PRACTICAL COOKERY

FOR THE LEVEL 2 TECHNICAL CERTIFICATE IN PROFESSIONAL COOKERY

DAVID FOSKETT

NEIL RIPPINGTON

STEVE THORPE

PATRICIA PASKINS

HODDER EDUCATION

AN HACHETTE UK COMPANY

City & Guilds have endorsed this product as a supporting resource for the hospitality and catering sector. However, this endorsement does not guarantee exact coverage of any City & Guilds qualification and is not directly linked to any City & Guilds assessment.

Although every effort has been made to ensure that website addresses are correct at time of going to press, Hodder Education cannot be held responsible for the content of any website mentioned in this book. It is sometimes possible to find a relocated web page by typing in the address of the home page for a website in the URL window of your browser.

Hachette UK's policy is to use papers that are natural, renewable and recyclable products and made from wood grown in sustainable forests. The logging and manufacturing processes are expected to conform to the environmental regulations of the country of origin.

Orders: please contact Bookpoint Ltd, 130 Park Drive, Milton Park, Abingdon, Oxon OX14 4SE. Telephone: (44) 01235 827720. Fax: (44) 01235 400454. Email education@bookpoint.co.uk Lines are open from 9 a.m. to 5 p.m., Monday to Saturday, with a 24-hour message answering service. You can also order through our website: www.hoddereducation.co.uk

ISBN: 978 1 5104 0185 3

First published in 2017 by
Hodder Education,
An Hachette UK Company
Carmelite House
50 Victoria Embankment
London EC4Y 0DZ

www.hoddereducation.co.uk

Impression number 10 9 8 7 6 5 4 3 2 1

Year 2020 2019 2018 2017 2016

Typeset in by Aptara, Inc.

Printed in Slovenia

A catalogue record for this title is available from the British Library.

Contents

* The questions in the assessment strategy pages are aimed at giving learners a chance to practice their knowledge and prepare for their end assessment by answering questions in the style of the summative tests. Although this textbook is closely matched to the City & Guilds qualification and has been endorsed by City & Guilds as an excellent teaching and learning resource, these practice questions have been written by the publisher, and have not been designed, reviewed or approved by City & Guilds. They in no way represent sample exam questions from City & Guilds, rather they are practice questions, loosely in the style of the formative assessments required by the DFE for all awarding organisations end tests.

Picture credits: P9 b © AVAVA – Fotolia; p14-15 © Food Standards Agency; p16 © Photo by Eric Erbe; digital colorization by Christopher Pooley/ Material produced by ARS is in the public domain; p32 © Gelia – Shutterstcok; p33 l © Real Life Design – Shutterstock, r © stocksolutions – Shutterstock; p37 © WavebreakmediaMicro – Fotolia; p40 © Morgan Lane Photography/ iStockphoto.com; p41 Compass; p42 © auremar – Fotolia; p44 l © Samuel Borges – Fotolia, r © auremar – Fotolia; p47 © Ratchapol Yindeesuk/123RF; p48 © Sam Bailey; p49 © Monkey Business – Fotolia; p50 © Mark_KA - iStock - Thinkstock/Getty Images; p51 © Stephen Gibson – Shutterstock; p52 © Alexander Raths – Shutterstock; p53 © starush – Fotolia; p61 © Senol Yaman – Shutterstock; p62 (1-2) Russums, (3) © bradcalkins – Fotolia, (4) © Marc Dietrich – Fotolia; p63 (1-2) Russums, (3) © dbvirago – Fotolia, (4-8) Russums, (10) © Ric Esplana Babor - Fotolia, (11) Russums; p67 (1) Russums, (2) © Eugen Wais – Fotolia, (3) © Joe Gough – Fotolia, (4-5) Russums; p68 (2) © Coprid – Fotolia; (3) Russums), (6-7) Russums, (9) © vich – Fotolia, (10-11) Russums, (12) © shutswis – Fotolia, (15) Russums; p69 (1-4) Russums, (6-7) Russums, (8) © pioneer – Fotolia; (13) Russums, (14) © Schlierner – Fotolia, (15) © Metta image / Alamy; p70 (1) © Fotosearch / SuperStock, (3-4) Russums, (6) Russums; p72 tl Lincat Ltd, bl © chaoss – Fotolia, tr/br Enodis; p73 tl Enodis, bl Compass, tr Enodis, br Sam Bailey; p74 Enodis; p75 tl/ml Enodis, tr RH Hall, mr Sam Bailey, br Victor Manudacturing Ltd; p76 tl Enodis, br True Manufacturing UK; p149 Donald Russell; p224 b © foodfolio / Alamy Stock Photo; p252 r © I'm Photographer – Fotolia.

Except where stated above, photographs are by Andrew Callaghan.

Thanks to University College Birmingham and Summer Shore for appearing in the cover photo.

How to use this book

This book has been written to cover everything you need for the Level 2 Technical Certificate in Professional Cookery. The book is divided into 8 chapters, each covering one unit of your course.

You will find the following features in the book:

Learning outcomes at the start of each chapter describe exactly what you need to know and be able to do to complete the course.

Step-by-step photo sequences guide you through important preparation, cooking and finishing techniques.

Take it further boxes include links to other useful sources of information on certain topics in case you want to find out more.

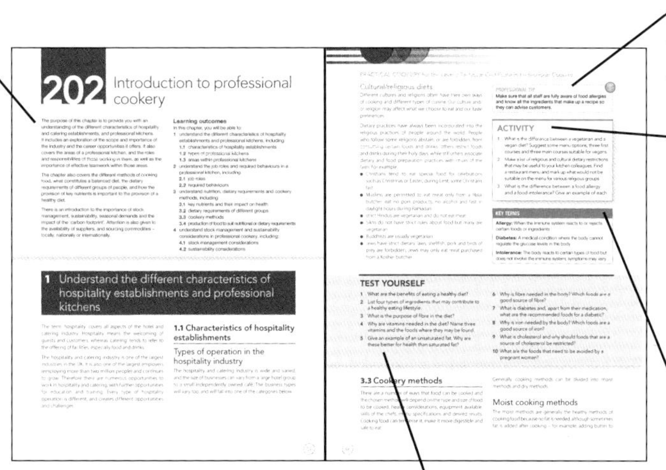

Professional tips give useful tips, information and advice from professional chefs.

Activities, including short questions, group activities and practical tasks, are included throughout each chapter to help you to develop your knowledge and skills.

Important **key terms** are defined in each chapter.

Important **health and safety** points are highlighted as a feature throughout – make sure you follow these to stay safe in the kitchen.

Test yourself questions at the end of each chapter help you to test your knowledge and prepare for short-answer and multiple-choice tests.

Recipes also include the following features:

Ingredients lists are provided for making smaller and larger quantities.

Nutritional data is included for most recipes to help you make informed choices about what to cook and eat.

Variation boxes suggest alternative ingredients, cooking methods or presentation, finishing and serving styles that could be used.

Healthy eating tips provide suggestions on how recipes can be adapted to make them healthier.

Notes boxes provides additional suggestions and tips relevant to the recipe.

Refer to the 'Assessment strategies' section on page 313 for more guidance on assessment and how this book can help you to prepare.

In the recipes, the main methods of cookery are shown by icons. So if you want to practise shallow frying for example, look for the relevant icon. They look like this:

Accessing the videos

There are free videos included throughout this book.

Look out for the QR codes throughout the book.

To view the videos you will need a QR code reader for your smartphone/tablet. There are many free readers available, depending on the smartphone/tablet you are using.

Once you have downloaded a QR code reader, simply open the reader app and use it to take a photo of the code. The file will then load on your smartphone/tablet.

If you cannot read the QR code or you are using a computer, the weblink next to the code will take you directly to the same place.

201 Safe working practices for the hospitality industry

The purpose of this chapter is to enable you to understand the how legislation applies when working in the hospitality industry. It deals with the laws covering food safety, health and safety, and allergen legislation as they apply to the industry to protect customers and employees.

The chapter also covers the range of knowledge necessary in food safety and health and safety as applied to working in kitchens and in the hospitality industry.

Learning outcomes

In this chapter, you will be able to:

1 know the legislative requirements applicable to the hospitality industry, including:
  - **1.1** legislation applicable to the hospitality industry
  - **1.2** employer and employee responsibilities

2 maintain food safety, including:
  - **2.1** following hygienic personal practices
  - **2.2** maintaining a hygienic working environment
  - **2.3** handling food safely
  - **2.4** allergenic ingredients or contaminants
  - **2.5** sources of food contamination
  - **2.6** identification and control of pests

3 maintain health and safety, including:
  - **3.1** factors that contribute to the risk of accidents
  - **3.2** common injuries and their causes
  - **3.3** maintaining health and safety by implementing control measures

1 Know the legislative requirements applicable to the hospitality industry

1.1 Legislation applicable to the hospitality industry

Food safety legislation

Food safety standards are protected by a range of legislation and enforced by Environmental Health Officers (Environmental Health Practitioners) employed by local authorities.

The Food Safety Act 1990

This provides the framework for all food safety law in Britain. It covers all types of food business in England, Wales and Scotland, and there is similar legislation in Northern Ireland. The act covers all food activities from food production right through to distribution, retail, catering and any other form of food activity.

The act places the following main responsibilities for all food businesses:

- to ensure that nothing is included in food, removed from food or food treated in any way making it damaging to the health of people eating it
- to ensure that any food served or sold is of the nature, substance or quality expected by consumers
- to ensure that the food is labelled, advertised and presented in a way that is not in any way false or misleading.

The act gives the government powers to make regulations on matters of detail. The Food Standards Agency is the principal government department responsible for preparing specific regulations under the act. For further information, see: www.food.gov.uk/business-industry/guidancenotes/

Food Hygiene Regulations 2006

These were applied throughout UK from 1 January 2006 to bring UK legislation in line with European legislation. The regulations:

- updated, consolidated and simplified the previous EU food hygiene legislation
- applied effective and proportionate controls throughout the food chain, from primary production to sale or supply to the consumer; this is referred to as 'from farm to fork'
- focused on the necessary controls for public health protection
- clarified that it is the primary responsibility of food business operators to produce safe food.

The regulations also require that:

- all food businesses are registered with the relevant authority; which authority will depend on the type of business
- food business operators must put in place, implement and maintain permanent procedures, based on HACCP principles (see below)
- the appropriate level of public health protection is in place
- food businesses apply the legislation flexibly and appropriately according to the nature of the business.

The Food Information for Consumers Regulations 1169/2011

This came into force in 2014 and enables local authorities to enforce the European Food Information to Consumers Regulation. It brings together EU rules on general food labelling and nutrition labelling into one piece of legislation.

Much of what appears in these regulations was detailed in Food Labelling Regulations 1996. There is no change in the principles of providing safe food that is honestly described and not misleading. In addition, foods cannot be labelled to state that they will prevent, treat or cure an illness. The following information must be required in English on prepacked food labelling:

- a true name or description of the food
- the ingredients it contains, in descending weight order
- how it should be handled, stored, prepared or cooked
- who manufactured, packed or imported it
- origin information if its absence would mislead the consumer
- specific information declaring whether the food is irradiated or contains genetically modified material or aspartame, high caffeine, sweeteners, packaging gases, etc.
- net quantity in metric measure – grams, kilograms, litres, etc.
- alcoholic strength where there is more than 1.2 per cent alcohol by volume.

If food is non-pre-packed (such as in a restaurant or café) the information about allergens can be supplied on the menu, on menu screens, boards or provided verbally by an appropriate member of staff as well as in other formats. It must be clear, easily visible and legible. If verbal information is to be provided, it is necessary to make it clear to customers that staff can provide this information on request.

Allergen information must be specific to the actual food, complete and accurate. Refusal to give information, inaccurate or incomplete information about allergenic ingredients used in foods offered for sale would be a breach of the EU Food Information to Consumers Regulation.

Health and safety legislation

Professional kitchens can potentially be dangerous places to work if not properly managed. It is a **legal requirement** for every establishment to identify risks, and introduce the necessary measures to minimise risks and possible workplace accidents and injury to ensure that the workplace is as safe as it can possibly be.

There is a significant amount of legislation in place to ensure that business owners comply with what is necessary to avoid employees being injured or made unwell in any way by their workplace or the work they complete.

Health and Safety at Work Act (1974), updated in 1994

The Health and Safety at Work act imposes a general duty on an employer 'to ensure so far as is reasonably practicable, the health, safety and welfare at work of all employees'. It is largely about establishing and maintaining good health and safety practice in the workplace. It requires that employers comply with all parts of the act including completing risk assessments of all areas and procedures, and introducing safe ways of working.

Employers will need:

- a health and safety policy that includes risk assessments (unless there are fewer than five employees)
- to keep premises and equipment in safe working order and provide/maintain personal protective equipment for employees.

Employees must:

- take reasonable care for the health and safety of themselves and of other persons who may be affected by their actions or omissions at work
- co-operate with the employer so far as is necessary to meet or comply with any requirement concerning health and safety
- not interfere with, or misuse, anything provided in the interests of health, safety or welfare.

The act is particularly relevant to the hospitality and catering industries where many hazards present themselves as a naturally occurring part of everyday work. Working areas themselves can present dangers, as can machinery and tools. Where so many hazards can be present in working areas it is of particular importance to make sure that staff partake in regular safety training, that risk assessments address any dangers and to regularly update the controls in place.

Control of Substances Hazardous to Health (COSHH) 2002

Under COSHH, risk assessments must be completed by employers of all hazardous chemicals and substances that employees may be exposed to at work, their safe use and proper disposal.

A range of chemicals will be used in kitchens. Each chemical must be given a risk rating that is recorded, and employees given relevant information and training on the chemicals they will be using. Data sheets or cards with information about the chemicals, how they must be used and what to do if an accident occurs must be kept in an easily accessible place so staff can refer to them when needed. Measures must be taken to ensure that all staff understand these, and that consideration is given to those who do not speak English as their first language or who have other possible barriers to understanding the information.

Everyone must be trained in the safe handling and use of chemicals, and proper dilution procedures where needed, and must wear protective equipment such as goggles, gloves and face masks as appropriate. Eye goggles should be worn when using oven cleaners, gloves when hands may come into contact with any chemical cleaner, and face masks when using grease-cutting and oven degreasers. Extra protective aprons or overalls may be needed. It is essential that staff are trained to take precautions and not to take unnecessary risks.

RIDDOR (Reporting Injuries, Diseases and Dangerous Occurrences)

These regulations require employers, and/or the person with responsibility for health and safety within a workplace, to report and keep records of any:

- work-related fatal accidents
- work-related disease
- accidents and injury resulting in the employee being off work for three days or more
- dangerous workplace events (including 'near miss' occurrences)
- major injuries, loss of limbs or eyesight.

Accidents and incidents under RIDDOR need to be reported and can be done so by contacting the Health and Safety Executive. You can find the RIDDOR form on its website: www.hse.gov.uk/riddor/

Management of Health and Safety at Work Regulations 1999

Where an employer has five or more employees there must be a written health and safety policy in place that is issued to every member of staff. This will outline the responsibilities of the employer and employee in relation to health and safety. It states that health and safety information must be provided for all employees.

Manual Handling Operations Regulations 1992

These regulations are in place to protect employees from injury or accident when required to lift or move heavy or awkwardly shaped items. A risk assessment must be completed, employees must be trained in correct manual handling techniques, and lifting or moving equipment should be provided where appropriate. Handling of objects can be more difficult in hospitality areas because the objects could be very hot, frozen or sharp.

Personal Protective Equipment at Work Regulations 1992

These regulations require employers to assess the need for and to provide suitable personal protective equipment (PPE) and clothing at work. In a commercial kitchen environment these may include chefs' uniforms and items for cleaning tasks, such as rubber gloves, goggles and masks. Employers must keep these items clean, in good condition and provide suitable storage for them. Employees must use them correctly and report any defects or shortages.

TEST YOURSELF

1. What are two requirements of food businesses under the Food Safety Act 1990?
2. What are two further requirements of a food business stipulated by the Food Hygiene Regulations 2006?
3. What do the Food Information for Consumers Regulations say about:
   a. ingredients listed on packaging
   b. amounts of alcohol in drinks
   c. where the food came from?
4. What does the above act say about allergens in food and giving allergen information to customers?
5. As laid out in the Health and Safety at Work Act, name one responsibility of an employer and three responsibilities of an employee.
6. What are the COSHH regulations and how do they affect employees?
7. Under RIDDOR (Reporting Injuries, Diseases and Dangerous Occurrences) regulations, which accidents and illnesses must be reported? Who must they be reported to?
8. Why may handling, carrying and moving certain items be more difficult or hazardous in hospitality areas than in other areas?
9. What must an employer and an employee do in relation to PPE?
10. A health and safety policy needs to be produced by an employer and given to every employee. What information will this give you?

1.2 Employer and employee responsibilities

All food businesses must be registered with the local authority, must co-operate with the Environmental Health Officer/Environmental Health Practitioner (EHO/EHP) and put proper food safety practices in place.

Employer responsibilities

Hazard Analysis Critical Control Point (HACCP)

Food safety legislation requires every food business to have a recorded food safety management system that will prove how they manage all aspects of food safety.

All food safety management systems must be based on **Hazard Analysis** Critical Control Point (HACCP). This is a system that identifies the hazards that could occur at **critical control points** (CCPs) or stages in any process and the safeguards in place to stop potential hazards from causing harm. The system must provide a documented and regularly updated record of the policies and procedures in place and all of the stages all food will go through right up until the time it is eaten.

Once the possible hazards have been identified, measures are put in place to control them and keep the food safe.

The HACCP system has seven stages:

1. Identify hazards – what could go wrong?
2. Identify critical control points (CCPs). These are the important stages where things could go wrong.
3. Set critical limits for each CCP – for example, temperature requirements on delivery of fresh chicken.
4. Monitor CCPs and put checks in place to stop problems happening.
5. Corrective action – what will be done if something goes wrong?
6. Verification – check that the HACCP plan is working.
7. Documentation – record all of the above.

The system must be updated regularly, especially when new items are introduced to the menu or systems change (for example, a new piece of cooking equipment is used). New controls must be put in place to include them.

Full written or electronic records must be available for inspection as part of the system.

When Environmental Health Officers/Practitioners inspect a food business they will check that food safety management systems are in place and are working effectively.

Ensuring appropriate food safety training for employees

As well as being a legal requirement, food safety training for staff '**commensurate**' to their job roles is essential in any food business, and needs to be planned, monitored and managed for staff, making sure that training records are accurate and up to date.

Before any new member of staff handles food, initial training must be carried out covering the most important food safety issues in the job role; the food handler will also need to be supervised until formal training takes place, which should be within a month.

The training methods chosen will depend on the type of business, the activities carried out and any previous training staff have been given. Training could take place by:

- formal and informal training delivered by supervisors/managers to meet the needs of the business as well as to satisfy legal requirements; planned retraining/refresher sessions are also essential at all levels to keep staff up to date and aware of any developments or related issues
- use of food safety management companies undertaking part or all of the food safety requirements for a business, including training at different levels
- partaking in recognised food safety qualifications accredited by CIEH, RSPH, City & Guilds, BIIAB, Highfield and others; food safety training courses are available at colleges and universities, through independent training providers, local authorities and adult education centres; training and testing for these can also take place in the workplace.

Training can also be completed by:

- online or computer package training, with end tests and certification
- food safety training packs, which could include books, workbooks, DVDs, activities, etc.
- as part of another qualification relevant to students
- use of a variety of materials, including, posters, leaflets, films, interactive games and quizzes
- food safety consultants/trainers delivering different levels of training
- training delivered by the local authority or **EHO (EHP)**.

The different levels for formal food safety qualifications are usually as follows.

- Level 1: for those new to food handling tasks, or those employed on non-complex or limited tasks.
- Level 2: this level is the most frequently completed and is for those handling a wide variety of foods, including 'open' and high-risk foods.

- Level 3: a qualification for supervisors of food premises and for those completing more complex tasks and requiring a greater depth of knowledge.
- Level 4: a management/senior supervisor level, and for anyone requiring a high-level food safety qualification, with responsibilities for managing food safety.

Registration of food businesses with the local authority

Almost all food businesses need to be registered with their local authority; this includes catering businesses run from home and mobile or temporary premises, such as stalls and vans. The business needs to be registered with the environmental health service of the relevant local authority at least 28 days before opening. Registration is free. If you have more than one premises, you will need to register all of them. You can find information about registering at: www.food.gov.uk/business-industry/startingup

Employee responsibilities when working in a food business

Employees have their own specific responsibilities under food safety legislation. It is the employees' own responsibility to:

- partake in food safety training relevant to the work they are doing so that they understand the principles of food safety and how to avoid food poisoning
- comply with the safe, hygienic working practices as established by their employer, and food safety legislation including working in a way that does not endanger or contaminate food, and not serve food they know is contaminated
- report anything that may have an effect on food safety, such as a fridge running at the wrong temperature, and co-operate with food safety measures the employer puts in place
- report any illness, especially if stomach related, to a supervisor before going near food or preparation areas; after suffering such an illness they must not return to work until 48 hours after the last symptom
- maintain high standards of personal hygiene, wear clean, suitable kitchen clothing and adopt hygienic working practices; there is more about this on page 7.

Impact of not complying with employer and employee responsibilities

Non-compliance with legislation can have very serious effects on a business as well as employees or customers, and could lead to:

- **injury and illness** from carelessly stored, prepared, cooked or served food; it could also occur from misuse of processes, machinery, equipment or packaging; non-compliance with safety regulations could, in some circumstances, result in the death of an employee or customer
- **complaints** from customers verbally, by phone or in writing about the products or services they receive
- **damage to reputation** can very soon follow complaints because dissatisfied customers tell others; it is worth remembering that, with social media and review sites, a complaint against a business can be sent worldwide in seconds
- **loss of business** will be a likely result of non-compliance to legislation because of bad publicity, negative press reports, poor reputation and possible enforced closure (see below)
- a **Hygiene Improvement Notice** is served if the EHO (EHP) believes that a food business does not comply with regulations; the notice is served in writing and states the name and address of the business, what is wrong, why it is wrong, what needs to be done to put it right and the time in which this must be completed (usually not less than 14 days; this does not apply to cleaning); it is an offence if the identified work is not carried out in the specified time without prior agreement
- a **Hygiene Emergency Prohibition Notice** is served if the EHO (EHP) believes that there is an imminent risk to health from the business; these would include serious issues such as sewage contamination, lack of water supply or rodent infestation; serving this notice would mean immediate closure of the business or part of the business for three days, during which time the EHO (EHP) must apply to magistrates for a Hygiene Emergency Prohibition Order to keep the premises closed; notices/orders must be displayed in a visible place on the premises; the owner of the business must apply for a certificate of satisfaction before they can reopen

- a **Hygiene Prohibition Order** prohibits a person such as the owner/manager from working in a food business
- fines and penalties for non-compliance
  - Magistrates Courts can impose fines of up to £5,000 per offence, a six-month prison sentence or both
  - for serious offences, such as knowingly selling food dangerous to health, magistrates could impose fines of up to £20,000
  - in a Crown Court unlimited fines and/or a sentence of two years' imprisonment can be imposed.

KEY TERMS

Critical control point (CCP): A point in a procedure or process where a hazard could occur if controls were not in place

EHO/EHP: Employed by local authorities to ensure that the required standards of food safety are met

Food safety: Putting measures in place to ensure food is safe to eat and will not cause illness

Hazard: Any area, activity or procedure with the potential to cause harm

Hazard analysis: Identifying all the possible hazards and putting in measures to prevent them causing harm

Legal requirement: Something that must be done by law

TEST YOURSELF

1. Where must every new food business be registered?
2. What is meant by HACCP and how many stages does it have?
3. What is meant by a critical control point (CCP)?
4. When are the times that a HACCP system would need to be updated?
5. What determines the level of food safety training needed by kitchen staff?
6. Suggest four ways in which food safety training could be completed?
7. What are two of an employee's food safety responsibilities when working with food?
8. What are two possible outcomes if a business does not comply with food safety legislation?
9. What is a Hygiene Improvement Notice and what information must be recorded on it?
10. What is the maximum penalty that can be imposed in a Magistrates Court for non-compliance with food safety legislation?

2 Maintain food safety

Every consumer has the right and expectation to be served safe food that will not cause them illness or harm. Food safety means putting in place all of the measures needed to make sure that food and drinks are suitable, safe, fit to eat and will not cause food poisoning.

Food poisoning is an illness usually caused by eating contaminated food. In most cases of food poisoning, the food is contaminated by pathogenic bacteria such as salmonella or by a virus such as norovirus. Symptoms are often similar, and include nausea, vomiting, diarrhoea, dehydration, headaches and fever. Food may also be contaminated by physical items or chemicals getting into it as well as by allergens that could severely affect someone allergic to it.

Good standards of food safety are essential to avoid food poisoning, comply with the law and avoid legal action. It will help to build a successful business with a good reputation, and to provide clean and safe premises for employees and customers. All food businesses are required to have a recorded food safety management system based on the principles of HACCP.

2.1 Following hygienic personal practices

It is very important for all food handlers to take care with **personal hygiene** and to adopt good practices when working with food to avoid contaminating the food, which can cause food poisoning.

Food handlers must:

- arrive at work clean (bath or shower daily) and with clean hair

- wear appropriate protective clothing; the food handler's own clothing must not be worn in the workplace
- keep nails short, clean and not bitten – no nail varnish or false nails should be worn
- not wear jewellery and watches when handling food; these items can trap bacteria and could cause physical contamination by falling into food
- not wear cosmetics and strong perfumes; these must be washed off before entering the kitchen
- avoid touching their nose, face and head/hair
- never smoke in food preparation areas
- not eat food or sweets or chew gum when handling food as this may transfer bacteria to food
- arrive fit to work and handle food, with no illnesses.

Protective clothing

Protective clothing is worn in the kitchen to protect food from **contamination**, as well as protecting the wearer from heat, burns and splashes. Some people allergic to certain food items, chemicals, plastics or cleaning materials can suffer a skin reaction called contact dermatitis. Good kitchen clothing can also protect the wearer from an allergic reaction.

Kitchen protective clothing usually consists of chef's jacket, trousers, apron and **safety shoes**. Jacket pockets should be on the inside, which will help to prevent items accidentally falling into food. Disposable gloves must be worn as appropriate, and hair must also be contained in a suitable hat and/or hair net. Kitchen clothing should be used only in the kitchen, should completely cover any personal clothing and ideally should be light in colour. At break times food handlers should not go outside and must not smoke while wearing kitchen clothing. For practical reasons many kitchens enforce the removal of aprons and hats when leaving the kitchen, and provide a white coat to wear over the rest of the uniform.

All items of clothing should fit well, be in good repair and suitable for the tasks being completed. Materials such as cotton that are comfortable, durable and can be easily laundered at high temperatures are the most usual.

> **PROFESSIONAL TIP**
> Kitchen clothing itself could contaminate food. If it gets dirty or stained, change it for clean clothing.

Avoiding unhygienic personal behaviour

Some personal behaviour is completely unacceptable in food areas because it could result in the contamination of food. Examples of unhygienic behaviour include those listed below.

- **Nail biting** – Putting fingers in and around the mouth then handling food would result in contamination. Badly bitten nails can cause bleeding or infection around the nail, which can also contaminate food.
- **Touching head and face** – All humans will carry some bacteria on their bodies so touching the head, hair or face could result in bacteria being transferred to food.
- **Smoking in the food environment** – Smoking is now prohibited in most buildings but it is especially important that there should be no smoking in a food environment. Smoking will involve touching the face or mouth so transferring bacteria to food. Smokers are also more likely to cough, which may also result in contamination. There is a risk of ash falling into food. The use of e-cigarettes is also not acceptable.
- **Sneezing and coughing** where there is open food can transfer bacteria. Do not work with food if you have a bad cough or cold. If a sudden sneeze or cough is unavoidable, step back, turn away from the food and cough or sneeze into the shoulder area. Wash hands thoroughly.
- **Tasting food with fingers** is bad practice and can contaminate food. Use a clean tasting spoon.

Hand washing

Contamination of food from hands can happen very easily. Thorough hand washing is essential to avoid this.

- Use a basin provided just for hand washing.
- Wet hands under warm running water.
- Apply liquid soap.
- Rub hands together between fingers and thumbs.
- Remember to wash the fingertips, nails and wrists.
- If a nailbrush is used make sure it is clean and disinfected.
- Rinse off under the running water.
- Dry hands on a paper towel, use the paper towel to turn off the tap then dispose of it into a foot-operated waste bin.

Hands should be washed:

- when you enter the kitchen, before starting work and handling any food
- after a break
- after using the toilet
- after smoking or eating
- between different tasks, but especially after handling raw and before handling cooked/high-risk food
- if you touch hair, nose or mouth/face
- after coughing/sneezing and nose blowing
- after you apply or change a dressing on a cut or burn
- after using cleaning materials, or cleaning preparation areas, equipment or contaminated surfaces
- after handling kitchen waste, external food packaging, money or flowers.

Ensure fitness to handle food

Report any illness to the supervisor as soon as possible and before handling any food. This is a legal requirement and would include:

- diarrhoea and/or vomiting, nausea and stomach pain; this may well be food poisoning
- infected **(septic)** cuts, burns or spots
- eye or ear infections
- cold or flu symptoms, including sore throat
- skin problems such as dermatitis.

Also report illness you had when away from work and family members or friends you have contact with who have the above symptoms, especially where they are stomach related.

Cuts and wounds

Any infected (septic) cuts and wounds should be reported to a supervisor. Wash, dry then cover any cuts, burns or grazes with a brightly coloured waterproof dressing, then wash hands and if necessary use a disposable plastic glove.

KEY TERMS

Commensurate: Completed at the right level for the job being undertaken

Contamination: Anything in food that should not be there; contaminated food could cause harm or may just be unpleasant

Personal hygiene: Keeping yourself clean and hygienic to avoid contaminating food

PPE: Personal protective equipment (and clothing) worn for safety reasons at work

Safety shoes: Strong, enclosed shoes with reinforced toecaps to protect the feet from heavy or sharp objects and hot liquids

Septic: Cuts, burns and so on infected with pathogenic bacteria; they are often wet, with a white or yellow appearance

TEST YOURSELF

1. Suggest six personal hygiene rules you would include in a kitchen instruction leaflet used for staff training.
2. What are the main reasons that jewellery and watches should not be worn in the kitchen?
3. What is the correct procedure to follow if you arrive at work feeling unwell and with stomach pains?
4. What are the main reasons for wearing protective clothing in the kitchen? What would you consider to be a good range of protective clothing for a chef?
5. Why should kitchen clothing not be worn outside of the kitchen? What may be considered acceptable if you need to go outside at break time?
6. Why must the face and hair not be touched when handling food?
7. List three occasions when hands should be thoroughly washed if working with food?
8. What should be worn after washing and drying a small cut on the hand?

2.2 Maintaining a hygienic working environment

Cleaning procedures

It is a legal requirement that food areas are kept clean and hygienic and that food premises are designed with good food safety in mind. Clean food areas play an essential part in the production of safe food, and it is a requirement to plan, record and check all cleaning as part of a planned **cleaning schedule**.

As a food handler it is your responsibility, along with those working with you, to keep food areas clean and hygienic at all times, and it is important to be aware of the following.

- **Clean as you go** and do not allow waste to build up; clean up any spills straight away. Put items away when no longer using them, and clean, **sanitise**/disinfect surfaces and equipment regularly.
- **Pre-cleaning** means removing any food waste, debris and excess grease, trimmings, crumbs and other items from surfaces and equipment then cleaning the area with detergent and water before more thorough cleaning, sanitising or **disinfection** takes place.
- **Detergents** remove grease and dirt, and hold them in suspension in water; they do not kill bacteria. **Detergent** works best with hot water.
- **Sanitising** is usually completed using a spray sanitiser, which cleans and disinfects. It is very useful for work surfaces and equipment, especially between tasks, and also for **hand contact surfaces** such as fridge handles.

- **Disinfecting** can be completed by using very hot water. For example a dishwasher rinse cycle runs at around 82°C, which kills most bacteria, so this is a very effective way to clean and disinfect small equipment. A disinfectant is a chemical designed to destroy bacteria if used properly. Disinfectants must be left on a cleaned grease-free surface for the required amount of time to be effective and work best when used with cool water.
- **Rinsing** is the washing off or removal of detergent or disinfectant, usually to avoid tainting food. Follow the manufacturers' instructions for rinsing their products. Some products such as sanitisers may not need rinsing. A dishwasher rinses at a very high temperature to disinfect and allow items to dry quickly.
- **Drying** – When surfaces or equipment needs to be dried, cloths are not recommended because they hold on to bacteria that can be transferred to food. Use of disposable kitchen paper or allowing surfaces and equipment to air dry is preferable. Very high temperatures such as in a dishwasher will facilitate rapid drying.
- **Deep cleaning** – This is special intense cleaning of whole areas, specific areas or equipment, completed at certain times as planned. It could include items such as filtration and ventilation systems, large pieces of equipment or refrigeration and ceiling and walls. Deep cleaning needs to be planned for a time when the area could be out of use for the required time and could be completed in house or by a specialist contractor.
- **High priority/risk cleaning** – This is a special and thorough clean of whole areas or specific completed for an identified need. Times when such cleaning may be completed include:
  - after an EHO inspection where a cleaning need was highlighted
  - after an outbreak of food poisoning from the business
  - after a problem with pest infestation which has now been resolved
  - after building or repair work
  - after there has been an identified illness such as norovirus affecting staff.

Some items, especially in high-risk areas and where high-risk foods are handled, need both cleaning and disinfection. These are:

- **all food contact surfaces**, such as chopping boards, bowls, spoons, whisks
- **all hand contact surfaces**, such as fridge handles and door handles
- **cleaning materials and equipment**, such as mops, buckets, cloths, hand wash basins.

Colour-coded chopping boards

Sanitising a surface

KEY TERMS

Cleaning schedule: Planned and recorded cleaning of all areas and equipment

Corrosive: Something that can eat away or destroy solid materials

Detergent: Removes grease and dirt and holds them in suspension in water; it may be in the form of liquid, powder, gel or foam; detergent will not kill pathogens

Disinfection: Action to bring micro-organisms to a safe level; this can be done with chemical disinfectants or heat

Hand contact surfaces: Anything in the kitchen that hands touch, including surfaces, equipment and a wide range of objects used in the kitchen

Sanitise: To clean and disinfect together with one product

Characteristics of different work surfaces and equipment

Kitchen surfaces and equipment must be hard wearing, suitable for the food environment and be installed to allow for efficient cleaning and disinfection of the equipment itself and of the surrounding area. Equipment and surfaces need to be in good condition, smooth, impervious (not absorb liquids) and must be non-**corrosive**, non-toxic, non-tainting and must not crack, chip or flake. Many kitchens have a 'no glass' policy to prevent the possibility of broken glass getting into food. Table 1.1 provides examples of the types of materials and requirements of work areas.

Table 1.1 Requirements of work areas

Lighting	Must allow for tasks being completed safely and without eye strain so that cleaning can be carried out efficiently.
Ventilation	Using extraction and air replacement canopies over essential areas prevents excessive heat, condensation, circulation of air-borne contaminants, grease vapours and odours and gives a more comfortable working environment.
Floors	Need to be hard wearing and in good condition; they must be impervious, non-slip and easy to keep clean. Edges between floor and walls should be coved (curved) to prevent dirt collecting in corners.
Walls	Need to be non-porous, smooth, easy to clean and light in colour. Suitable wall coverings are plastic cladding and stainless steel sheeting.
Ceilings	Ceiling finishes must resist build up of condensation, which could encourage mould. They should be of a non-flaking material and be washable. Non-porous ceiling panels and tiles are often used; non-flaking paints are also useful.
Drainage	Drainage must be adequate for the work being completed without causing flooding. If channels, grease traps and gullies are used they should allow for frequent cleaning.
Windows/ doors	These provide possibilities for pests to enter the building so should fit well into the frames with no gaps. They should be fitted with screening, strip-curtains and doors should have metal kick plates.

Maintenance

All food premises, fittings and equipment must be kept in good repair to ensure food safety. Cracked surfaces or chipped equipment could support the multiplication of bacteria and a fridge running at the wrong temperature may allow bacteria to multiply in food. If you notice anything is damaged, broken or faulty report it to a supervisor immediately. You may have specific reporting forms to do this.

2.3 Handling food safely

Receiving food, storing it correctly, handling and cooking it safely all play essential parts in maintaining good food safety standards.

Food deliveries

Ordering and taking delivery of food will be the first point in achieving the required food safety standards. Only approved suppliers who can assure that food is delivered in the best condition should be used. Food must be delivered in perfect condition in suitable, undamaged packaging, within the required use by or best before dates and at the correct temperature. Items should then be labelled with the name of the commodity, the date it was put into storage and use by/best before date.

All deliveries should be checked against the delivery note then moved to the appropriate storage area as soon as possible. Chilled/frozen food must be stored within 15 minutes of delivery. Use a **food probe** to check the temperature: chilled food should be below 5°C; frozen foods should be at or below -18°C. Many suppliers will now provide an electronic printout of temperatures at which food was delivered.

Storage

Correct storage is essential to keep all food items in best condition and safe to eat. Remove food items from outer boxes before placing the products in the refrigerator, freezer or dry store. Food should be stored with correct labelling so it is clear what the commodity is. Table 1.2 gives storage instructions and temperatures for different commodities.

Table 1.2 Storage instructions and temperatures

Food type	Storage temperature	Storage instructions
Dry goods (including items such as rice, dried pasta, sugar, flour, grains)	A cool, well-ventilated dry store area	Should be kept in clean, covered containers on wheels or in smaller sealed containers on shelves to stop pests getting into them. No food should be stored on the floor even if in boxes or bags. Storage should be in a cool, well-ventilated dry and pest proof store area away from direct sunlight. Well-managed stock rotation is essential. Retain packaging information as this may include essential **allergy advice**.
Canned products	Dry store area	Cans are usually stored in the dry store area and once again rotation of stock is essential. Canned food will carry best before dates and it is not advisable to use it after this date. 'Blown' cans must never be used, and do not use badly dented or rusty cans. Once opened, transfer any unused canned food to a clean bowl, cover and label it, and store in the refrigerator for up to two days.
Raw meat and poultry	In a refrigerator running between 1°C and 4°C	Wherever possible store in refrigerators just for meat and poultry, to avoid drip contamination. If not already packaged, place on trays, cover well with clingfilm and label. If it is necessary to store meat/poultry in a multi-use refrigerator make sure it is covered, labelled and placed at the bottom of the refrigerator and is well away from other items.
Fish	In a refrigerator running between 1°C and 4°C	A specific fish refrigerator is preferable. Remove fresh fish from ice containers and place on trays, cover well with clingfilm and label. If it is necessary to store fish in a multi-use refrigerator make sure it is well covered, labelled and placed at the bottom of the refrigerator, well away from other items. Remember that odours from fish can get into other items such as milk or eggs.
Dairy products/eggs	Milk and cream, eggs and cheese should be stored between 1°C and 4°C Sterilised or UHT milk can be kept in the dry store Eggs should be stored at a constant temperature and a refrigerator is the best place to store them	Milk and cream, eggs and cheese should be stored in their original containers. For sterilised or UHT milk follow the storage instructions on the label.
Fruit, vegetables and salad items	Dependent on type; refrigerated items should be stored at around 8°C to avoid any chill damage	Storage conditions will vary according to type, e.g. sacks of potatoes, root vegetables and some fruit can be stored in a cool, well-ventilated store room but salad items, green vegetables, soft fruit and tropical fruit would be better in refrigerated storage.
Cooked foods	Below 5°C	These include a wide range of foods, e.g. pies, pâté, cream cakes, desserts and savoury flans. They will usually be 'high risk' foods so correct storage is essential. For specific storage instructions see the labelling on the individual items, but generally keep items below 5°C. Store carefully, wrapped and labelled, and well away from and above raw foods to avoid any cross-contamination.
Frozen foods	Freezer running at -18°C or below	Make sure that food is wrapped or packaged. Separate raw foods from ready-to-eat foods in the freezer and do not refreeze once it has defrosted.

Defrosting frozen food

If you need to defrost frozen food, a defrosting cabinet would be the best place to do it. Alternatively, place the food in a deep tray, cover with film, and label with what the item is and the date when defrosting was started. Place at the bottom of the refrigerator where thawing liquid can't drip on to anything else. Defrost food completely but do not let the temperature rise above 8°C, then cook thoroughly within 12 hours. Make sure that you allow enough time for the defrosting process – it may take longer than you think. (A 2 kg chicken will take about 24 hours to defrost at 3°C.)

Some foods can be cooked directly from frozen, but this tends to be very thin foods such as pizza, flat breadcrumbed fish fillet or frozen vegetables.

Cooking

Cooking food to a core (centre) temperature of 75°C (use a disinfected food probe to check) for at least two minutes will kill most bacteria. These temperatures are important, especially where large amounts are being cooked or the consumers are in the high-risk categories.

However, some dishes on hotel and restaurant menus may be cooked to a lower temperature than this if it is considered that higher temperatures would be detrimental to the food or to meet customer requirements. Lower temperatures – but no lower than 63°C – can be used when a whole piece of meat such as a steak is cooked. Always cook to the higher recommended temperature where meat has been boned/rolled or minced or where food is part of a made up dish such as fishcakes or fish pie.

PROFESSIONAL TIP

Sometimes where customers choose dishes cooked to temperatures lower than those recommended a warning is put on the menu stating that customers eat these at their own risk.

Chilling

If food is being cooled/chilled to serve cold or for reheating at a later time, it must be cooled to **8°C** within **90 minutes**. This will help prevent multiplication of any bacteria that may be present and avoids any possible problem with spores. The best way to do this is in a blast-chiller.

Reheating

If reheating previously cooked food, reheat to **75°C+** (the recommendation is **82°C** in Scotland). The temperature in the centre of the food must be maintained for at least two minutes and reheating must only be done once.

Holding for service, serving and transporting

Cooked food being held for service, served or transported must be kept above **63°C** for hot food or below **8°C** for cold food (below **5°C** is strongly recommended).

Labelling

All food being stored should be labelled on delivery with the name of the commodity, the date it went into storage and the date by which it must be used. Also carefully observe labelling and dates placed on the food packaging by manufacturers and fresh food suppliers.

Stock rotation

A stock rotation procedure must be in place. Adopt a 'first in–first out' (**FIFO**) policy to use older stock first and observe storage dates (best before) on packaged food.

- **Use-by dates** are given for perishable foods that need refrigeration (this must be observed by law).
- **Best before dates** are provided for items with a longer storage life and not needing refrigerated storage. The food should still be used within these dates.

Unsafe food

Unsafe food must never be used and it is unlawful to do so. Never accept inferior food deliveries. You may become aware that food is unsafe because:

- it has exceeded its best before or use by date, or has been stored at the wrong temperature – for example, the refrigerator is faulty and running at too high a temperature
- the appearance, smell, colour or texture of the food is suspect
- you know that it has become contaminated in some way.

For any of the above it is important to take action and not just leave the food where it is. Report the problem to a supervisor or line manager immediately and follow their instructions.

If you are asked to dispose of unsafe food:

- label clearly, 'unsafe' or 'not for human consumption'
- separate well away from other foods and general waste
- dispose of correctly as advised
- record the disposal according to workplace policy.

Temperature control

Temperature control plays a very important role in food safety. The temperatures between 5°C and 63°C are referred to as the **danger zone** because this is the temperature range where it is possible for bacteria to multiply, with most rapid activity at around 37°C. When food is cooked it should be taken through the danger zone quickly. Most food should be cooked to 75°C to kill bacteria. Cool food quickly (within 90 minutes) so it is not in the danger zone longer than necessary.

Electronic temperature probes can be used to measure the temperature in the centre of food (this is known as the core temperature). They are also good for recording the temperature of deliveries and for checking food temperatures in fridges. Make sure the probe is clean and disinfected before use; disposable disinfectant wipes are useful for this. Place the probe into the centre of the food, making sure it is not touching bone or the cooking container.

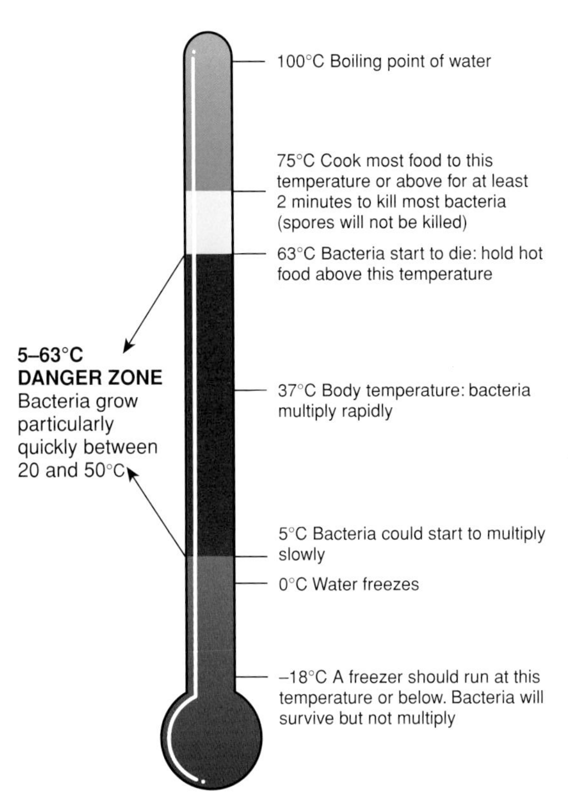

Danger zone thermometer

The running temperature of refrigerators, freezers and chill cabinets should be checked and recorded at least once a day. Refrigerators and chill cabinets should be below 5°C and freezers below -18°C. Good food safety practice is to store cold/chilled food at or below 5°C even though the temperature stated in food safety legislation is 8°C; this is now considered too high because this takes food into the 'danger zone'.

Systems are now available to log temperatures of all fridges, freezers and display cabinets in a business. Temperatures are recorded and sent to a central computer several times a day. These can then be printed or stored electronically as part of due diligence record-keeping. Units not running at correct temperatures will be highlighted.

TEST YOURSELF

1 What is meant by 'clean as you go'?
2 What is the difference between a disinfectant and a detergent?
3 What is deep cleaning and when may it be carried out?
4 Name six kitchen items that would need both cleaning and disinfecting.
5 What does it mean if a kitchen surface is impervious?
6 When food is delivered it should be labelled. What information should go on the label?
7 How soon should chilled and frozen food go into storage?
8 What is the recommended running temperature for a freezer and for a fridge used for cooked food?
9 When cooling food to chill it, how quickly should this be done?
10 When holding hot food for service what is the temperature that must be maintained?

ACTIVITY

1 What is the temperature range referred to as the danger zone? Why should food be kept out of this zone as much as possible? Suggest three good working practices that will prevent food from being in the danger zone for too long.
2 Show on the diagram below where you would position these different chilled foods in a multi-use refrigerator: raw chicken, cooked ham, cream, salmon fillets, cooked vegetable quiche, eggs, cheese, cooked pasties, pâté, fresh pasta, rump steak, milk, raw sausages, butter, frozen chicken drumsticks that need to be defrosted.

1
2
3
4

3 There is already some cream cheese in the refrigerator with a use-by date of today, crème fraîche with a use-by date of tomorrow and some yoghurt with a use-by date of yesterday. What should be done with these items? At what temperature should the fridge be running?
4 How could you inform other kitchen staff of the ways required for storing food in a refrigerator?

2.4 Allergenic ingredients or contaminants

Allergens can cause certain consumers to suffer a range of reactions. An allergy is when the immune system in some people reacts to certain food, causing swelling, itching, rashes, breathlessness and may even cause **anaphylactic shock** (a severe reaction causing swelling of the throat and mouth that blocks airways). Food intolerance is different and does not involve the immune system, but there may still be a reaction to some foods and some of these reactions can be serious. The foods most usually associated with allergies and intolerances are listed below but many other foods and ingredients may cause reactions, especially certain fruits, vegetables, plants and mushrooms.

Under EU regulation FIR 1169/2011 specific information on 14 allergens/ingredients must be available irrespective of whether the food is packaged or chosen from a menu.

The 14 identified allergens are listed below.

1. **Celery:** this includes celery stalks, leaves root and seed, celery salt and items seasoned with it, as well as the root vegetable celeriac.
2. **Foods containing gluten:** including wheat and wheat flour, spelt, rye, barley and oats. Be aware of the wide range of food containing wheat, such as bread, pasta, pastry, biscuits, batters and many more.
3. **Crustaceans:** these include shellfish such as lobsters, prawns, crabs and scampi. Also be aware of products such as fishcakes and shrimp paste or fish sauce used in oriental dishes.
4. **Eggs:** eggs are used alone and in a number of egg dishes. Eggs are also a frequently used ingredient in a range of foods as well as being used as a glaze.
5. **Fish:** used as a menu item in a variety of ways but also appears in ingredients such as Worcestershire sauce and salad dressings.
6. **Lupin:** best known as a flower but the seeds can be ground into flour for addition to bread, pastries and pasta (check labels). Seeds can be used in salads.
7. **Milk:** as a drink on its own or used in a variety of ways, commonly used in soups, sauces and desserts. Also includes cheese, yoghurt, butter and other spreads where components of butter may be added.
8. **Molluscs:** includes shellfish such as mussels, oysters and snails; also oyster sauce.
9. **Mustard:** may be in liquid, powder or paste form and is a frequent addition to soups, sauces, salad dressings and marinades.
10. **Tree nuts:** these include almonds, hazelnuts, walnuts, brazil nuts, cashews, pecans, pistachios and macadamia nuts. Apart from being eaten on their own, nuts are ingredients in a wide range of foods either whole, chopped or ground. Also be aware of the use of nut oils.
11. **Peanuts:** also sometimes called groundnuts. Apart from being a popular snack food, peanuts are ingredients in a wide range of foods either whole, chopped or ground. Also be aware of the use of peanut oils.
12. **Sesame seeds:** these have a number of uses in bread, biscuits and pastries. They are frequently sprinkled on the top of bread or burger buns. Also used as an ingredient in some curries and in pastes such as tahini.
13. **Soya:** edamame beans are actually soya and are eaten whole. Also made into bean curd, textured soya products, meat products, desserts and ice cream, and can be an ingredient in bread too.
14. **Sulphur dioxide and sulphates:** these are used as preservatives in soft drinks, wine, beer, prepared fruit and vegetables, and some vinegars.

Legal responsibilities relating to allergens have been strengthened by the Food Information Regulations 2014. For more information and advice visit the Food Standards Agency website: www.food.gov.uk/business-industry/allergy-guide

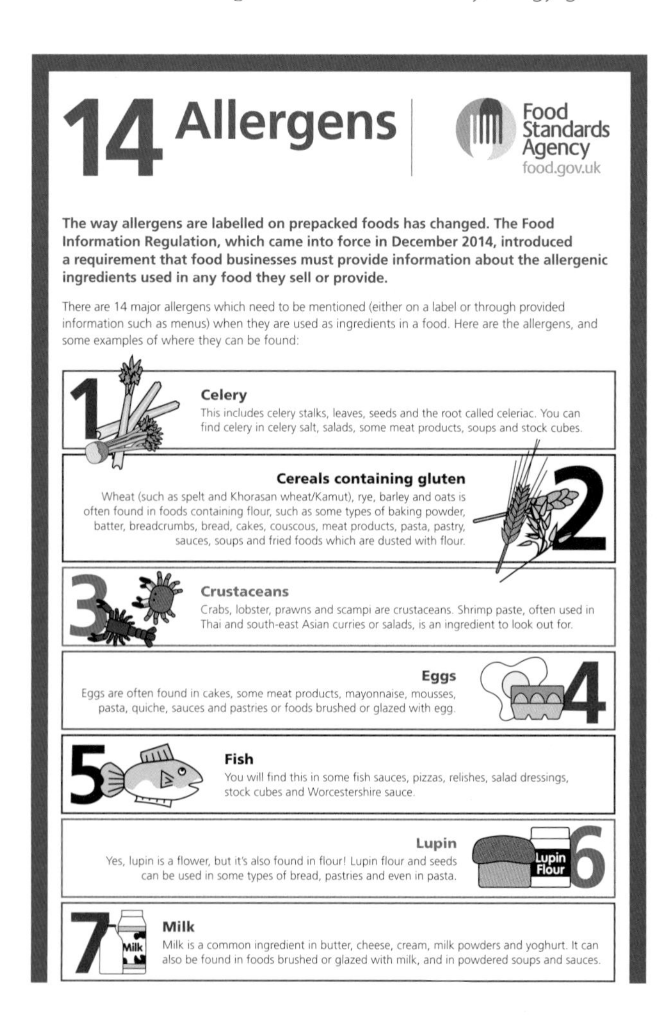

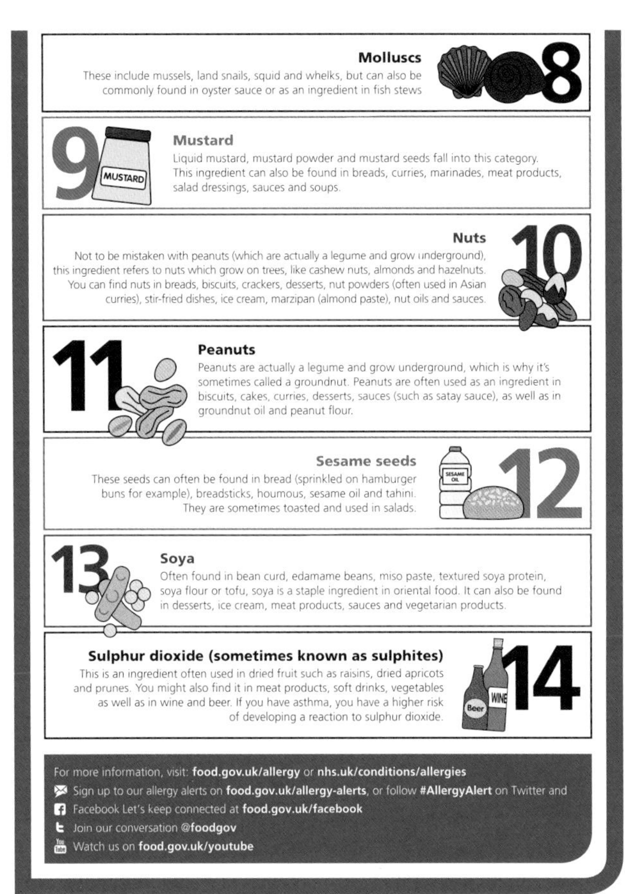

You can avoid allergenic contamination by:

- remaining aware of possible allergens in the food that you prepare and cook
- providing accurate information for customers on menus, notice boards, information cards, screens, verbally or in any other suitable way
- being aware that packaged food such as sandwiches must have allergens in the food listed and in bold.

Avoid allergen cross-contamination by:

- cleaning areas thoroughly between different food types
- using specific equipment for allergic customers
- taking care that items such as sauces and garnishes do not contain allergens
- retaining food packaging for allergen information.

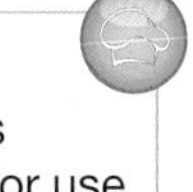

PROFESSIONAL TIP

Specific colour-coded equipment (purple) such as chopping boards and spatulas are now available for use in the preparation of food for allergy suffers.

TEST YOURSELF

1. In the Food Information Regulations how many allergens are identified?
2. What is anaphylactic shock?
3. What colour is the coded kitchen equipment that has been produced for use with food for allergy sufferers?
4. What is the difference between molluscs and crustaceans?
5. Name four popular foods that contain milk that could not be given to someone with a milk intolerance.
6. How could allergen information be given to customers in a restaurant?

2.5 Sources of food contamination

Contamination of food means that there is something present that impairs the quality of the food, changes the taste, could cause harm or illness, or could cause an allergic reaction.

Contamination of food could lead to food poisoning, which can be an unpleasant illness for anyone, and can be very serious or even fatal for 'high risk' people who may have low or reduced immune systems. This includes:

- babies and the very young
- elderly people
- pregnant women
- those who are already unwell or recovering from an illness.

How is food contaminated?

There are four main ways that food can become contaminated:

1 allergenic contamination (as described in section 2.4)
2 biological contamination
3 chemical contamination
4 physical contamination.

All must be avoided and are described in more detail below.

PROFESSIONAL TIP

If you are aware that food has become contaminated or become unsafe in any way during in its storage, preparation, cooking or preparation for service, it is essential that you do not serve it to a customer. Always report your concerns to someone in charge and remain aware of how to avoid contamination.

KEY TERMS

Best before date: Date coding appearing on packaged foods that are stored at room temperature and is an indication of quality. Use of the food within the date is not legally binding but it is bad practice to use foods that have exceeded this date

Danger zone: The temperature range at which bacteria are most likely to multiply; the danger zone temperature range is between 5°C and 63°C, with most rapid activity around 37°C

FIFO: First in–first out; refers to using older food stocks before new deliveries

Food spoilage: Foods spoiled by the action of bacteria, moulds yeasts or enzymes. The food may smell or taste unpleasant, be sticky, slimy, dry, wrinkled or discoloured. Food spoilage is usually detectable by sight, smell or touch

Pathogenic bacteria: Bacteria that can cause illness either by infection or by the toxins they may produce

Spore: A resistant, resting phase for some bacteria when they form protection around the essential part of the cell that can then survive, boiling, freezing and disinfection

Toxin: A poison produced by some bacteria as they multiply in food or as they die in the human body

Use-by date: Date coding appearing on packaged perishable foods that need to be stored in the refrigerator; use of the food within this date is a legal requirement

Biological risks – pathogenic bacteria

Biological (microbial) contamination could occur from **pathogenic bacteria** (the bacteria associated with food poisoning) and the **toxins** they may produce, viruses, yeasts, moulds, spoilage bacteria and enzymes. These can be found in the environment, on raw food, on humans, animals, birds and insects. There are many different types of bacteria and other biological organisms; many of them are completely harmless and even beneficial to the body.

However, when pathogenic bacteria multiply in food or use food to get into the human body, illness can result. Bacteria are so small that you would need a microscope to see them; you would not be able to taste them or smell them on food. This is why pathogens are so dangerous – you cannot tell if they are in food or not. When bacteria have food, warmth, moisture and time, they can multiply every 10–20 minutes by dividing in half.

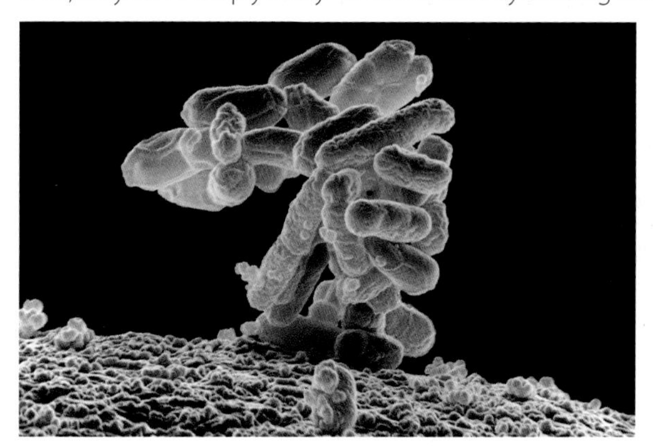

Bacteria multiplying by dividing in two; this is called binary fission

Pathogenic bacteria may act in different ways to cause food poisoning. They can multiply in food then infect the person eating it. Some bacteria can produce toxins (poisons) as they multiply or die. Toxins can survive boiling temperatures for half an hour or more. Some can produce **spores** to protect themselves from very high or low temperatures or from chemicals such as disinfectant. Normal cooking procedures do not destroy spores.

The main biological contaminants involved with food poisoning are shown in Table 1.3.

Table 1.3 The main biological contaminants involved with food poisoning

Major food poisoning pathogens	Sources of bacteria	Preferred temperature for growth	Illness onset time	Symptoms	Can it form spores?
Salmonella There are many different types of Salmonella. Poisoning can be passed on through human carriers (someone carrying salmonella but not showing any signs of illness).	Raw meat/poultry, raw egg, intestines and excreta of humans and animals Sewage/untreated water Pests and domestic pets Food sources include raw meat and poultry, raw eggs, untreated milk and shellfish	7–45°C	12–36 hours	Stomach pain, diarrhoea, vomiting, fever (1–7 days)	No
Clostridium perfringens Food poisoning incidents from this organism have occurred when large amounts of meat are brought up to cooking temperatures slowly then allowed to cool slowly for later use, or if meat does not get hot in the centre. Poultry where the cavity has been stuffed has also caused problems because the middle does not get hot enough to kill the bacteria. All these examples can lead to the formation of spores. Spores are very resistant to any further cooking and allow the survival of bacteria in conditions that would usually kill them.	Animal and human intestines and excreta Soil and sewage Insects Raw meat and poultry Unwashed vegetables and salads	15–50°C	12–18 hours	Stomach pain and diarrhoea (12–48 hours) Vomiting is rare	Yes
Staphylococcus aureus Produces a toxin in food; is heat resistant and very difficult to destroy. To avoid food poisoning from this organism, food handlers need to maintain very high standards of personal hygiene.	Humans – mouth, nose, throat, hair, scalp, skin, boils, spots, cuts, burns, etc.	7–45°C	1–7 hours	Stomach pain and vomiting, flu-like symptoms, maybe some diarrhoea, lowered body temperature (6–24 hours)	No
Clostridium botulinum A spore-forming organism that produces toxins, which fortunately is fairly rare in the UK. Symptoms can be very serious, even fatal. It multiplies in conditions where there is very little or no oxygen so is of concern to canning industries and where food is vacuum packed.	Soil, fish intestines, dirty vegetables and some animals	7–48°C	2 hours – 8 days (usually 12–36 hours)	Difficulty with speech, breathing and swallowing Double vision, nerve paralysis Death	Yes
Bacillus cereus Produces spores and two different types of toxin. One toxin is produced in food as the organisms multiply or expire and the other in the human intestine as the organisms expire. Bacillus cereus can survive whether oxygen is present or not, and is more difficult to destroy when fats and oils are present. It is often associated with cooking rice in large quantities, cooling it too slowly and then reheating. The spores are not destroyed and further bacterial multiplication can then take place.	Cereal crops, especially rice, spices, dust and soil (unwashed vegetables)	3–40°C	1–5 hours 8–16 hours	Vomiting, abdominal pain, maybe some diarrhoea (12–24 hours) Stomach pain, diarrhoea, some vomiting (1–2 days)	Yes

Food-borne illness

Different organisms from those described above cause what is described as food-borne illness. These do not multiply in food, but use food to get into the human gut, where they then multiply and cause a range of illnesses, some of them very serious. They include those described in Table 1.4.

Table 1.4 Organisms that cause food-borne illness

Bacteria or virus	Sources	Preferred temperature for growth	Illness onset time	Symptoms	Can it form spores?
Campylobacter jujuni/enteritis This now causes more food-related illness than any other organism. One of the reasons thought to contribute to this is the increase in consumption of fresh chicken, which is a significant source of this organism.	Raw poultry/meat, untreated milk or water, sewage, pets and pests, birds and insects	28–46°C	2–5 days	Headache, fever, bloody diarrhoea, abdominal pain (mimics appendicitis)	No
E. coli 0157VTEC There are many strains of E. coli but significant problems have been caused in recent years by E. coli 0157VTEC. Symptoms can be very serious – even fatal.	Intestines and excreta of cattle and humans Untreated water and sewage Untreated milk Raw meat, under-cooked mince, unwashed salad items and dirty vegetables	4–45°C	1–8 days (usually 3–4 days)	Stomach pain, fever, bloody diarrhoea, nausea Has caused kidney failure and death	No
Listeria monocytogenes This organism is of concern because it can multiply (very slowly) at fridge temperatures, i.e. below 5°C. It is also of concern because of the serious outcomes that poisoning from this organism can cause.	Pâté, soft cheeses made from unpasteurised milk, raw vegetables and prepared salads Cook/chill meals	0–45°C	1 day – 3 months	Meningitis, septicaemia, flu-like symptoms, stillbirth	No
Norovirus An air-borne virus, widely present in the environment and highly contagious. Passed from person to person. Does not grow in food – viruses grow only in living cells.	Can survive on surfaces, equipment and cloths for several hours	N/A	24–48 hours	Severe vomiting and diarrhoea	No
Typhoid/paratyphoid People who have suffered from this can become long-term carriers, which means they could pass the organism on to others through food (food handlers need six negative faecal samples before returning to work after illness).	Sewage, untreated water, dirty fruit/vegetables	N/A	8–14 days	Fever, nausea, enlarged spleen, red spots on abdomen Severe diarrhoea Some fatalities	No

Viruses such as norovirus are even smaller than bacteria and can be seen only with a powerful microscope. They multiply on living cells, not on food, though they may be transferred into the body on food or drinks, and may live for a short time on hard surfaces such as kitchen equipment. Viruses can be air-borne and water-borne, and are easily passed from person to person.

Toxins (poisons) can be produced by some bacteria as they multiply in food. They are heat resistant and may not be killed by the normal cooking processes that kill bacteria, so remain in the food and can cause illness. Some bacteria produce toxins as they die, usually in the intestines of the person who has eaten the food.

Spores can be formed by some bacteria in conditions such as a rise in temperature or in the presence of chemicals such as disinfectant. A spore forms a protective 'shell' inside the bacteria, protecting the essential parts from the high temperatures of normal cooking, disinfection, dehydration, etc. Once spores are formed the rest of the cell disperses and cannot divide and multiply as before but simply survives until conditions improve, e.g. high temperatures drop to a level where the cell can re-form and multiplication can start again. Prolonged cooking times and/or very high temperatures are needed to kill spores. Time is very important in preventing the formation of spores. Large amounts of food such as meat for stewing, when brought slowly to cooking temperature, allows time for spores to form; these are then very difficult to kill. Food should be brought up to cooking temperature and cooled quickly.

Food spoilage

Food spoilage refers to food that has spoiled or 'gone off'. Unlike contamination with bacteria it can usually be detected by sight, smell, taste or texture. Signs of spoilage include:

- visible mould
- slimy, over-wet or over-dry food
- sour smell or taste
- discoloured and wrinkled food
- other texture changes.

It is caused by natural breakdown and ageing of the food by organisms such as spoilage bacteria, enzymes, oxidation, moulds and yeasts, which in some cases may not be harmful themselves but cause the food to deteriorate. Spoilage may also be caused by poor storage, poor handling or by contamination of the food.

Food spoilage can account for a significant amount of unnecessary waste in a business, and if food stock is being managed and stored properly it should not happen.

Any food that has spoiled or is out of date must be reported to the supervisor/line manager then disposed of appropriately and marked 'not for human consumption'. It should be separated from general waste and disposed of away from food storage areas.

To avoid **biological contamination**, store food correctly at the recommended temperatures. Observe personal hygiene requirements, especially thorough hand washing, keep all areas and equipment clean and sanitised, and report any illness you may have before starting work.

Chemical contamination can occur when chemical items get into food accidentally. These can then make the consumer suffer discomfort or become ill. The kinds of chemicals that can get into food could be cleaning fluids, disinfectants, machine oil, degreasers and pesticides/rodenticides. Problems can also occur when there are chemical reactions between such things as metal containers and acidic foods.

To avoid chemical contamination, keep chemicals well away from open food, and when cleaning/disinfecting use the chemical exactly according to manufacturers' and data sheets' instructions. Keep all items in their original containers and do not use containers for anything else.

Physical contamination is caused when something gets into foods that should not be there. This could include a wide range of items, such as glass, nuts, bolts and oil from machinery, flaking paint, pen tops, threads from worn clothing, buttons, blue plasters, hair or insects, among many others.

To avoid physical contamination, work with care, and keep work areas clean and free of any items that could cause contamination (this is knows as 'clean as you go'). High standards of personal hygiene and the correct work clothing will also help to prevent physical contamination.

Cross-contamination

Cross-contamination is when bacteria, allergens or other contaminants are transferred from contaminated food (often raw food) to ready-to-eat food. It is a cause of food poisoning and care must be taken to avoid it. Causes of cross-contamination include:

- foods touching – for example, raw and cooked meat or foods containing allergens and non-allergen foods
- raw meat or poultry dripping on to high-risk foods
- soil from dirty vegetables coming into contact with high-risk foods
- use of dirty cloths or dirty equipment
- equipment such as chopping boards or knives used for raw then cooked food, or allergen then non-allergen food, without proper cleaning or disinfection
- equipment, surfaces or hands used for foods or ingredients containing allergens then being used for preparation of food for an allergy sufferer without thorough cleaning
- hands touching raw food then cooked food, or not washing hands thoroughly between tasks and after breaks.

Controlling cross-contamination

Ways of avoiding cross-contamination in any food business should be part of the food safety management system (HACCP); see section 1.2 for further details. Having separate areas for different foods, storage, processes and service will help to reduce the risk of contamination, and assist efficient working and effective cleaning. Thorough and ongoing staff training on how cross-contamination can be avoided is of great importance. This must be planned and recorded in the **food safety** management system, but informal training should also occur in every working day.

Colour-coded equipment

Worktops and chopping boards will come into contact with the food being prepared so need special attention. Make sure that chopping boards are in good condition; cracks and splits could hold on to bacteria and this could be transferred to food. Colour-coded chopping boards are a good way to keep different types of food separate.

PROFESSIONAL TIP

As well as colour-coded chopping boards some kitchens also provide colour-coded knives, cloths, cleaning equipment, storage trays, bowls and even staff uniforms to help prevent cross-contamination.

TEST YOURSELF

1. What is meant by the term food poisoning? What are the main symptoms?
2. What are the four main ways that food can become contaminated?
3. What is a spore? Name three pathogens that can produce spores.
4. What is a toxin and how can toxins cause illness?
5. What are the products and chemicals that may be present in a kitchen and could cause chemical contamination if care is not taken?
6. What is meant by food spoilage and how is it different to food being contaminated by pathogenic bacteria?
7. Which people would be included in the 'high risk' group for food poisoning and why are they high risk?
8. In relation to illness from food, what is a virus and how is a virus different from bacteria?
9. What are the temperatures between 5°C and 63°C called? Why are these temperatures important?
10. In relation to certain bacteria, what is meant by a human carrier?

2.6 Identification and control of pests

Pests in food premises can be a serious source of contamination and disease; having them near food cannot be allowed and is against the law.

Pests that can cause problems in food premises include rats and mice, flies and wasps, cockroaches, ants, weevils, birds, domestic pets and wild cats.

Pests can be attracted to food premises because there is food, warmth, shelter, water and possible nesting material; all reasonable measures must be put in place to keep them out.

Signs of pest infestation include:

- sightings of animal, insect or bird droppings
- unpleasant smells
- smear marks (dirty, greasy marks where rodents run close to walls)
- damaged commodities, gnawed packaging and food spillages
- pupae, larvae, eggs or cases, holes in skirting boards, door and window frames or gnawed wires.

Pests in food premises can also lead to:

- contamination, spread of disease and the cause of food poisoning
- legal action against the business, which could include large fines
- loss of reputation leading to loss of business and therefore financial losses
- closure of the business
- poor staff morale, because somewhere infested with pests would probably have other problems too, making it an unpleasant place to work
- damage to equipment, buildings, fittings and wastage of food.

Pests can be kept out of the building or dealt with in a number of ways:

- block entry – make sure there are no holes around pipework; remove any gaps and cavities where pests could get in; seal all drain covers; damage to the building or fixtures and fittings must be repaired quickly to block the ways in
- use window/door screening/netting
- check deliveries/packaging for pests
- place bait boxes and traps in relevant places; pest control contractors will advise
- use an electronic fly killer or 'insectocutor'
- seal containers and do not leave food out in the open
- avoid a build-up of waste in the kitchen and dispose of waste appropriately

- do not keep outside waste too close to the kitchen; ensure containers are emptied regularly and the area is clean and tidy
- metal kick plates on the bottom of doors will help to prevent rodents gaining entry
- arrange for professional and organised pest management control, surveys and reports.

Any suspicion of pests being present must be reported to the supervisor or manager immediately. Pest problems are best dealt with by a recognised pest contractor; they can also complete audits and give advice.

PROFESSIONAL TIP

The only pests a food business can deal with itself are flying insects with an electronic fly killer. For all other pests professional help is needed.

TEST YOURSELF

1. Name five pests that may find their way into a kitchen.
2. If you entered the kitchen in the morning and saw small black pellets, chewed packaging and spilled flour, what would you think the problem was and what would you do about it?
3. Suggest three ways that you could prevent pests entering the kitchen.
4. If small flying insects came into a kitchen how could they be dealt with?
5. What is the best way to deal with a pest problem in a kitchen?
6. What could happen to a food business if it was found to have a pest problem?

ACTIVITY

1. Produce a leaflet for new kitchen staff highlighting ten ways that they can avoid cross-contamination in a kitchen. Use illustrations where appropriate and include allergen cross-contamination.
2. Suggest some pieces of new kitchen equipment that will help to reduce the risk of cross-contamination.
3. How could cross-contamination occur when food is stored in a refrigerator? What measures could you put in place to avoid this?
4. Which colour-coded chopping board would you use to cut each of the following:
   a. raw salmon
   b. cooked chicken
   c. bread
   d. cucumber
   e. uncooked carrots
   f. raw fillet beef
   g. cooked savoury flan
   h. food for someone with an allergy?

Small equipment can be cleaned and disinfected very effectively by putting it through a dishwasher. Loose debris is scraped or sprayed off, the machine washes at approximately 55°C using a detergent then rinses at 82°C, which disinfects and allows items to air dry quickly.

Large equipment, such as large mixing machines and ovens, cannot be moved so need to be cleaned where they are. This is called 'clean in place' and each item will have a specific method outlined on the cleaning schedule. Sometimes steam cleaning methods are used that also disinfect the items.

TAKE IT FURTHER

After an engagement party for 50 guests at a hotel there was an outbreak of food poisoning. Guests were suffering from severe vomiting about two hours after eating the food. The EHO investigating the incident was concerned about levels of staff hygiene in the kitchen. Only partial uniforms were worn and these were in poor repair. The only hand wash basin was blocked and there was no soap or towels. It was also mentioned that there were no health and safety signs in the kitchen.

1. Which organism do you think was responsible for the outbreak?
2. What are the measures that you think would be recommended to put matters right?
3. What training needs to be put in place?
4. Make an itemised list of which items and equipment need to be bought to assist with the improvements.
5. Suggest a good online source of information on food safety matters. What are two food safety information matters you could find there?

3 Maintain health and safety

Health and safety are very important in the hospitality industry. It is essential that working safely becomes part of the culture of every workplace to prevent accidents and injuries, to maintain health and to increase productivity. Working safely can increase productivity because there will be fewer interruptions to deal with minor injuries, collisions, falls, faulty equipment and a wide range of other safety-related issues. You need to understand the principles of health and safety and how to apply them when you are working.

3.1 Factors that contribute to the risk of accidents

The reasons why accidents can happen in kitchens and other hospitality areas can be divided into the categories below.

Occupational factors

Kitchen and restaurant premises and equipment can potentially be very dangerous. You will need to consider the safe use of knives and other sharp tools, mixing and cutting machinery, open gas jets or flames, steam, smoke (from smoking equipment), very hot surfaces such as solid top stoves and a wide range of other items.

The food you work with and the process you complete can also be hazardous. For example, those working frequently with flour can suffer from inhaling the dust (a mask could be worn); some can develop an allergy to items such as yeast or nuts; frequent handling of items such as fish or some vegetables can cause skin irritation (use of gloves or masks may be needed). Occasionally sharp fish or meat bones may cause cuts.

You will be dealing with chemicals for cleaning, disinfection, grease removal and a range of other processes. It is important to handle these with care and follow instructions to prevent skin and possible inhalation problems. Use the required personal protective equipment (PPE) such as gloves. Long sleeves will help to prevent skin contact and masks reduce inhalation problems.

Environmental factors

Employers are legally bound to provide suitable working conditions and facilities. They must also consider the layout of your working area so it does not become overcrowded with too much crossover of activities that could make it dangerous.

Accidents and ill health can occur when consistently working in very high temperatures, where you can become over-hot, dehydrated, dizzy and feel unwell.

Good lighting must be provided. Poor lighting can make working conditions difficult and poor visibility could lead to accidents.

Kitchens can become very noisy, especially large kitchens. Prolonged high noise levels can result in ear damage, and high levels of noise could lead to accidents when called instructions or warnings are not heard.

Human factors

It is important that those working in a kitchen have the required experience or adequate supervision. Proper training is essential for all tasks to be completed to avoid accidents or injury. Anyone without the skills or experience needed must be supervised until full training is given.

Someone who is not concentrating fully on what they are doing, or is just being careless, foolish or immature in their actions (sometimes called horseplay) can cause injury to themselves or to someone else. A lack of concentration and poor performance can be because of someone's mental or physical state. For example, they may have a physical condition such as a back injury, be suffering from stress, feel overworked or have personal concerns, all of which may result in them losing concentration. Anyone at work under the influence of alcohol, drugs or other substances may lose concentration and the ability to complete their job well; they should not be working and certainly should not be operating machinery. No one should ever suffer physical or verbal abuse in their workplace and if this happens it must be reported immediately to the relevant person.

HEALTH AND SAFETY
Work in an organised, clean and tidy way. This will help to reduce the risk of accidents and injury.

3.2 Common injuries and their causes

A wide range of injuries can occur in kitchens and other hospitality areas if correct precautions are not taken (see Table 1.5).

Table 1.5 Examples of common injuries

Injury type	Examples
Head injuries	• Falling from height or down stairs, slipping and hitting head on equipment or fittings • Doors closing on to head • Standing from crouched position and hitting head on shelving, etc. • Objects falling on to head, e.g. from high equipment storage or boxes in a store room
Musculoskeletal, e.g. breaks (fractures), strains, sprains, bruising	• Lifting something too heavy or lifting wrongly • Using equipment wrongly or without training • Slipping or tripping, falling from a height • Falling objects (as above) • Collisions with moving objects such as loaded trucks or trolleys
Cuts and grazes	Injury from a wide range of items in a food environment including: • incorrect use of sharp equipment • cuts from meat or fish bones or shells • cuts from packaging
Burns and scalds	Burns (from dry heat) or scalds from wet sources can be fairly common in food environments because of the wide range of hot equipment and processes used

There are a number of common causes of injury, as described below.

Inadequate training

It is a legal requirement that employees are given the necessary training and supervision for the tasks they complete, and training procedures form part of employers' risk assessments. Never complete work or use a piece of equipment if you are unsure about it; ask for training and instruction. Use and cleaning of some equipment, such as slicing machines, are regulated by age (i.e. over 18) and on the correct recorded training having been completed.

Slips, trips and falls

These are the most frequent causes of accident and injury in food premises, not just because of the incident itself. The person could fall on to something very hot like a deep fryer or solid-top stove, could spill something they are carrying on to themselves, such as a pan of hot soup, or could fall on to a sharp object such as a knife. They could also hit their head on a table or piece of equipment as they fall, or they could fall on to moving machinery. All reasonable measures must be taken to avoid slips, trips and falls in working areas.

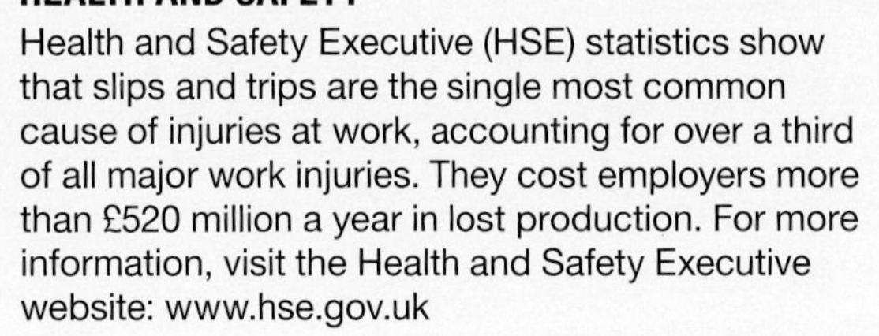

HEALTH AND SAFETY

Health and Safety Executive (HSE) statistics show that slips and trips are the single most common cause of injuries at work, accounting for over a third of all major work injuries. They cost employers more than £520 million a year in lost production. For more information, visit the Health and Safety Executive website: www.hse.gov.uk

Incorrect use of equipment

Machinery and food production equipment is designed to be used in certain ways without causing any injury or strain to the operator. However, if these are used wrongly, not assembled correctly or the required safety procedures are not in place, accidents and injuries may be the result. If you think that equipment is unsafe or that you are being asked to use it in an unsafe way, seek advice from a manager or someone in charge. Always make sure you have had full training before using any piece of equipment or machine, and if you are still unsure ask for further training before using it.

Faulty equipment

All equipment must be in good working condition and regularly maintained to do the job for which it is intended without causing any injury. Report any faulty or dangerous equipment to a supervisor immediately and warn others not to use it by use of a written sign as well as verbal warnings if necessary. Faulty equipment can cause serious injury.

Incorrect use of PPE

Personal protective equipment (PPE) and clothing is designed to protect employees as they work. Typical PPE for a food environment may consist of a full chef's uniform, which protects the body from heat, spills and sharp objects, and reinforced safety shoes to protect feet from hot, heavy or sharp items. PPE may be provided for special tasks, such as a padded jacket and gloves for working in a freezer, goggles and mask when using strong oven-cleaning chemicals, and strong rubber gloves when cleaning pots and pans.

Employers have a responsibility to provide the correct PPE for their employees for the tasks to be completed and, where necessary, to provide training in its correct use. Employees must attend and follow this training. It is the employee's responsibility to use and look after the equipment properly and not to misuse it. It must be kept in good, clean condition and the employer must be informed of damage, defects and when it needs replacing. There must be somewhere provided such as a locker for an employee to store their PPE; changing facilities must also be available. PPE used incorrectly can result in accidents and injury.

Inadequate housekeeping

For a working area to be safe it needs to be kept as clean, tidy and organised as possible. Injuries can be caused by poor housekeeping – for example:

- leaving boxes and other items on walkways where they could be tripped over
- not cleaning up spills of liquid or oil on the floor immediately
- storing equipment and deliveries badly so they can fall.

Regular planned cleaning and good working practices can greatly assist in maintaining good housekeeping standards.

Inadequate lighting

Good lighting is essential in workplaces such as kitchens, and minimum lighting levels are covered by health and safety law. Lighting not sufficient for tasks being completed results in dim or dark areas; poor vision can lead to hazards and warning signs not being seen. Good lighting will also show areas that need to be cleaned and that cleaning has been done properly. Lighting systems need to be sufficient for the tasks being carried out, well maintained so they work properly, and replaced as necessary. They must also be kept clean – dirty, greasy light fittings will not give off as much light.

Bad behaviour

The safety of the working environment and those working in it is the responsibility of every employee. Bad, irresponsible and foolish behaviour in what can be a potentially dangerous environment is never acceptable, and can lead to accidents and injury. Anyone found to be behaving badly or irresponsibly should expect disciplinary procedures and possibly dismissal. Bad behaviour also includes bullying, and physical and verbal abuse.

Inadequate signage

Kitchens and other hospitality areas will display a range of health and safety signage in appropriate places. It is important that employees are aware of these and understand what they mean. They should be clearly visible, not covered with other items and if illuminated should be working properly. Any worn or out-of-date signs should be replaced. Inadequate signage would mean that an employer is not meeting its legal health and safety responsibilities, and that it is more likely that accidents and misunderstandings could occur.

3.3 Maintaining health and safety by implementing control measures

Appropriate training

It is a legal requirement that all employees, especially young employees, be fully trained in the procedures they complete and the equipment and chemicals they use. Training should be ongoing and must reflect any changes in procedures, equipment or legislation. Formal training should be recorded, with updates as necessary. Training must also reflect the needs of employees who need extra support in understanding procedures and instruction, and those for whom English is not their first language.

Good housekeeping

This plays a vital role in keeping a workplace and the employees in it healthy and safe. Good housekeeping is everyone's responsibility. Clean up spills immediately and warn others, put equipment and ingredients back into their proper storage, and develop a 'clean as you go' method of working. If you notice anything that is preventing proper and safe housekeeping taking place – for example, a shortage of cleaning materials or equipment not working – report it immediately.

Correct use of PPE

PPE is not a replacement for other safety measures but an additional safety precaution and other relevant safety procedures must be considered first. The actual equipment or clothing issued will be related to the job being completed. For example, an employee working in frozen storage areas over long periods will be issued with a range of padded clothing, gloves and goggles. It is of great importance that items are used with care and exactly as intended. Anything that doesn't fit properly will not be as effective, so ill-fitting items and any damaged or worn items should be reported to the employer so they can be replaced. PPE must also be worn properly – for example, if a uniform has long sleeves for arm protection they should not be rolled up. Also take care that PPE does not produce a hazard – for example, an apron that is too long could be tripped over.

Following manufacturers' instructions

The preparation, cooking and other equipment you use in a food production area will carry manufacturers' instructions for their safe and proper use. It is very important that you follow these instructions properly; this should be an ongoing part of your training. If you do not understand how something works, ask for further explanation and training. Take special care to follow instructions with electrical and gas equipment. If you suspect that a piece of equipment is faulty, do not use it and report it immediately.

In hospitality areas there are also a number of substances you may use that could be hazardous to health if not used properly. They include cleaning chemicals such as detergents, disinfectants, sanitisers, degreasers and descalers, fuel gels and spirits, and cooking liquids and gases. Anyone using chemicals in their job must be fully trained in their correct use and provided with suitable protective equipment or clothing such as gloves or goggles.

Always follow the manufacturer's instructions for chemical use; how they should be diluted or mixed, how spillages should be dealt with (especially if spilt on the skin or eyes) and how used products should be disposed of. Kitchen areas will display safety data sheets with information on chemicals, how they are to be used, and how to deal with spillages and accidents. Make sure you are familiar with this information and never mix different chemicals

The Control of Substances Hazardous to Health (COSHH) regulations were consolidated in 2002 and are the main legislation dealing with hazardous substances. See section 1.1 for more details of the COSHH regulations.

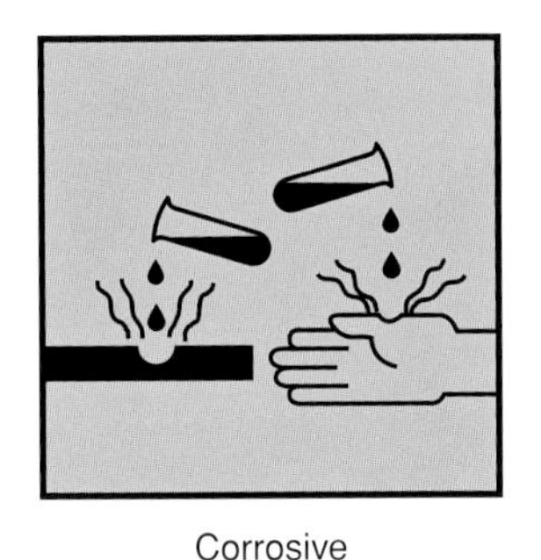

Corrosive

Flammable

Harmful

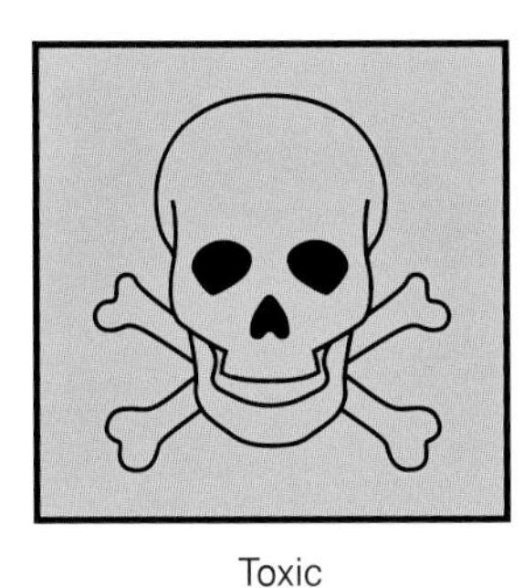

Toxic

Labels for hazardous chemicals

For information on the safe use of chemicals see page 2.

Correct manual handling techniques

In kitchens and hospitality premises a wide range of lifting and handling will be done. It could include boxes of deliveries, various foodstuffs and ingredients, preparation and cooking equipment, laundry and many other items. The hazards from these may be increased because the item may be hot, such as a baking tray or pan of soup; it could be heavy, such as a large, full baking tray; it could be wet, such as deliveries of fresh fish; or very cold, such as frozen food deliveries. Never lift anything too heavy or large for you to handle well. Get help or use equipment such as trolleys.

The main injuries that can occur from incorrect manual handling are:

- back and spinal injuries
- muscular injuries
- fractures
- sprains
- cuts, bruises and burns.

Avoiding injury from lifting and carrying

- Always consider the item to be moved – its weight, size, temperature and shape. Is it possible to make the load smaller – for example, unloading large cans of tomatoes from their outer cases?
- Consider the distance you need to move the item and whether that distance could be minimised.
- Ask for help – the task is often easier with two people.
- Consider the use of any available lifting equipment.
- Consider using a trolley, but do not lift anything on to the trolley that is too heavy for you. Do not load the trolley too high because you will not be able to see what is in front of you and the load may become unstable and fall off.
- Consider the environment – are there any uneven floors, stairs, high or low temperatures, or low lighting? These will all make a difference.
- Avoid handling wet or greasy loads and do not try to move items when floors are wet or slippery.

- Wear the correct PPE.
- Do not unload, carry or store heavy items, sharp items or hot items above shoulder height.
- Do not lift and carry heavy, hot or awkward items if you feel unwell.
- If you are lifting, unloading or moving heavy items as a regular part of your job you should receive manual handling training.

Correct lifting technique

1. Assess the load – can it be made smaller? Can lifting or carrying equipment be used? Consider the weight and shape and where you need to move it to.
2. Stand close to the load, with your feet apart and your weight evenly spread, chin tucked in, shoulders level.
3. Bend the knees, keeping the back straight, and grip the load at the base or with handles, keeping it close to your body.

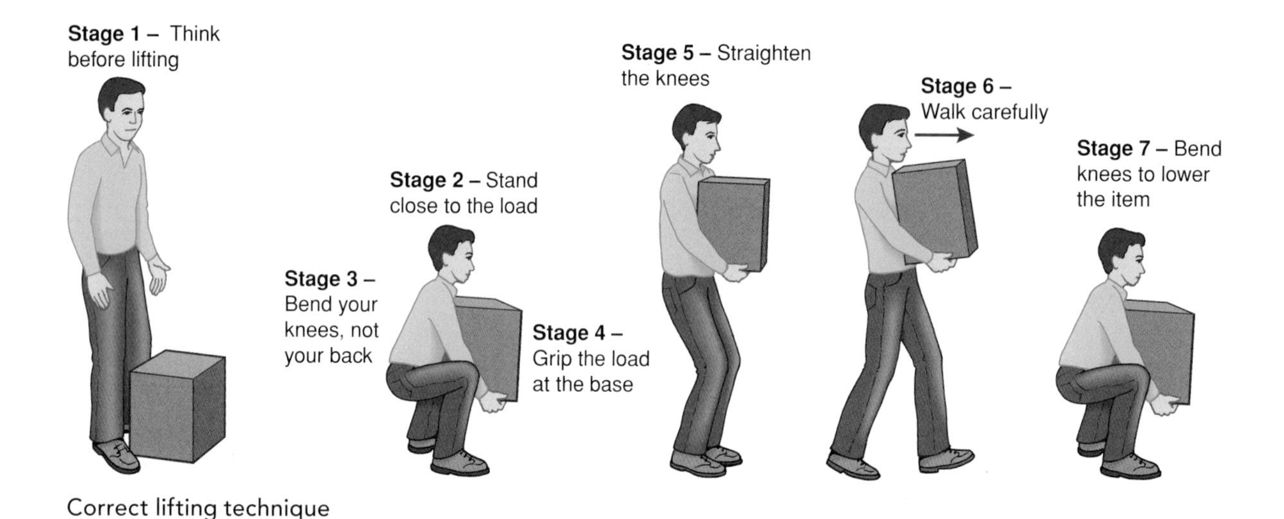

Correct lifting technique

4. Bring the load up to waist height and straighten the knees.
5. Walk carefully, making sure that you can see where you are going.
6. Lower the item in place again with bent knees and straight back.

Colour-coded safety signs

Health and safety signs point out messages using shape, colour, symbols, pictures and words, but should not replace other methods of controlling risks. Ideally they should be easy to understand by those speaking other languages. The signs are divided into four general categories, as described below.

Yellow sign

Yellow signs/warning signs

These warn of various dangers such as wet floors, hot surfaces or **corrosive** materials. Probably the most frequently used yellow sign is the tent-shaped wet floor sign.

Blue signs/mandatory signs

These inform about precautions that must be taken, such as how to progress safely through certain areas or the PPE that must be used.

Blue sign

Red signs/prohibition or fire-fighting signs

Red signs inform of what must not be done in a particular area – for example, no entry or no smoking. Red signs are also used for fire-fighting equipment such as hose reels.

Red sign

Green signs/safe signs

Green signs are used to guide people to fire escapes and emergency exits. Green is also used to point out where first aid equipment is kept or where first aid rooms are.

Green signs

Reporting issues or problems

It is sometimes necessary for employees to report matters they think may affect health and safety. These would usually be reported to a supervisor or line manager and would include:

- damage, decay or misuse of the building or equipment
- ill health, including dermatitis or infectious diseases
- injury when at work
- environmental problems, including excessive noise or heat or cold
- abuse from others, such as bullying, physical or verbal abuse.

No one should be working in hospitality premises if they feel unwell. There are some illnesses where the sufferer must not go near or handle food but must report to their supervisor for advice.

Accident reporting procedures

All accidents (and near misses) that happen in the workplace should be recorded correctly. It is important to report and record any accident or injury you may have at work, no matter how small. This may be in the form of verbal or written reports. The system most workplaces use for this is individual paper accident report forms, which are then stored in a file. Sometimes an electronic system may be used but all systems must conform to data protection requirements.

The recording must include:

- the date, time and place of the event
- the date when the report is made
- personal details of those involved
- a brief description of the nature of the event or accident.

Serious accidents must be reported to the relevant authority under RIDDOR (see section 1.1). There is more accident reporting information on the Health and Safety Executive website: www.hse.gov.uk

Fire handling and evacuation procedures

Fire safety must be completed as part of the employer's risk assessment. Employees must only ever tackle a fire when they are sure how to do so and if it does not put them at risk. Many companies run fire extinguisher training sessions for staff. Various pieces of fire-fighting equipment will be present in hospitality premises, with the relevant extinguishers placed where certain fires may occur – for example, a wet chemical extinguisher and a fire blanket may be placed near frying equipment.

KNOW YOUR FIRE EXTINGUISHER COLOUR CODE

Water	Dry powder	Foam	CO_2 Carbon dioxide	Wet chemical
For use on: A Wood, Paper, Textiles etc.	For use on: A Wood, Paper, Textiles etc.; B Flammable liquids; C Gaseous fires; Live electrical equipment	For use on: A Wood, Paper, Textiles etc.; B Flammable liquids	For use on: B Flammable liquids; Live electrical equipment	For use on: F Cooking oil fires
Do not use on: B Flammable liquids; Live electrical equipment		Do not use on: Live electrical equipment	Do not use in a confined space	

Types of fire extinguisher and their uses

Fire fuel, heat/ignition, oxygen

Fire and possible explosions are always risks that need to be considered in hospitality premises. They may be caused by gas jets or open flames, overheated oils and other hot liquid substances, and by fuel gels. They could also be caused by electrical faults or faulty equipment, gas leaks or gas build-up and chemicals, but also by carelessness and misuse of equipment. Smoking can be a cause of fire and is not allowed in most buildings; smoking should also not be allowed outside near gas canisters, waste oil, or items such as paper and cardboard.

The business owner or employer must conduct a **fire risk assessment** of the premises and business, identify the risks and put measures in place to make them as safe as possible. This may include:

- Installing fire alarms and testing them regularly to make sure they are working
- making sure that escape routes are clearly marked and there are no obstacles in the way
- ensuring that fire detection systems are in place
- providing suitable equipment for extinguishing fires.

Three elements are needed for fire: heat, oxygen and fuel. If one of these is taken away the fire will not start or continue. Extinguishing fires relies on removing one of these elements, such as restricting the supply of oxygen (a foam extinguisher acts in this way) or removing the heat (a water extinguisher cools the burning material down).

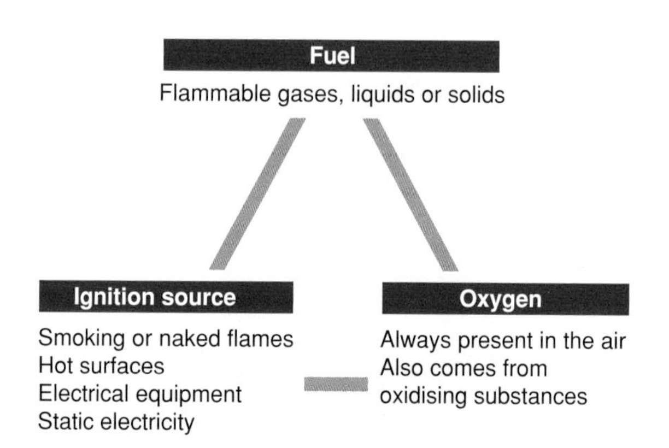

Fire triangle

Fire evacuation

Training in procedures to follow in case of fire, explosion, security threat or other emergency is essential for all staff. There must be a fire and evacuation plan in place that is fully recorded in the risk assessment. Staff must know how to follow the evacuation plan and leave the building safely, assisting customers and visitors where appropriate. Planned practice and training procedures need to be part of the risk assessment.

If a fire breaks out in your work area:

- raise the alarm and warn others verbally
- turn off gas supplies using a central cut-off point if possible
- never put yourself in danger; only tackle small fires and then only if you have been trained in doing this

- leave by the appointed escape route and go to the assembly point; remain there and do not re-enter the building until told to do so.

Risk assessments

As part of managing the health and safety procedures in a business and to comply with legislation, an employer must control the potential **risks** in the workplace (Management of Health and Safety at Work Regulations 1999).

To do this an employer must have conducted a full **risk assessment** of premises and procedures including the consideration of anything with the potential to cause harm. They must then put the necessary controls in place to keep employees safe, and keep records of this. All employees must be given a copy of the risk assessment.

If there are fewer than five employees a full written risk assessment is not required but the employer still has a duty of care for the health and safety of employees at work.

KEY TERMS

Risk: The possibility that someone could be harmed by a hazard

Risk assessment: The process of identifying and evaluating hazards and risks, and putting measures in place to control them; this process should be recorded and reviewed

Managing risk need not be a complicated procedure, and guidance – including useful templates – is available on the Health and Safety Executive website: www.hse.gov.uk

You will also find useful information on the website of the Royal Society for the Prevention of Accidents: www.rospa.com

Security procedures

Hospitality premises need to be kept as secure as practically possible to ensure the safety of employees, customers, guests and others who may be authorised to be in the building. Security is also necessary for the protection of equipment and fittings, as well as cash. Increasingly security will also include remaining alert to any possibility of terrorist attacks. There will be various security measures around the building that could include, among others:

- limited access and keys to certain areas
- key pads
- electronic swipe cards
- security cameras with recordings
- security staff.

All staff need to remain aware of security issues and report anything they think is of concern and could affect security of the premises or the people working there.

Waste management

It is important that all employees keep waste to a minimum, especially as there is increasing concern about the amounts of waste going into landfill sites and most businesses will be charged for the amount of waste collected from their premises. Waste should be collected as frequently as is practical because excess waste on the premises can be a contamination, pest and fire hazard.

Most businesses will be required to separate their waste into different types – for example, waste food, bottles, cans, cardboard, paper and plastic items.

Waste disposal

Kitchen waste should be placed in waste bins with lids, preferably foot-operated and lined with a strong bin liner. They need to be strong, kept in good condition and away from direct sunlight. Bins should be emptied regularly to avoid cross-contamination and odour, and should never be left unemptied in the kitchen overnight as this could result in the multiplication of bacteria and attracting pests.

TEST YOURSELF

1 Suggest four effects there could be on staff working in a kitchen with poor lighting and ventilation.
2 What are four ways that an accidental fire could start in a kitchen? How could these be prevented?
3 What are the most common kinds of accident in hospitality workplaces? Suggest three ways that these could be avoided.
4 What is meant by each of the following terms:
   a hazard
   b PPE
   c evacuation procedure
   d risk assessment
   e data sheets?
5 Which fire extinguisher would be used on a deep fat or oil fire? Which fire extinguisher would be used on an electrical fire?
6 Give an example of each of the following health and safety signs. What information is each giving?
   a Yellow sign
   b Blue sign
   c Red sign
   d Green sign
7 Name three health and safety-related concerns you should report to a supervisor or line manager?
8 It is necessary to keep business premises secure. What could happen without adequate security? What are the security measures that could be put in place?

ACTIVITY

A large restaurant has been criticised because it is not completing the necessary recycling of waste.

1 Produce a chart of the waste that is likely to be produced in a kitchen and restaurant, and separate it into types that can be recycled. Include information on the chart about what needs to happen before recycling, e.g. do bottles and containers need to be washed, do bottle tops go into recycling?
2 What are the different containers (bins) you will need for various items both inside and outside?
3 Can used fryer oil be recycled and how would you do this?
4 Produce some information for kitchen staff (a poster, leaflet or PowerPoint presentation) to explain how the recycling is going to work and the necessity of separating waste into the different containers.

202 Introduction to professional cookery

The purpose of this chapter is to provide you with an understanding of the different characteristics of hospitality and catering establishments, and professional kitchens. It includes an exploration of the scope and importance of the industry and the career opportunities it offers. It also covers the areas of a professional kitchen, and the roles and responsibilities of those working in them, as well as the importance of effective teamwork within those areas.

The chapter also covers the different methods of cooking food, what constitutes a balanced diet, the dietary requirements of different groups of people, and how the provision of key nutrients is important to the provision of a healthy diet.

There is an introduction to the importance of stock management, sustainability, seasonal demands and the impact of the 'carbon footprint'. Attention is also given to the availability of suppliers, and sourcing commodities – locally, nationally or internationally.

Learning outcomes

In this chapter, you will be able to:

1 understand the different characteristics of hospitality establishments and professional kitchens, including:
 - **1.1** characteristics of hospitality establishments
 - **1.2** types of professional kitchens
 - **1.3** areas within professional kitchens

2 understand the job roles and required behaviours in a professional kitchen, including:
 - **2.1** job roles
 - **2.2** required behaviours

3 understand nutrition, dietary requirements and cookery methods, including:
 - **3.1** key nutrients and their impact on health
 - **3.2** dietary requirements of different groups
 - **3.3** cookery methods
 - **3.4** production of food to suit nutritional or dietary requirements

4 understand stock management and sustainability considerations in professional cookery, including:
 - **4.1** stock management considerations
 - **4.2** sustainability considerations

1 Understand the different characteristics of hospitality establishments and professional kitchens

The term 'hospitality' covers all aspects of the hotel and catering industry. Hospitality means the welcoming of guests and customers, whereas 'catering' tends to refer to the offering of facilities, especially food and drinks.

The hospitality and catering industry is one of the largest industries in the UK. It is also one of the largest employers (employing more than two million people) and continues to grow. Therefore there are numerous opportunities to work in hospitality and catering, with further opportunities for education and training. Every type of hospitality operation is different, and creates different opportunities and challenges.

1.1 Characteristics of hospitality establishments

Types of operation in the hospitality industry

The hospitality and catering industry is wide and varied, and the size of businesses can vary from a large hotel group to a small independently owned café. The business types will vary too, and will fall into one of the categories below.

Sole trader

A sole trader is the simplest form of a business and is suited to the smallest of operations. The sole trader owns the business, takes all the risks, is liable for any losses and keeps any profits. The advantage of operating a business as a sole trader is that very little formality is needed. The only official records required are those for HM Revenue & Customs (HMRC), National Insurance and VAT. The accounts are not available to the public.

Independent companies

These usually fit in to one of the following categories.

- **Small to medium-sized business enterprises (SMEs)** – These have up to 250 employees. In the UK as a whole, SMEs account for more than half of all employment (58.7 per cent). These are usually private companies that may become public limited companies if they become very large.
- **Public limited companies and private companies** – The key difference between public and private companies is that a public company can sell its shares to the public, while private companies cannot. A share is a certificate representing one unit of ownership in a company, so the more shares a person has, the more of the company they own.
- **Limited liability companies** – These are companies that are incorporated under the Companies Acts. This means that the liability of their owners (the amount they will have to pay to cover the business's debts if it fails, or if it is sued) is limited to the value of the shares each shareholder (owner) owns. Limited liability companies are much more complex than sole traders and partnerships. This is because the owners can limit their liability. As a consequence it is vital that people either investing in them or doing business with them need to know the financial standing of the company. Company documents are open to inspection by the public.

Partnership

A partnership consists of two or more people working together as the proprietors of a business. Unlike limited liability companies, there are no legal requirements in setting up as a partnership. A partnership can be set up without the partners necessarily being fully aware that they have done so.

The partnership is similar to a sole trader in law, in that the partners own the business, take all the risks, stand any losses and keep any profits. Each partner individually is responsible for all the debts of the partnership. So, if the business fails, each partner's personal assets are fully at risk. It is possible, though not very common, to have partners with limited liability. In this case the partner with limited liability must not play any active part in the management or conduct of the business. In effect, he or she has merely invested a limited sum of money in the partnership.

The advantages of operating a business as a partnership can be very similar to those of the sole trader. Very little formality is needed, although everyone contemplating entering into a partnership should seriously consider taking legal advice and having a partnership agreement drawn up.

The main official records that are required are records for the Inland Revenue, National Insurance and VAT. The accounts are not available to the public. There may be important tax advantages when compared with a limited company. For example, partnerships might be able pay the tax they owe at a later date, or treat deductible expenses more generously.

Groups or brands

These will consist of a company owning or managing a group of hotels, restaurants, coffee shops or other outlets. The group will have a number of establishments under the same or similar name that function in a wide area, sometimes worldwide. The groups may directly own the business or operate them through a franchise or management agreement. Well-known names in this category include luxury hotels such as Radisson group, Dorchester Collection, Mandarin Oriental, Intercontinental and Four Seasons, through mid-range to budget brands such as Best Western, Holiday Inn, Novotel, Four Pillars and Travelodge. Some groups may run hotels at different levels – for example, Hilton Hotels has five-star properties but also runs some three- and four-star hotels. There are numerous branded restaurant groups – for example, Garfunkel's, Harvester, Carluccio's, Café Rouge, Pizza Hut, Pizza Express, and fast food outlets such as McDonald's, Subway and Burger King.

The branded coffee shop, such as Starbucks, Costa and Pret A Manger, has been a particularly fast-growing area, providing a wide variety of good-quality coffee and other drinks, along with a selection of food items. They provide for both a fast takeaway and more leisurely café-style consumption, with tables and chairs, sometimes with sofas and low tables. Some of these coffee shops provide franchises for others to run so may be available in colleges, offices or retail shops. As with other franchises, the product and ingredients must come from the main company, along with branded products such as cups and napkins.

Franchise

A franchise is an agreement where a person or group of people pay a fee and some set-up costs to use an established name or brand that is well known and therefore likely to attract more customers than an unknown or start-up brand. Many of the groups/brands discussed above are also franchises, with 65 per cent of McDonald's outlets being franchised.

An example of a franchise agreement

The contract caterer Compass Group buys a franchise in the Burger King brand from its owners. It pays Burger King a fee and a proportion of the takings. The franchisor (the branded company franchise provider) will normally lay down strict guidelines, or 'brand standards', that must be met. These may include which ingredients and raw materials are used and where they come from, as well as portion sizes and the general product packaging and service. The franchisor will check on the brand standards regularly to ensure that the brand's reputation is not being put at risk. The franchisor will normally also provide advertising and marketing support, accounting services, help with staff training and development, as well as designs for merchandising and display materials.

Hospitality businesses

Hospitality businesses can be:

- **local or independent** – trading within a local or limited area; this would include small businesses, those providing a speciality service or maybe local or regional food and drinks; examples would be a small bed and breakfast business or a fish and chip shop
- **regional** – trading within a specific regional area such as Cornwall, Wales or the Highlands of Scotland; the regionality may be reflected within the provision – for example, wild salmon on a menu in Scotland or handmade pasties in Cornwall, and the regional provision may be a tourist attraction or selling point
- **national** – businesses operating within one country, which once again may use their national identity as a selling point; examples could be Harry Ramsden's fish and chip shops or National Trust restaurants
- **multinational/global** – a multinational business is one that has its headquarters in one country but has businesses operating in other countries; a global business refers to a company running businesses across the world.

1.2 Types of professional kitchens

Each establishment will have its own kitchen or kitchens. The size, type, layout and equipment will depend on the workload and the food being produced. Modern kitchens can be divided into two broad categories.

Standalone kitchens

These are specific to the actual business and can be of any size depending on the work to be completed. One kitchen may be supplying a number of dining areas in an establishment such as in a large hotel, and may need to produce food for banqueting, corporate events, conferences, in-room dining, room service, lounges, gardens, spa and any other areas requiring kitchen services, including staff and contractor meals. The kitchen may be divided into different areas to service differing requirements and there may also be other kitchens in the same establishment for specific uses – for example, a banqueting kitchen. Restaurants are more likely to have one kitchen but may still need to take account of different dining areas. Small businesses will have a kitchen relevant to their needs.

Centralised kitchens with satellite outlets

This is an area that has seen very significant growth in many parts of the industry. It involves a large production unit producing dishes for its outlets, which are then chilled or frozen and transported to a restaurant. The restaurant would have a finishing or regeneration kitchen/satellite outlets where the food would be finished, reheated or regenerated, with extras like garnishes and salad being added. In some operations the entire meal would be delivered ready for service. Vacuum packaging of food and cook/chill methods are widely used for this type of operation. Hotels with large banqueting facilities may operate a large production kitchen with finishing facilities close to the dining areas.

There are some significant advantages in this type of production:

- standardised product across all outlets
- good portion control
- smaller kitchens will be needed for finishing, with only specific regeneration equipment needed
- fewer skilled staff needed in the finishing kitchen
- faster service and turnover.

This type of production is now used for a number of high-street and popular restaurants as well as places where high volumes of food are needed at one time, such as hospitals and airlines.

1.3 Areas within professional kitchens

Kitchen

The kitchen of most hospitality/catering establishments is where the majority of food preparation, cooking and presentation will take place (although, as noted above, there is an increasing move to produce food in a **centralised kitchen** or production unit, and regenerate or finish it in a **satellite kitchen**). The size and organisation of the kitchen will vary according to the volume and complexity of the operation and what is actually required. A large kitchen may be divided into different sections with specific chefs and other support staff in each. A small kitchen would be less formal, with more flexible staff who may cover more than one area.

All kitchens need to be carefully planned with, wherever possible, a linear work flow in place to avoid cross-over of procedures, which can be chaotic and could lead to possible cross-contamination occurring (see Unit 201, section 2.5). The main kitchen will need some easily accessible food storage for chilled, frozen and ambient foods, although some of this may be in a separate storage area. Some establishments may have more than one kitchen to cover different parts of the business – for example, different restaurants within a large hotel. A smaller business may have just one kitchen producing all of the food for the business with no separate sections. However, these tasks are often completed in their own area to allow for better organisation and to reduce the likelihood of cross-contamination. All kitchens must have suitable access for deliveries and removal of refuse.

Larder

In most professional kitchens the larder is the 'cold kitchen' or the cold section, where cold **mise en place** is done. Cold savoury items such as hors d'oeuvres, salads and cold first courses would be prepared and finished in the larder. Cold meat and fish items and cold sauces would also be prepared. Prepared fruit items for buffets and first-course items may come from the larder. Depending on the type of establishment and kitchen organisation, the larder may also prepare cold buffets, food for events and conferences, salad bars, sandwiches, canapés and food display items such as elaborate seafood displays or cold joints of meat to be sliced on a buffet table. In larger establishments the larder section is further subdivided and may complete butchery and meat/poultry preparation for the rest of the kitchen. It is essential that there are separate preparation areas and well-organised and separate refrigeration in the larder to prevent any possibility of cross-contamination, especially when a wide variety of foods are being prepared.

Pastry section

The kitchen pastry section makes the different types of pastry for sweet and savoury pastry dishes, as well as making hot and cold desserts. Depending on the type and size of the business, it may also produce ice creams, sweet sauces, chocolate items, petits fours, afternoon tea items, celebration cakes, dough products and bread.

The pass

This is the area dividing the kitchen and restaurant entry areas. There may be **still room** facilities in between for storage of crockery, tea and coffee making facilities and other items that are not stored elsewhere. Orders from the restaurant will arrive somewhere near the pass (usually electronically) and the orders will be called or passed to the individual sections. Completed food orders will arrive at the pass and be checked, usually by one of the more senior chefs before being given to waiters or **restaurant runners** to take to the restaurant. The long stainless steel pass will have heat lamps to keep food hot before it leaves the kitchen and hot cupboards underneath for plates and other items. In a smaller kitchen this may just be a specified area where the food service staff collect food from the kitchen.

A still room

KEY TERMS

Centralised kitchen: A production kitchen producing dishes that are then chilled or frozen and transported to finishing kitchens, often as part of a restaurant group or chain

Mise en place: A French phrase that means 'putting in place'; it refers to the set-up required before cooking or before service, and may include the preparation of ingredients or garnishes, and is an essential part of the work of a professional kitchen

Restaurant runner: A member of the restaurant team who collects food from the kitchen and delivers it to the waiter for service; they would also assist with clearing

Satellite kitchen: A kitchen where food produced in a centralised kitchen would be finished

Still room: An area between the kitchen and the restaurant, or somewhere close to both, where tea, coffee and other drinks may be prepared, along with other tasks such as slicing/preparing bread for the restaurant

Preparation being undertaken in a kitchen

2 Understand the job roles and required behaviours in a professional kitchen

2.1 Job roles

Executive chef

A manager and senior member of the team who oversees the whole kitchen operation. This may include the planning and organisation of the kitchen, overseeing menus, purchasing, budgeting and forecasting. Along with the head chef the executive chef may be involved with staff recruitment and may oversee necessary training. The executive chef would liaise with other senior managers in the establishment.

Head chef

Depending on the size of the establishment the head chef has a similar role to an executive chef. The difference may be that the head chef runs a major kitchen operation and an executive chef may manage several operations. The head chef would be involved in recruiting staff and dealing with staff issues including training, planning menus, recipe creation, establishing suppliers and making sure the kitchen is operating to the required standards.

Sous chef

Deputises for the head chef or executive chef and has a range of similar responsibilities. They would work very closely with the head chef or executive chef. In larger kitchens they may be supported by a second or junior sous chef.

Chef de partie

Reports to the sous chef or head chef and is responsible for a specific section – for example, the pastry or larder sections. They supervise any commis chefs or apprentices in their section and will support their training.

Commis chef

This is a more junior chef role and considered to be a training role. They are likely to move around the different sections to gain experience. Commis chefs usually prepare and cook food under the supervision of the chef de partie.

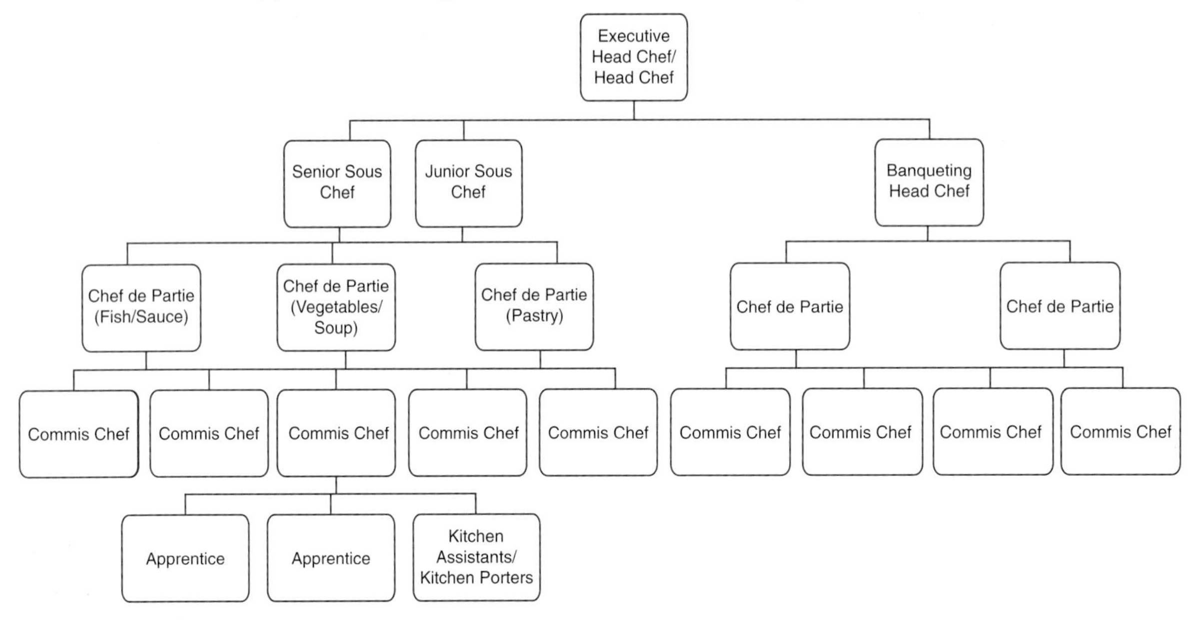

Staffing structure for a large medium-sized hotel kitchen

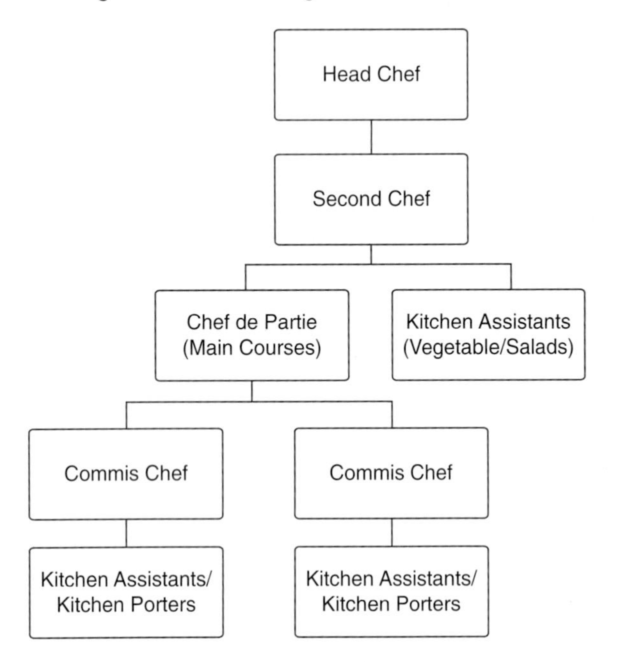

Kitchen organisation structure for a brasserie

Catering manager

Plans, organises and develops the food and beverage services of a hospitality business. Their responsibilities will vary according to the size and type of business. In a small establishment, the catering manager may have a hands-on role in the day-to-day running of the operation, including supervision of staff. They would have a responsibility for food safety, health and safety, forward planning, budgets and purchasing, recruiting staff and negotiating contracts, and would be involved in menu planning with the chefs, as well as other tasks as required by individual businesses.

Catering managers may work for a variety of organisations, including hospitals, schools, workplaces, prisons, cruise ships, hotel chains, educational establishments and visitor attractions, or may be employed by a contract catering company covering a range of clients.

Catering supervisor

Someone in this role would take a more 'hands on' role than the catering manager, working directly with the kitchen and restaurant team and liaising with the catering manager and other management. They would deal with the day-to-day running of the establishment, staff rotas, ordering food and other items, overseeing food safety and health and safety for the establishment, and any other duties assigned to them.

Production chef

This term may be used to cover different roles in different organisations where food is being produced, however a production chef is usually employed in a production kitchen where food is prepared and cooked for distribution to satellite units for finishing or regeneration. The role can vary greatly according to the company, its size and its requirements.

Development chef

Often employed by a national food manufacturing company, a large contract caterer or a restaurant/hotel chain organisation to create, develop and modify new dishes or food products for retail sale, restaurants or branded outlets creating new ready meals, menu ideas and food products. Their role is to respond to and stay ahead of customer trends by creating new dishes and recipes, modifying existing dishes and ensuring that new dishes are sustainable, which means the ingredients will be reliable and remain available. This is especially important when large-scale production is intended. It is likely that development chefs will work alongside food scientists, technicians, nutritionists and marketing teams.

Kitchen porter

Kitchen porters are essential in most kitchens and support the work of the chefs, enabling them to work more efficiently. They will complete a wide range of tasks including collecting and cleaning pots, pans and other equipment, cleaning food preparation areas and dealing with kitchen waste. They may unload and put away food and equipment deliveries and keep store areas tidy and organised.

Apprentices

An apprenticeship is a training contract between the employer and a trainee chef where the apprentice learns the skills needed to become a chef and completes necessary qualifications at the same time. Apprentices are paid while they are learning and working. They may combine formal training from a college with work-based training or complete all of their training in the workplace supported by a college or training provider who will manage their qualifications. Apprenticeships are available at different levels enabling progression of skills and qualifications.

2.2 Required behaviours

The importance of managing time effectively to meet establishment and customer expectations

Careful and efficient time management is essential when working in the hospitality industry. This means planning your work so that you use the time available to you to full advantage. Chefs and others employed in producing and serving food often work to tight, non-flexible schedules. Lunch, dinner and food for events need to be served at the time the customer wants and expects them. Therefore, you may be working to tight deadlines and targets as an individual and as a team. This involves prioritising tasks and knowing how long each procedure will take so they can be fairly distributed amongst the team. Good time management means that work will be completed on time and to the standard required by the organisation and customers. Chefs often produce a daily time plan for the work they need to complete in a specific time. Planning may involve allocating a realistic amount of time for each task, prioritising the most important and integrating tasks – for example, making a sauce while meat is cooking.

Working as part of a team

Having the ability and willingness to work well as part of a team is essential for employment in the hospitality industry. A successful hospitality business may have many teams working together, interacting with one another and liaising with other teams. Teams could include those working in reception, bars and lounges, in food service, kitchens, maintenance, housekeepers, porters and many others. All of the different departments need to work together as a larger team to ensure efficient provision of required services and to meet employer and customer expectations.

Effective communication within your own team and between the different teams will always be of the greatest importance to ensure a successful business, to develop a good team spirit and to form positive working relationships. Discussing work with colleagues, exchanging ideas and skills, prioritising team tasks and helping and supporting one another are all part of effective teamwork.

Assisting colleagues as required – Kitchens can be very busy places and because of the nature of the business the workload is often not evenly distributed throughout the day. There will be quieter times, maybe spent in preparation or training, and very busy times when orders are coming into the kitchen, food for an event or banquet is required or a self-service operation is about to open. Because of these fluctuations in demand, junior chefs and others may be required to assist their colleagues to make sure work is completed on time and to customer expectations. Assist when you are asked to but first check that leaving the work you were previously completing will not adversely affect another area.

Contributing to achieve overall goals – Traditionally kitchen teams have worked closely together to ensure that work is completed to the required standards, on time, with all team members understanding their roles and responsibilities. Full commitment is essential from all team members and an individual contribution can affect the outcome of the whole team. Working as part of a team gives a great sense of achievement as well as allowing for the learning of skills and expertise from one another. In a good team people feel supported in their role, allowing for personal job satisfaction and overall team achievement. It is the outcome of the whole team that defines the quality and success of a business, never one person working in isolation, so developing good teamwork skills is essential to achieve overall goals.

Listening to and respecting colleagues' opinions – There will be many occasions when you may need to listen to the opinion of others. These opinions may directly affect the work you are doing or may be of a more general nature. Generally, when an opinion comes from a more senior colleague about aspects of your work you need to respect that opinion and complete the actions necessary. At other times you may listen to opinions you do not agree with; however, you will still need respect these opinions. Opinions of a racist, sexist or bullying nature should not be tolerated and should be reported to someone in charge.

Recognising impact of own behaviour on colleagues – It is an expectation that your behaviour at work will always be professional and reflect well on you and on your employer, even if others you may work with do not achieve the same high standards. The way that you behave will be noticed by colleagues and sometimes others will recognise you as a role model for their own style of behaviour. Professional behaviour will include:

- always being punctual, reliable and ready for work at the agreed time
- communicating well with others, using positive speech and not swearing
- taking pride in appearance; always being, clean, smart and well groomed
- completing work on time
- being helpful and respecting others
- remaining open to feedback and comment
- always being ready to learn new skills and build on existing skills.

Responding positively to feedback from colleagues – In your learning role you will frequently receive feedback from colleagues, especially those with responsibility for your training. Responding positively to this feedback is important. It will help you to learn from mistakes, build on successes and achieve the standards required of you. Use the time spent on feedback to ask questions about anything you may not have understood and to ask for further training in areas that may particularly interest you. Discuss how your training is progressing and the progression opportunities that may be available to you.

The importance of communicating effectively and with appropriate methods

Effective communication is essential when working in a kitchen or other areas of hospitality. Communication is how you make yourself understood and how you understand others. It is the way that information is passed from one place or person to another. There will be many different communication methods used between:

- individuals working together
- other kitchen sections and service staff
- other departments and management
- suppliers and contractors
- customers/guests.

Verbal and non-verbal communication

Speaking and listening is the most widely used form of communication in a kitchen so it is important that it is carried out effectively.

- Speak clearly and listen carefully so the message is completely understood.
- Avoid using abbreviations or acronyms for equipment or procedures as not everyone will understand them.
- Non-verbal gestures such as facial expressions and hand gestures may be used alongside speech to help reinforce the message and will confirm understanding.
- Take time to communicate properly; avoid speaking from a distance, with your back to someone or while walking past the other person.
- Avoid interrupting and avoid distractions; listen to what is being said, then respond.
- Do not shout or use inappropriate language.
- When receiving verbal instruction, ask questions where necessary and summarise the instruction at the end.

Body language and non-verbal gestures such as a nod, a raised hand or 'thumbs up' are a common means of communication. These can be very useful but make sure they are not misunderstood, especially when communicating between different nationalities and cultures. Your facial expression and body language can express your opinions and how you are feeling or your attitude to work, so avoid scowling, a slumped posture or leaning on work benches. Don't stand with your arms folded – this is a closed gesture and makes you appear uninterested or unhelpful.

Written communication

This is very widely used in kitchens and restaurants for:

- ordering food, drinks and equipment from suppliers or from other departments
- writing menus, explanation of menu dishes and additions to menus
- messages and notes for colleagues
- records of telephone messages
- records of stock and food safety records
- formal and informal letters and emails.

Make sure that written communication is clear and presented in a way that the recipient will fully understand. Take time when writing by hand that your writing and numbers can be understood. If unsure of how to spell something, ask for help because the wrong spelling could completely change the meaning. The incorrect spelling of menu items looks very unprofessional.

Pictorial communication

Pictures or diagrams often form part of instructions and signs used around the kitchen, especially health and safety instructions. These are often standardised and are recognised internationally. A picture, diagram or sketch could also be used to convey meaning where there is a language barrier.

Telephone and electronic communication

Telephone remains a very widely used method of com–munication and there may be specific systems used in an establishment. Make sure you know how to use these appropriately.

Fax messaging is now considered 'older technology' but still has numerous uses, especially when exact copies, signed copies, drawings or diagrams need to be sent elsewhere.

Electronic systems have become increasingly more sopisticated. Frequently used systems include email, text messaging, QR codes, electronic ordering systems, data logging systems and systems designed for specific company use, such as Vocera, Maytas or Opera. In some restaurants the menu is displayed on an electronic screen or on individual tablet devices given to each customer.

Employees are often given access to their own company email or other communication system. When using email at work or from home to work, apply the same care and professionalism to your message as you would to a written message. Do not use all capital letters or any unnecessary abbreviations. Keep your message factual and positive, and remember that an email can be sent on to many other people.

When sending a text message to work, also keep this factual and without abbreviations where this can be avoided.

Increasingly, communication takes place through social media such as Twitter, Facebook, Instagram, YouTube, LinkedIn and many more. Hospitality businesses may use these for promotional purposes and they are often very effective. However, when using social media personally, take care what is entered; remember that this too can be sent to a large number of users – including your employer.

TEST YOURSELF

1 Many high-street restaurants are part of a group or brand. Name three that would fall into this category.

2 Many food outlets are run as a franchise. What is meant by a franchise and can you name some of them?

3 What are the differences between multinational businesses and global businesses?

4 What are centralised kitchens and satellite kitchens, and why are they important to each other?

5 What types of work are completed in the larder section of a large kitchen?

6 What duties are likely to be completed by a chef de partie?

7 What is a development chef? What kind of tasks would they complete and who employs development chefs?

8 When may you be asked to assist other colleagues in a kitchen? Before assisting them, what is it important to check first?

9 What is meant by body language, and how may it be used in a busy kitchen?

10 When may you need to communicate in writing in a kitchen area? Why is it important that the information written on a menu is correct?

3 Understand nutrition, dietary requirements and cookery methods

3.1 Key nutrients and their impact on health

The types and the balance of the foods we eat have an impact on our health. All food we eat is made up of components called nutrients in differing amounts. **Nutrients** in foods help our bodies to do everyday things like moving, growing and seeing. They also help our bodies to heal themselves if they are injured, and a balanced diet can help to prevent illness and disease.

The main nutrients are:

- carbohydrates
- protein
- fats
- vitamins
- minerals
- water.

Carbohydrates

We need carbohydrates for energy. There are three main types of carbohydrate:

1. sugars
2. starches
3. fibre.

Foods high in carbohydrates

Sugars

Sugars are the simple form of carbohydrate. There are several types of sugar:

- glucose – found in the blood of animals and in fruit and honey
- fructose – found in fruit, honey and cane sugar
- sucrose – found in beet and cane sugar
- lactose – found in milk
- maltose – found in cereal grains and used in beer making.

Starches

Starches are present in many foods, such as:

- pasta
- cereals
- cakes, biscuits and bread
- whole grains, such as rice, barley, tapioca
- powdered grains, such as flour, cornflour, ground rice, arrowroot
- vegetables
- unripe fruit, such as bananas, apples, cooking pears.

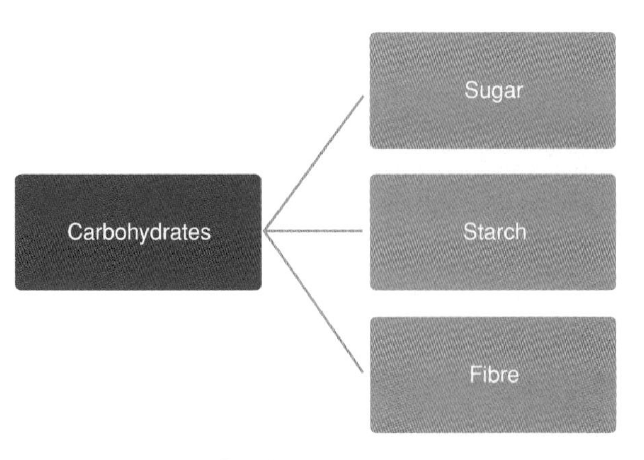

The three types of carbohydrate

Fibre

Unlike other carbohydrates, dietary fibre cannot be digested and does not provide energy to the body. However, dietary fibre is essential for a balanced diet because it:

- helps to remove waste and toxins from the body, and maintain bowel action
- helps to control the digestion and processing of nutrients
- adds bulk to the diet, helping us to stop feeling hungry; it is used in many weight control foods.

Fibre is found in:

- fruits and vegetables
- wholemeal and granary bread
- wholegrain cereals
- wholemeal pasta
- wholegrain rice
- pulses (peas and beans) and lentils.

ACTIVITY

Plan a high-carbohydrate menu with a high water and vitamin content for a team of road runners to eat the night before they run a marathon.

Proteins

We need protein so that our bodies can grow and repair themselves. The lifespan of the cells in our bodies varies from a week to a few months. As the cells die they need to be replaced. We need protein for our cells to repair and for new ones to grow.

We can also use protein for energy. Any protein that is not used up in repairing and growing cells is converted into carbohydrate or fat.

Animal protein is found in meat, game, poultry, fish, eggs, milk and cheese. Vegetable protein is found in vegetable seeds, pulses, peas, beans, nuts and wheat, and in vegetarian products such as Quorn.

Foods high in protein

Fats

Fats are naturally present in many foods and are an essential part of our diet.

- Fats provide the body with energy.
- Fats form an insulating layer under the skin that helps to protect the vital organs and to keep the body warm.
- Fat is needed to build cell membranes in the body.

Fats from an animal source include butter, dripping (beef), suet, lard (pork), cheese, cream, bacon, meat fat and oily fish.

Vegetable fats include margarine, cooking oils, nut oils and soya bean oils.

Too much fat is bad for us. It can lead to:

- being overweight (obesity)
- high levels of **cholesterol**, which can clog the heart's blood vessels (arteries)
- heart disease
- bad breath (halitosis)
- type 2 diabetes.

There are two basic categories of fats: saturated fat and unsaturated fat. A diet high in saturated fat is thought to increase the risk of heart disease. In an average western diet, the saturated fat mainly comes from:

- meat and meat products
- milk, cheese, cream and butter
- other oils and fats such as margarines and spreads
- biscuits cakes, pastries and savoury snacks.

Saturated fats are also present in eggs, some fish and poultry.

Use low-fat dairy products to provide calcium without excess saturated fats.

Current healthy eating guidelines advise cutting down on all fats and replacing saturated fat with unsaturated fat. This is mainly because of concerns about cholesterol – the fatty deposits that can build up, restricting the blood flow to the heart, brain and the rest of the body. It also increases the risk of a blood clot developing. The risk of developing coronary heart disease also rises as your blood's cholesterol level increases.

Unsaturated fats are found mostly in oils from plants and some fish; they can be either polyunsaturated or monounsaturated. Monounsaturated fats help protect the heart by maintaining levels of **HDL** (good cholesterol) while reducing levels of **LDL** (bad cholesterol).

Monounsaturated fats are found in:

- olive oil, rapeseed oil and their spreads
- avocados
- some nuts, such as almonds, brazils and peanuts.

Polyunsaturated fats can help lower the level of LDL (bad cholesterol). They are found in vegetable oils such as rapeseed, corn, sunflower and some nuts, and in some oily fish such as mackerel, kippers, herring, trout, sardines, salmon and fresh tuna.

KEY TERMS

Cholesterol: A substance produced by the body that can clog the arteries to the heart; not all cholesterol is bad – some types of cholesterol are important for the nervous system and other body functions

HDL: High-density lipoprotein, 'good cholesterol'

LDL: Low-density lipoprotein, 'bad cholesterol'

Foods rich in vitamins

Vitamins

Vitamins are chemicals that are vital for life. They are found in very small amounts in many foods. If your diet is deficient in any vitamins, you can become ill or unhealthy. Vitamins help with many of our bodily functions, such as growth and protection from disease.

Table 2.1 shows the most important vitamins, how they are used in the body and what foods they can be found in.

Table 2.1 Important vitamins

Vitamin	How it is used in the body	Examples of ingredients containing the vitamin
Vitamin A	Helps children to grow Helps the body resist infection	Fatty foods Dark green vegetables Eggs
Vitamin D	Controls how the body uses calcium Essential for healthy bones and teeth	Oily fish Dairy produce Egg yolks
Vitamin B	Helps convert carbohydrates into energy Helps children to grow Good for the nervous system	Yeast Liver and kidney Oats
Vitamin C	Helps cuts to heal Helps children to grow Prevents gum infections	Potatoes Green vegetables Fruit

Minerals

There are 19 minerals in total, most of which our bodies need, in very small quantities, to function properly.

- Minerals are needed to build our bones and teeth.
- Minerals help us to carry out bodily functions.
- Minerals help to control the levels of fluids in our bodies.

Table 2.2 Important minerals

Mineral	How it is used in the body	Examples of ingredients containing the mineral
Calcium	Builds bones and teeth Helps muscles to work Helps blood to clot	Milk Green vegetables Wholemeal bread
Iron	Helps keep blood healthy	Lean meat and offal Wholemeal flour and brown rice Fish Leafy green vegetables Nuts
Phosphorus	Builds bones and teeth Good for the brain	Cheese Eggs Fish
Salt and foods with added salt	Regulates water in the body Helps muscles and nerves to work	Salt
Iodine	Helps the thyroid gland to work (affecting growth and weight)	Seafood
Potassium	Regulates water in the body Helps muscles and nerves to work	Leafy vegetables Citrus fruit Bananas

Water

Water is vital to life. Without it we cannot survive for very long. We lose water from our bodies through urine and sweat, and we need to replace it regularly to prevent dehydration. It is recommended that we drink eight glasses of water a day.

Our organs require water to function properly:

- Water regulates our body temperature – when we sweat the water evaporates from our skin and cools us down.
- Water helps to remove waste products from our bodies – if these waste products are not removed they can release poisons, which can damage our organs or make us ill.
- We need water to help our bodies absorb nutrients, vitamins and minerals, and to help our digestive system.
- Water acts as a lubricant, helping our eyes and joints to work and stay healthy.

Sources of water are drinks of all kinds, foods such as fruits, vegetables, meat and eggs, and fibre.

PROFESSIONAL TIP

Always offer customers tap water in a restaurant. Tap water is more environmentally friendly than bottled water.

Advice on good nutrition

A healthy **balanced diet** contains a variety of types of food, including plenty of fruit, vegetables and starchy foods such as wholemeal bread and wholegrain cereals, some protein-rich foods such as meat, fish, eggs and lentils, and some dairy foods.

Nutritional advisers continue to emphasise the need to eat more healthily, especially with the introduction of nutritionally balanced school meals and by encouraging caterers to include nutritional labelling on menus.

Advice from nutritionists is issued as government guidelines. The easy-to-understand advice on healthy eating from the UK Food Standards Agency is:

- eat a range of foods to make sure you are getting a balanced diet
- eat the right amount of food for how active you are
- base meals on starchy foods such as wholemeal bread, pasta brown rice and starchy vegetables
- eat lots of fruit and vegetables
- eat more fish – including a portion of oily fish each week
- cut down on saturated fat and sugar
- try to eat less salt – no more than 6 g per day for adults
- get active and try to maintain a healthy weight
- drink plenty of water
- don't skip breakfast.

The Eatwell Guide was updated by The Food Standards Agency in 2016 and gives visual representation of how to achieve a healthier diet and more sustainable food. It shows the proportions that should come from each group of foods shown. This balance does not need to be achieved with every meal but as part of the overall diet. The Eatwell Guide is available on the NHS website: https://www.gov.uk/government/publications/the-eatwell-guide

Consequences of a poor diet

It is important to use healthier ingredients in the food we cook to help to establish good eating patterns and lifestyles. A lack of the healthier ingredients in the diet can lead to a low **immune system**, **obesity**, skin problems, lack of energy, poor dental health, higher risk of general ill health, and reduced bowel function. Increasingly diseases such as cancer and heart disease are being linked to dietary issues.

ACTIVITY

Take four high-sugar or high-fat desserts and either modify the ingredients to make them healthier or suggest a good dessert substitute.

Why is it important for catering establishments to offer healthier choices?

Chefs and those involved in providing food for others can be instrumental in the provision of a healthier diet and improving health. Chefs need to have a good understanding of the ingredients in the dishes they cook as customers are becoming more aware of the need for good nutrition and therefore there is an increased demand for healthier foods. Increasing the choice of healthier food could lead to increased sales; lack of healthier options could result in a decrease in sales.

KEY TERMS

Balanced diet: A balanced diet contains sufficient amounts of fibre and the various nutrients (carbohydrates, fats, proteins, vitamins and minerals) to ensure good health; food should also provide the appropriate amount of energy and adequate amounts of water

Immune system: A system of structures and processes in the human body that defend against harmful substances and maintain good health; occasionally the immune system in some people recognises ordinary food as harmful and a reaction occurs

Nutrient: A chemical providing nourishment and purpose in the diet

Obesity: A medical condition in which excess body fat has accumulated to the extent that it may have an adverse effect on health, leading to reduced life expectancy and/or increased health problems

3.2 Dietary requirements of different groups

There are certain groups of people in the population who have special nutritional needs.

Pregnant and breast-feeding women

Pregnant and breast-feeding women should avoid foods that have a high risk of food poisoning, such as soft mould-ripened cheese, pâté, raw eggs, undercooked meat, poultry and fish. They should also avoid liver and alcohol.

Expectant mothers require a well-balanced high nutritional diet, which is high in vitamins and minerals and includes folic acid and vitamin B9, found in leafy green vegetables like spinach, orange juice and enriched grains. They should not, however, significantly increase vitamin A in their diet, as too much could harm the baby.

Breast-feeding women need high levels of nutrition to support both the baby and their own well-being.

This young child has special dietary needs – and so does her pregnant mother

Children

As children grow their nutritional requirements change. Children need a varied and balanced diet rich in protein, carbohydrate, vitamins and minerals.

Children are growing and developing very quickly, which means they have high nutrient needs. Their diet requires plenty of foods that provide not just the energy they need to be active, but also foods that deliver vitamins and minerals too.

Very young children, who are weaned, can eat the same types of foods as adults but because their stomachs are relatively small, it is easy for them to fill up quickly. Pre-school children should have small, regular, frequent meals and regular snacks containing nutrient-dense foods – for example, milk and egg. Very young children should be given full-fat milk rather than skimmed or semi-skimmed.

Children over the age of five can eat the same meals as the rest of the family, including more starchy foods and plenty of fruit and vegetables, but their portion sizes should be smaller and with low amounts of saturated fat.

Older children need to have a good, nutritionally balanced diet. Girls need to make sure that they are getting enough iron in their diet to help with the effects of puberty, so their diets should include lean meat and offal, wholemeal grains and brown rice, nuts, leafy green vegetables and fish.

The elderly

As we get older our bodies start to slow down and our appetite will get smaller. However, elderly people still need a nutritionally balanced diet to stay healthy.

The elderly often require small nutritional meals throughout the day. Elderly people are at increased risk of nutrient deficiencies and should ensure an adequate intake of calcium, folic acid, vitamins C, D, E, B12 and B6, minerals, magnesium, potassium and fibre. They should have a reasonable amount of protein in their diet but reduce their salt intake. They should also avoid foods that have a high risk of causing food poisoning.

People who are ill or have a weakened immune system

People who are ill, at home or in hospital, need balanced meals with plenty of nutrients to help them recover. Food should look appetising and be easy to eat and digest. Portions should not be too large. People may have a weaker immune system as they get older; the immune system may also be weakened by certain illnesses or certain medications being taken. This means some people may be vulnerable to fighting off any possible food poisoning. Strict standards of food safety must be in place and it is wise to avoid certain foods such as undercooked or raw fish, meat or eggs. Reheated rice dishes should never be used.

Special diets

Diabetic

Diabetes is a medical condition where the body cannot produce insulin or cannot use insulin properly. Insulin is a chemical hormone that controls the level of sugar in the blood. Type 1 diabetes is when the body's immune system attacks and destroys the cells that produce insulin. Type 2 diabetes is when not enough insulin is produced or the body doesn't react to insulin. Type 2 diabetes is far more common and in the UK around 90 per cent of all adults with diabetes have type 2.

Diabetes may be treated by diet alone; reducing sugars in the diet may be all some diabetics need, but others will need treatment with tablets or regular injections. Each diabetic will have different dietary requirements; as a result, there is no one diabetic diet that will work for everyone and people should follow medical advice and follow a diet that matches their individual needs. Diabetics should eat regular meals based on starchy carbohydrate foods such as bread, pasta, chapattis, potatoes, yam, noodles, rice and cereals but avoid refined sugary foods. They should also include plenty of fresh fruits and vegetables in their diet.

Allergies and intolerances

Food allergies occur when the body's immune system sees certain foods as harmful, which causes an allergic reaction. Food allergies can cause anaphylactic shock (which makes the throat and mouth swell so that it is difficult to swallow or breathe); they can also cause nausea, vomiting and unconsciousness. Some allergic reactions can be fatal.

Food **intolerance** is different and does not involve the immune system, but there may still be a reaction to some foods and some of these reactions can be serious. Foods most usually associated with allergies and intolerances are listed on page 14 but many other foods and ingredients may cause reactions especially certain fruits, vegetables, plants and mushrooms.

All businesses offering food to customers must provide accurate allergy information. Avoid problems with allergies by remaining aware of possible allergens in the food that you prepare and cook, avoiding allergen cross-contamination, which will mean separate storage of different foods, cleaning areas thoroughly after using different food types and using specific equipment for allergic customers (purple colour-coded equipment is now available when preparing food for allergy sufferers). Care must be taken that items such as sauces and garnishes do not contain allergens, and food packaging should be retained for allergen information.

For more information on allergenic ingredients, see Unit 201, section 2.4.

Low-cholesterol/low-fat diet

A low-fat/low-cholesterol diet may be recommended for some people who have high levels of cholesterol in their blood. Cholesterol is a fatty substance known as a lipid and is vital for the normal functioning of the body. It is made in the human body but is also in some foods, especially those containing animal fats.

Too much cholesterol in the blood may result in a greater risk of developing cardiovascular (heart disease) than in people with lower levels. Increased exercise and a good balanced diet low in saturated fats is recommended

A low-fat diet is recommended for a number of other medical conditions or just as a lifestyle choice. Once again a good balanced diet is recommended, low in fats – especially animal fats. Provide food naturally low in fat, do not add fats when cooking if it can be avoided, cut excess fat from meat before cooking, remove skin from chicken, and do not add fat after cooking, such as butter on potatoes. Avoid foods high in fat such as butter, cream, cakes, biscuits, full-fat cheeses, etc. Increase fresh fruits and vegetables, wholegrain cereals and rice.

Obesity

The term 'obese' describes a person who is very overweight, with excess body fat. It is usually caused by consuming more calories than are being burned through exercise. The excess energy is stored by the body as fat. It is thought that around one in every four adults and around one in every five children aged 10 to 11 in the UK is obese. Diet recommendations are similar to those for low fat, i.e. increase exercise, reduce the amount of fats in the diet, increase fruits, vegetables, whole grains and rice, and reduce sugars such as in cakes and biscuits.

Vegetarians

Most vegetarians choose their diet because they believe it is healthier or because they would rather not eat food from animals rather than for a medical reason. They avoid foods that would cause an animal to be killed.

Vegetarians tend to have a lower risk of heart disease, stroke, diabetes, gallstones, kidney stones and colon cancer than people who eat meat. They may also be less likely to be overweight or have raised cholesterol levels. However, to remain healthy, vegetarians need to eat a wide range of foods, such as fruit, vegetables, grains, brown rice, pasta and bread. Dairy foods should be included where possible but not large amounts of cheese, and care should be taken with vegetarian convenience products as some are high in fat.

Vegans

Vegans do not eat meat, fish, dairy products, eggs or any other animal product.

Cultural/religious diets

Different cultures and religions often have their own ways of cooking and different types of cuisine. Our culture and/or religion may affect what we choose to eat and our taste preferences.

Dietary practices have always been incorporated into the religious practices of people around the world. People who follow some religions abstain, or are forbidden, from consuming certain foods and drinks, others restrict foods and drinks during their holy days, while still others associate dietary and food preparation practices with rituals of the faith. For example:

- Christians tend to eat special food for celebrations such as Christmas or Easter; during Lent, some Christians fast
- Muslims are permitted to eat meat only from a Halal butcher, eat no pork products, no alcohol and fast in daylight hours during Ramadan
- strict Hindus are vegetarian and do not eat meat
- Sikhs do not have strict rules about food but many are vegetarian
- Buddhists are usually vegetarian
- Jews have strict dietary laws; shellfish, pork and birds of prey are forbidden; Jews may only eat meat purchased from a Kosher butcher.

PROFESSIONAL TIP

Make sure that all staff are fully aware of food allergies and know all the ingredients that make up a recipe so they can advise customers.

ACTIVITY

1. What is the difference between a vegetarian and a vegan diet? Suggest some menu options, three first courses and three main courses suitable for vegans.
2. Make a list of religious and cultural dietary restrictions that may be useful to your kitchen colleagues. Find a restaurant menu and mark up what would not be suitable on the menu for various religious groups.
3. What is the difference between a food allergy and a food intolerance? Give an example of each.

KEY TERMS

Allergy: When the immune system reacts to or rejects certain foods or ingredients

Diabetes: A medical condition where the body cannot regulate the glucose levels in the body

Intolerance: The body reacts to certain types of food but does not involve the immune system; symptoms may vary

TEST YOURSELF

1. What are the benefits of eating a healthy diet?
2. List four types of ingredients that may contribute to a healthy eating lifestyle.
3. What is the purpose of fibre in the diet?
4. Why are vitamins needed in the diet? Name three vitamins and the foods where they may be found.
5. Give an example of an unsaturated fat. Why are these better for health than saturated fat?
6. Why is fibre needed in the body? Which foods are a good source of fibre?
7. What is diabetes and, apart from their medication, what are the recommended foods for a diabetic?
8. Why is iron needed by the body? Which foods are a good source of iron?
9. What is cholesterol and why should foods that are a source of cholesterol be restricted?
10. What are the foods that need to be avoided by a pregnant woman?

3.3 Cookery methods

There are a number of ways that food can be cooked and the chosen method will depend on the type and size of food to be cooked, health considerations, equipment available, skills of the chefs, menu specifications and desired results. Cooking food can tenderise it, make it more digestible and safe to eat.

Generally, cooking methods can be divided into moist methods and dry methods.

Moist cooking methods

The moist methods are generally the healthy methods of cooking food because no fat is needed, although sometimes fat is added after cooking – for example, adding butter to boiled vegetables, or stewed food such as meat may be fried in a little oil before stewing or braising. There will be no crisp textures as in baking or deep frying and some items cooked by these methods, such as chicken, may be lacking in colour; sauces and garnishes are often added.

Boiling

Boiling is when food is covered in liquid, which is then heated until the liquid starts to bubble (boil). The heat is then turned down so the liquid bubbles gently.

Boiling is a healthy method of cooking food as it does not use any fat and, when done with care, will keep the flavour and nutritional value of most foods. Boiling makes raw food safe to eat, easy to digest and gives it good flavour. The texture of the finished food can vary according to length of cooking and desired result – for example, dried beans may need lengthy cooking to soften and tenderise them but vegetables are boiled for a shorter time to retain colour and leave them slightly crisp.

Table 2.3 Suitable foods for boiling

Suitable foods for boiling	Suitable liquids for boiling	Equipment used for boiling
Vegetables	Water	Saucepans (large enough for the food and the liquid)
Eggs	Milk	Saucepan lids
Pasta	Stock	Colander or 'spider' for draining
Pulses, rice and grains	Infused liquid	
Some meat and poultry		
Stocks and some sauces		
Soups		

Methods of boiling

The amount or type of liquid used for boiling depends on the food to be cooked and the result required. When boiling vegetables make sure there is enough water and that it is boiling before adding the vegetables. When boiling meat, place it in cold water, bring to the boil and skim off the scum produced regularly.

Once the liquid is boiling, food should be simmered rather than boiled vigorously. This means the liquid does not evaporate too quickly and also the more gentle bubbles are less likely to damage the food. If you place the food in already boiling liquid the liquid will stop boiling because the food cools it. Bring back to the boil then turn the heat down so the liquid just bubbles gently, i.e. simmers.

You can also cover the food with cold water and heat to boiling point, reduce the heat and allow it to simmer.

HEALTH AND SAFETY

When you place food into boiling water, you should lower it into the water gently to prevent splashing and scalding.

Make sure that the handles on pots of boiling liquids are turned in when on stoves, so that sleeves and hands do not catch them. When removing the lid from the cooking pot, tilt it away from your face to allow the steam to escape safely. If you open it towards you the hot steam may burn your face.

Poaching

Poaching is when food is cooked in a liquid just below boiling point. Again this is considered a healthy method of cooking that makes food easy to digest as well as retaining flavour, nutrients and colour.

Suitable foods for poaching include eggs, fish, fruit and chicken. The same liquids used for boiling could be used with the addition of stock syrups and fruit juices.

For most food the liquid is heated first, the food is placed in the liquid and cooked just below boiling point.

Methods of poaching

Ways of poaching include the following.

- **Shallow poaching** – Cook the food in a small amount of liquid. Keep the temperature just below boiling. One way to control the temperature and stop it from actually boiling is to get the liquid to boiling point, add the food, cover the pan and place into the oven running at 180°C. This would be suitable for pieces of fish or chicken.
- **Deep poaching** – Ensure the liquid is around 8–10 cm deep, bring it to boiling point then reduce the heat. Add the food so it is completely covered. Cook, keeping the temperature just below boiling. Suitable for eggs, fruit, fish and chicken.

A wide semi-deep pan should be used for poaching. A fish kettle may also be used. A lid is used for some foods, such as whole salmon, and a spider or slotted spoon should be used to remove food from the liquid.

Steaming

Steaming is another method using moist heat, but instead of placing the food in liquid it is cooked by the steam produced from boiling liquid.

Steaming retains nutrients and existing colour well. Changes in texture will occur depending on the food being steamed – for example, a sponge mixture will be well risen and light on steaming. Steaming is sometimes used as part of another process – for example, chips may be steamed before blanching or frying them in oil. Chicken breast may be steamed then a sauce added for serving.

Methods of steaming

The two main steaming methods are as follows.

1. **Atmospheric steaming** – This is steaming under low pressure where the steam is produced by boiling water in the bottom of a saucepan. Food is placed in a perforated container (with a lid) on top of the boiling water. Steam enters the container through the holes and cooks the food. Steaming can also be done in a combi oven on steam settings.
2. **High pressure steaming** – This can be done in high-pressure steamers such as a pressure cooker or a commercial steaming unit, which can vary in the levels of steam pressure achieved. The high steam pressure is forced through the food, which makes it cook faster.

PROFESSIONAL TIP

High-pressure steaming enables food to be cooked or reheated quickly. It is often used for 'batch' cooking, where small quantities of vegetables are cooked frequently throughout the service. This means the vegetables are always freshly cooked, so they keep their colour, favour and nutritional content.

HEALTH AND SAFETY

Boiling water is used in the bottom of steamers, so the same safety points apply to steaming as to boiling. Steam is extremely hot and can cause serious burns and scalds. To avoid injuring yourself:

- make sure you know how to use steamers properly and use them with great care
- check the pressure in high-pressure steamers continually and allow the pressure to return to the correct level before opening doors or removing pressure-cooker lids
- allow time for the pressure to return to normal before opening commercial steamers; stand well away from the door as you open it, to avoid the full impact of the escaping steam.

Because food is enclosed in steamers, care must be taken not to overcook it. This is especially important in high-pressure steamers where food cooks very quickly and with small pieces of food. When using a high-pressure steamer, wait until the pressure gauge shows the correct pressure has been reached then open the door carefully a little at a time to allow steam to escape slowly. Stand back when steam is escaping on opening the doors to avoid burns to the face and hands.

Stewing

Stewing is cooking by a slow, gentle moist heat in which the food is completely covered by a liquid. If the liquid is not thickened the stew may be cooked on top of the stove. If a thickened liquid is used then the cooking vessel (casserole) should be covered and cooked at a gentle simmer in the oven. Stewing is a nutritious method of cooking as both liquid and food are eaten, which means that any vitamins and minerals leaked into the cooking liquid are not lost.

Stewed food achieves a good rich flavour because it is a slow, gentle method with very little shrinkage.

Suitable foods for stewing include:

- meat – lamb, beef and pork
- poultry – chicken and turkey
- vegetables
- fruit.

Suitable liquids for stewing include:

- stock
- stock syrup (for fruit)
- wine
- beer and cider
- sauces, e.g. curry sauce.

Liquids are added to stews at various points in the cooking process. Some are thickened in the cooking process, others are thickened once the main ingredient is cooked, such as in a **blanquette**. If stewing has been done correctly very little liquid will escape, leaving a good sauce to serve as part of the stew. When stewing, the amount of liquid used should be enough to cover the food throughout the cooking process. Consistency should be monitored to ensure there is sufficient liquid/sauce for each portion of the finished dish.

Time and temperature

The time needed for a stewed dish will depend on the type and quality of food used. Generally, red meat will need longer than poultry and some vegetables need longer than fruit. Good stews are cooked slowly so it is important to control the temperature carefully. The liquid should barely simmer. Use a tight-fitting lid to keep in the steam; this helps to keep the temperature correct and reduces evaporation.

Methods of stewing

Stews can be cooked on top of the stove in a covered pan. Bring the ingredients to boiling point then cook on a very slow simmer with a lid on the pan. Check and stir frequently to ensure it is not cooking too fast. Stews may also be cooked in the oven in a dish with a lid, called a casserole dish. For some stews meat is browned in a frying pan before the stewing process. This is called sealing; it enhances the colour and flavour of the stew.

All stews have a thickened consistency achieved by:

- the unpassed ingredients (i.e. those not strained out), especially the potatoes in the stew such as Irish stew
- thickening of the cooking liquor, such as white stew (blanquette)
- cooking in the sauce, such as brown stew (**navarin**).

KEY TERMS

Blanquette: A white stew; the sauce is made by thickening the cooking liquor at the end of the cooking process

Fricassée: A white stew; the sauce is thickened as part of the cooking process

Mirepoix: A mixture of roughly cut onion, carrot, leek and celery

Navarin: A brown lamb stew; the sauce is thickened as part of the cooking process

Velouté: A basic white sauce made using stock and a blond roux

Braising

Braising is generally used for cooking larger pieces of meat or poultry, or whole joints in a covered pan, usually in an oven. The food item is initially browned on all sides, vegetables, herbs and a liquid is added to come halfway up the joint or to cover smaller pieces of meat and other ingredients. A tight-fitting lid is added and the cooking should then be done slowly with the liquid gently moving. Braising has the advantage of being suitable for less expensive meats and poultry, and also maximum flavour and nutritional value are retained.

Braising will:

- give variety to the menu and the diet
- break down tissue fibres in food such as tougher meat, making it soft and tender so the less expensive cuts of meat can be used
- produce and enhance flavour, texture and eating quality.

As well as meat, foods often braised include vegetables and rice.

A suitable liquid such as stock, wine, beer or cider needs to be added when braising.

Time and temperature

When braising the temperature should be carefully controlled so that liquid is barely simmering. The time needed for a braised dish will depend on the type, shape and size of food being cooked. For example, if lamb shanks are cooked too quickly the meat can detach from the bone before it is tender enough to meet dish specifications. A suggested oven temperature for braising food is 160°C. Use a tight-fitting lid to keep in the steam, retain an even temperature and reduce evaporation.

Once the braised food is cooked and tender the liquid is usually strained from the food. For braised meat dishes this is then usually made into a sauce by reducing or thickening. When braising a whole joint of meat, remove the lid three-quarters of the way through cooking and baste the joint frequently to glaze it.

Methods of braising

- **Brown braising** – Used for whole joints of meat such as beef and venison, and also for portion-size cuts of meat. The meat is sealed quickly by browning on all sides in a hot oven or in a pan on the stove. This helps retain flavour and nutritional value, and gives an attractive brown colour. Joints are then placed on a bed of root vegetables (**mirepoix**) in a braising pan with the liquid and other flavourings, covered with a lid and cooked slowly in the oven.
- **White braising** – Suitable for vegetables, rice and sweetbreads. Foods may be blanched, refreshed and cooked on a bed of root vegetables with white stock in a covered container in the oven. Alternatively ingredients may be gently sweated before adding to the braising pan with stock (braised rice) or all the ingredients added to the braising pan together (red cabbage). When braising rice it may be covered with greaseproof paper or foil to allow a little evaporation in the cooking process.

Equipment for stewing and braising

- Saucepans, sauté pans and, where large numbers of portions are being cooked, bratt pans are all considered to be traditional types of equipment for stewing and braising. These should be clean and in good repair, with no loose handles and with correct-fitting lids.
- A number of kitchens are now using non-traditional equipment to stew and braise foods; this includes slow cookers and steamers.
- Casserole dishes are usually deep, round, ovenproof dishes with handles and a tight-fitting lid. They can be made of glass, metal (cast iron), ceramic or any other heatproof material. They are available in various sizes, some of which are then used to serve the food at the table. Always make sure you use the appropriate size and type of dish for the food that you are cooking.

Dry cooking methods

Dry cooking methods generally have no liquid added in the cooking process, although methods such as frying use fats and oils.

Baking

Baking is the cooking of food by dry heat in an oven in which the action of the dry convection heat is modified by steam either created in the food or by added steam. The purpose of baking is to produce attractive and distinctive dishes with appealing colour and texture, creating variety on the menu.

A wide range of foods are suitable for baking, producing different finished results. Suitable foods include:

- flour-based products, which can be sweet or savoury, and might contain meat, fish, fruit or vegetables
- milk- and egg-based products
- fruit and vegetables
- pre-prepared dishes such as lasagne.

Important considerations when baking

- The correct temperature is essential and ovens must be preheated prior to baking. Check the temperature before adding each batch to be cooked.
- Most foods contain moisture, which will produce steam when baking, creating humidity in the oven. Some ovens create injections of steam, which are used when cooking certain dough products.
- The time that different items will need to cook generally depends on their size and density. Bread rolls will cook more quickly than a loaf of bread, and biscuits will cook very quickly.
- Most baking is now done in convection ovens where a fan ensures even temperature in all parts of the oven. However, if using a traditional oven without a fan you will

need to consider the position of the shelves; the oven will be hottest at the top.
- Follow your recipe carefully, being accurate with the ingredients. This will affect how the products bake.
- Prepare trays, tins and moulds correctly. Do they need greasing or lining? Keep baking trays level in the oven and do not overload them.
- Use the available space in the oven efficiently.
- Treat products with care when baking and on removing them from the oven. They may be soft and unstable and the product could be spoiled by opening the oven too often, banging the door shut, removing from the oven too soon or mishandling.

Methods of baking

- **Dry baking** – This is done in a dry oven. Steam is produced from the water content of the food; this combines with the dry heat to cook the food. The majority of baking is done in this way, and this method is used for biscuits, cakes, pastry, baked jacket potatoes, finishing pasta dishes and some dough products.
- **Baking with increased humidity** – when baking certain foods, such as bread, the oven humidity is increased by placing a bowl of water or injection steam into the oven (there will be a switch on the oven to do this), increasing the moisture content of the food and so improving texture and quality.
- **Baking with heat modification** – placing food in a container of water (bain-marie), such as baked egg custard, modifies and evens up the heat so that the food cooks more slowly, does not overheat and lessens the possibility of the egg mixture overcooking.

HEALTH AND SAFETY

Use thick, dry oven cloths when removing trays from the oven.

Do not open oven doors too quickly as there is likely to be a lot of steam, which may burn your face.

Roasting

Roasting is cooking in dry heat or on a spit in an oven, with the aid of fat or oil. Roasting is started in a hot oven but the heat is reduced once the food starts to colour. This reduction of heat helps to reduce the hardening of the food. Roasting is a popular way to cook meat but is suitable only for the better-quality (and more expensive) cuts of meat that can be cooked quickly. When roasting meat or poultry, frequent basting is essential to keep the item moist and succulent.

Roasting creates a distinctive flavour and aroma, and enhances the flavour and colour of the food. When the correct meats are used it produces a tender and appealing addition to the menu.

Suitable foods for roasting

These include:

- meat of the required quality
- poultry
- game
- vegetables
- small items and accompaniments such as kebabs or sausages.

When roasting, consider the following.

- Always preheat the oven to the required initial cooking temperature. The temperature will be reduced once cooking starts.
- Ensure oven shelves are in the right position to allow for the size of item to be roasted. If the oven is not the convection type, remember that the hottest part will be at the top.
- Cooking time is affected by the size, weight and shape of the item as well as the proportion of bone in meat.
- Use a food probe to check core temperatures (temperatures at the centre). Take care not to touch the bone or cooking tin with the probe because this will give a false reading.
- Remove roasting trays carefully from the oven as they may be heavy as well as very hot. Use a thick oven cloth.
- It is possible to roast several items at the same time – for example, roast meat and roast vegetables.

Methods of roasting

- **Roasting on a spit** – Place the prepared meat or poultry on a rotating spit over or in front of fierce radiated heat.
- **Roasting in the oven** – Place prepared foods such as poultry or joints of meat on a trivet. This will prevent

burning at the bottom. A trivet can be a metal rack or roughly cut vegetables to raise the item being cooked from the base of the cooking tin. Items such as vegetables to be roasted are placed directly in the roasting tin with the desired fat or oil (vegetables may have been blanched first). Place food into the preheated oven according to recipe instructions. The heat may be reduced once cooking starts.

Grilling

Grilling is a fast method of cooking using radiant heat either:

- over preheated charcoal, barbecues, gas or electric grills/griddles
- under heat, such as gas or electric salamanders (overfired grills)
- between heat – for example, using electrically heated grill bars or plates.

Grilling (sometimes called broiling) is a healthy way to cook because the cooking is quick, nutrients are retained and no fat needs to be used, though food is frequently brushed with oil when grilling to add some moisture, prevent the food sticking to the grill bars, add flavour and assist even browning.

Grilling creates a distinctive flavour and aroma, and grilled foods look attractive. Some restaurants now have grill areas open to the restaurant so customers can see grilling take place. When the correct foods are used, grilling produces an interesting and appealing addition to the menu.

Grilling enhances the flavour and colour of the food as well as retaining nutrients because it is such a fast process. Because food is cooked so quickly, grilling allows all items to be freshly cooked with no waste. Grilled dishes are non-complex and add good variety to the menu.

Grill bars must always be brushed with oil and preheated before use otherwise the food will stick to them. Grilling is suitable only for tender, good-quality foods such as steaks, which because of the speed of cooking retain the maximum of nutrients and flavours.

Do not overcook grilled food as it will become dry and unpalatable. Small, thin items may cook very quickly. You will need to understand degrees of cooking such as rare, medium and well done, especially with steaks. Start the cooking process on the hottest part of the grill then move the food to a cooler area.

PROFESSIONAL TIP

Quadrillage is a term used for the markings that can be achieved on grilled items such as steaks by placing food in one direction on hot grill bars then giving a quarter turn to achieve a crossed effect

Suitable foods for grilling

Foods suitable for grilling need to be fairly small and tender, so any meat used will probably be the most expensive cuts such as steaks. Other suitable foods include:

- meat – beef, pork, lamb, offal
- poultry – cuts of chicken, duck and turkey
- minced meat and poultry items such as burgers
- vegetables
- fish – whole fish or firm fillets
- pre-prepared items such as kebabs.

Methods of grilling

Grilled foods can be cooked:

- over heat, such as charcoal, barbecues, gas or electric heated grills/griddles
- under heat, such as gas or electric salamanders (overfired grills)
- between heat – for example, using electrically heated grill bars or plates.

HEALTH AND SAFETY

- When reaching over to turn a steak at the back of the grill, be careful of the heat coming up from underneath, which may burn your forearm.
- If meat or fish has been marinated in an oil marinade, ensure that it is well drained before you place it on the grill. Food with too much oil on it may be a fire hazard if it is moved directly from the marinating container to the grill.
- Always use the correct equipment to turn and lift food on the grill. Use tongs to turn and lift cutlets and steaks; use fish slices to turn and lift tomatoes, mushrooms and whole or cut fish.

Deep frying

Deep frying is a process for cooking small, tender pieces of food quickly and totally immersed in hot oil or fat. The hot oil produces a crisp surface on the food as well as an attractive colour. Heat from the oil cooks the food.

Deep frying:

- cooks food quickly making it suitable for cook-to-order and fast food
- produces an appealing colour, flavour and texture, enhancing presentation
- maintains the original nutrients but does add fat content to the finished dish.

Fat and oil are prevented from penetrating the main food item, which would make it greasy by applying a coating to the food. This is often a batter or an egg and breadcrumb coating (pané).

Suitable foods for deep frying

Foods suitable for deep frying are small items that cook quickly and include:

- tender meat (beef pork and lamb)
- minced meat products such as meatballs
- cuts of poultry and poultry products
- fish and fish products such as fishcakes
- vegetables, especially chips and other potato products
- fruit, especially as fritters
- flour-based and dough products (sweet and savoury)
- ready prepared and convenience products.

Fish and chips are still the UK's most popular fried food. British consumers eat around 382 million portions of fish and chips every year – the equivalent of six servings for every person in the country. The annual spend on fish and chips in the UK is in the region of £1.2 billion.

Cooking fats and oils

A variety of fats and oils may be used for deep frying, and often a blend or mixture is used. The most usual oils are:

- sunflower
- corn
- rapeseed
- vegetable
- olive (though this is usually mixed with another oil).

Some establishments may deep fry in goose fat, duck fat or dripping. These have gained popularity for the flavour they add. Traditionally deep frying was done in lard, which does not add flavour.

Points to consider

- Deep fried food remains very popular but it is one of the least healthy cooking methods so consider limiting the number of deep fried items on the menu.
- Serve deep fried items with vegetables or salad rather than other deep fried items.

HEALTH AND SAFETY

- Never overfill fryers with fat or oil or with the food to be cooked.
- Maintain the oil in the fryer at an even temperature. The normal frying temperature is 175°C to 195°C. A slight heat haze will rise from the oil when it reaches this temperature. Overheated oil is very dangerous and also impairs the flavour of the food. Most deep fat fryers are thermostat controlled so will cut out before the oil overheats.

- Consider timing – thicker items will take longer to cook so the temperature may need to be reduced for them to cook through. You may also need to allow extra time for food cooked directly from frozen.
- Allow temperature recovery time between batches of food. Remember that large amounts of food or frozen food will reduce the fryer temperature.
- Serve deep fried food as soon as it is cooked to retain the crisp texture.
- Strain the oil between uses (allow the oil to cool first), cover the oil when not in use to help prevent oxidation and completely change the oil frequently.
- Cook food to a golden brown colour. Once food is cooked, drain it thoroughly on kitchen paper before serving.

Blanching

Partly cooking food before deep frying is called blanching. Food is partly cooked by boiling, steaming or frying at a lower temperature in advance of service, then deep frying to order. This works particularly well with chips, giving a floury texture inside and a crisp exterior. It also saves time at busy service periods.

HEALTH AND SAFETY

- Stand back when placing food into the fryer to avoid steam and splash burns. Avoid putting your face, arms or hands over the deep fryer.
- Before using a deep fryer, know how to put out a fat fire. Do not try to put out a fat fire with water. Cover the pot or fryer with a lid or fire blanket and then use the correct fire extinguisher. Fire extinguishing equipment should be kept nearby and staff should be trained in how to use it.

Shallow frying

Shallow frying is the cooking of food in the minimum quantity of oil or fat in a strong shallow pan, (sauté or frying pan) or on a flat surface (griddle plate). As the food is in direct contact with the oil it will cook rapidly. Shallow frying has the advantage of being able to cook food to order quickly and easily. The high temperature gives the food an attractive colour and surface texture. Shallow frying will retain nutrients in food but will add to fat and calorific content.

Shallow frying produces good colour, flavour and texture, enhancing presentation. A coating, e.g. flour or egg/breadcrumbs, may be added to shallow fried foods before cooking to prevent oil/fat penetrating the food.

Points to consider

- As shallow fried food is likely to be cooked to order make sure the food is completely prepared and ready to cook.
- Do not overheat the pan before placing the food into it.
- Clean the pan between each use to ensure best presentation of food.
- When cooking food, always cook presentation side down first.
- Make sure the food is dry when placed in the pan and lower it into the pan away from you.

Suitable foods for shallow frying

These include:

- tender, thin cut meat (beef, pork and lamb)
- cuts of poultry
- minced meat products such as burgers
- fish – whole fish, fillets, cuts and fish products such as fishcakes
- vegetables and vegetable products
- eggs and omelettes
- flour-based products (sweet and savoury)
- ready prepared and convenience products.

Suitable fats and oils for shallow frying are similar to those used for deep frying. Butter is much more widely used for shallow frying, especially clarified butter. Sometimes a mixture of oil and butter is used.

HEALTH AND SAFETY

Add food to the pan carefully, away from you, to avoid being splashed by hot fat. Always keep your sleeves rolled down to prevent splashing fat from burning your forearms.

Methods of shallow frying

- **Shallow fry** – Cook the food in a small amount of oil or fat in a frying pan or sauté pan. Fry the presentation side (the side the customer will see) first, as this will be the more attractive side. Turn the item carefully and cook the other side.
- **Sauté** – This means to toss or jump, and can be used for a variety of foods that don't break up easily. Suitable foods include tender cuts of meat or poultry, cooked sliced potatoes, onions and mushrooms.
- **Stir frying** – Strips of fish, meat, poultry and vegetables can be fast-fried in a little oil using a wok, often with a small amount of a suitable sauce added at the end.

- **Griddle** – Suitable for cook-to-order items such as bacon, sausages, fried eggs, burgers, onions tomatoes and mushrooms. The cooking is completed on a griddle (a solid, under-heated metal plate). Some items, such as onions, may be stirred or turned several times. Pancakes can also be cooked on a griddle, but turn only once.

Equipment

Most kitchens will have a variety of equipment suitable for shallow frying and their use depends on what is to be cooked. The usual items are: frying pans of various sizes, wok, sauté pan, griddle, bratt pan (for large quantities), omelette pan, blini pan, tawa (a disk-shaped shallow pan for cooking flat bread).

TEST YOURSELF

1 Which methods of cookery are referred to as the moist methods?
2 Which oils are suitable for deep frying?
3 What is meant by baking with increased humidity?
4 Which methods of cookery may be suitable for cooking eggs?
5 What are the different ways that food can be grilled?
6 What are the advantages of steaming food?
7 Which methods of cookery could be used for tougher cuts of meat to tenderise them?
8 Which coatings could be added before frying to prevent oil penetrating the food?
9 Suggest three foods that are suitable for cooking by braising.
10 What are two ways that food can be poached?

ACTIVITY

Find menus online for two different styles of restaurants (or hotel restaurants) in your area. Identify the methods of cooking being used for each dish. Could you suggest other ways that the menu items could be cooked?

3.4 Production of food to suit nutritional or dietary requirements

Those employed across the wide range of hospitality businesses can play a significant part in changing diets and tastes as well as encouraging more healthy eating choices (see section 3.1).

With consideration and skill, a substantial contribution can be made to providing a healthy balanced diet without loss of flavour or texture, or restricting consumer choice. Healthier food provision need not cost more or affect the financial margins of the business. Being creative with menus could lead to improved profits, with high added value while using less expensive ingredients.

There are many practical changes that can be made to the way food is prepared and cooked, which will lead to healthier choices and variety for the consumer. It is not difficult to adapt recipes to make them healthier. Always look for alternative healthier ingredients as well as healthier ways to cook.

To get the best results, experimentation and some trial dishes are recommended, with tastings and comments from staff.

Changes that can make dishes healthier

- **Substitute healthier ingredients** such as fruit, vegetables and skimmed milk. For example, use:
  - lean cuts and joints of meat or skinless poultry
  - fish such as salmon, mackerel, herring or trout, which are rich in oils beneficial to health
  - white fish as it has very little fat
  - dishes that can be oven baked, grilled, steamed or poached instead of fried
  - sugar-free breakfast cereals
  - fruit juices and products in their natural juices/ unsweetened
  - oils, fats and spreads that are high in monounsaturates or polyunsaturates
  - pre-prepared and convenience products that are low in salt/sugar/fat.

For further information, see section 3.1, pages 40–46.

- **Adapt recipes**:
  - use alternative flavourings rather than salt and proprietary products high in salt
  - reduce quantities of fat/oil
  - replace butter with unsaturated oils or a mixture of butter and oil
  - thicken soups and sauces with purées of vegetables/fruit/pulses or potatoes in place of a roux or butter-based sauces
  - use natural fruit juice to sweeten
  - use wholemeal alone or along with white flour for pastry.
- **Change the balance on the plate** by reducing the size of the main item, especially red meat, and add more vegetables or salad. Add extra vegetables where possible when garnishing dishes, and think about fresh vegetables to increase the fibre, vitamins and minerals in the meal.
- **Reduce added fat and change to healthier cooking methods** – Where possible, cook food by steaming, poaching, grilling or stir frying using a little oil spray. In recipes where fat or oil is needed for cooking, use small amounts of olive oil or sunflower oil instead of butter or other animal fats; use yoghurt or crème fraîche in place of cream.
- **Grill, bake, poach, microwave, stir fry** (quick cooking, minimum oil), using spray oils shallow fry in non-stick pans (to use less or no oil), steam chips to blanch. Keeping the temperature of oil slightly lower can protect its structure and therefore make it healthier to use. See section 3.3, pages 46–55.
- **Reduce or eliminate sugar** – Gradually reduce sugar content in desserts, sugar substitutes can be used if necessary. Use fruit juices where appropriate – for example, in fruit salad.
- **Reduce salt** – Gradually reduce salt in recipes. Herbs and spices can be used in its place. See section 3.1, page 40.
- **Use wholegrain ingredients** such as wholemeal flour, brown rice and pasta.
- **Adjust preparation methods** – Trim visible fat and remove poultry skin; leave skin on potatoes, vegetables and fruit to increase fibre content and reduce vitamin loss; use chunky/thick cuts of vegetables to reduce fat absorption/vitamin loss.
- **For vegetables, choose cooking methods that reduce vitamin loss** – Steam, microwave or stir fry, and cook in small batches to reduce hot holding time
- **Think about additions to the main dish item and consider the garnishes used** – Add a mixed salad rather than chips. Top soup with chopped fresh herbs rather than fried croutons.
- **Keep all menu items safe** – Use separate storage, preparation, cooking, finishing and storage areas for different foods and processes to avoid cross-contamination with bacteria and allergens. Be aware of allergens and your responsibilities to those with allergies (see Unit 201, pages 2 and 14).
- **Include information on the menu about which items are the low-fat/lower-calorie dishes**. Explain how you are making your menu healthier – this could provide useful information for customers and could increase business.
- **Where there is a children's menu, include healthier choices** and cooking methods here too (see section 3.2, page 43).

ACTIVITY

1. Why should a caterer offer healthy alternatives on the menu? What could the consequences be if an establishment did not have alternative healthy ingredients available?
2. Suggest ways in which the following menu items can be made healthier and how would you describe the dish on the menu?
   - Avocado and prawn salad in a creamy mayonnaise topped with crisp fried onions
   - Stir fry beef with fried rice and prawn crackers
   - Pan fried fillet of sole with lemon butter and sauté potatoes
3. Write a suitable statement for a popular restaurant stating how customers can be informed of possible allergens in food on the menu. List six popular salads that might be included in a salad bar. Next to each, include the allergens from the 14 listed on page 14 that would be in them.

4 Understand stock management and sustainability considerations in professional cookery

4.1 Stock management considerations

Availability of suppliers and frequency of delivery

Selecting suppliers of food and other items is an important part of the purchasing process. It must be considered how a supplier can best meet the needs of an individual business; the main considerations will be price, delivery arrangements, quality, suitability, traceability and sustainability. Every business will have its own individual needs and discussing those needs with the supplier is essential. Information and recommendations of suppliers can be obtained from other businesses that have used them, and visiting the potential suppliers is to be encouraged. When discussing your needs with prospective suppliers, you need to question how reliable the supplier will be compared to the competition and how stable they will be under varying market conditions. It is advisable to communicate well and build understanding and rapport with suppliers to ensure the best service at all times. Frequency and actual times of delivery must be agreed with the supplier as late or missed deliveries can have a serious impact on the business and the smooth running of the kitchen.

Other topics to discuss are:

- how the deliveries are made
- whether there is a refrigerated van and you will receive a printout of delivery temperature
- how individual items are packaged and whether any of the packaging is returnable
- how much of the packaging is recyclable and what the procedure is if unsuitable items need to be returned.

Once an agreement is reached it then needs to be formalised in writing.

Commodities must meet organisational and customer requirements

It is of great importance to agree with the supplier the quality and type of items to be supplied. This will depend partly on the kind of establishment, the menu, prices charged and customer expectations. Consideration of quality needs to be given the highest priority. Good quality does not always mean most expensive; drawing up specifications of the quality expected along with the supplier will help to ensure getting the best for what is paid. Anything considered below the expected quality should not be accepted on delivery but returned to the supplier with an explanation of why it does not meet the quality agreement.

Financial impact

Sourcing food and other items has a huge financial impact on a business, so efficient stock control levels are essential to help ensure the profitability of the business. The main difficulties of controlling food costs are as follows.

- Food prices fluctuate frequently because of inflation and falls in demand and supply due to poor harvests, bad weather conditions and even food trends.
- Transport costs rise due to wage demands and the cost of petrol and diesel.
- Fuel, heating and refrigeration costs rise, which affects costs for food companies and producers.
- Any food subsidies or grants made available by governments might be removed.
- Changes occur in the amount demanded by the customer; increased advertising increases demand; changes in taste and fashion influence demand from one product to another.

Media focus on certain products that are labelled healthy or unhealthy will affect demand, such as butter being high in saturated fats or sunflower margarine being high in polyunsaturates. TV cookery programmes and celebrity chefs can make certain dishes and ingredients more popular.

Financial impact of stock management

Stock levels must be maintained at the correct level. Carrying too much stock ties up the business's available finance. The stock needs to be carefully managed to avoid deterioration, which could result in valuable commodities being thrown away, with high cost implications. If you have a large amount of stock, suitable storage needs to be found, which ties up space that could have a better use.

Too little stock could result in the inability to produce certain menu items or running out of certain items during service. Both could affect the business financially. Carrying too low a stock of cleaning materials and running out of them could have serious implications for the cleanliness and legality of the company. Carrying the right amounts of stock is something that is learned with experience.

Managing waste

It is important to control waste in any food business, for financial and ethical reasons. Waste often occurs because of over-ordering, poor purchasing or incorrect storage. Significant amounts of wastage also occur because of careless preparation and cooking. Waste management should be part of the training and feedback given to everyone working in the area. As well as excess waste resulting in a direct financial loss to the business, most local authorities and refuse companies charge businesses for the amounts of waste they take away, so the amount of waste produced each week should be monitored and the kitchen team should work together to reduce waste.

Most businesses are involved in recycling suitable items such as glass, plastics, paper, cardboard, foil, oil and any other items identified for recycling. Some local authorities now collect waste food. This most frequently goes for anaerobic digestion where micro-organisms break down the waste biodegradable material in the absence of oxygen. This can then be used for a number of purposes, including fuel production.

Minimum and maximum stock levels

Carrying the wrong amounts of stock can have a serious impact on finance and cash flow of a business. Those in charge of the kitchen or business need to decide the minimum and maximum levels of stock to be held at any time, and to make sure that this is managed correctly. A number of records and systems are kept to manage and control stock. One form is the traditional **bin card** or stock management record for each item held in stock. In larger catering operations, the bin number system has been computerised, with different software systems being available. These show the name of the commodity, issuing unit, date of receipt, supplier, maximum/minimum stock levels and balance in stock.

Stores ledgers have also been used for tracking levels of stock. Traditionally, this was a loose-leaf file with one sheet for each item held in stock. Such records are now more likely to be stored on a computerised system.

Even with electronic systems it is still necessary to complete a physical stock-take at specified intervals. This will be a physical count of what is actually in stock, and should match what either the paper or electronic system states. Small discrepancies will inevitably happen due to things such as breakages but large discrepancies need to be investigated.

Quality of commodities

The quality of commodities supplied to any business is of the greatest importance. Quality could define the reputation of a food business and have an impact on everything sold through the business. Quality specifications will have been agreed with suppliers; staff receiving deliveries must be aware of this, refer to it and not accept commodities that are below the agreed standard. Staff must be aware of the procedure for non-acceptance of deliveries.

Quality may refer to type, grade, weight, size or levels of preparation, such as washed potatoes or trimmed leeks. Other information may include: country or region of origin, maturity or degree of ripeness, colour, shape and anything else relevant to the item.

Failure to meet quality requirements would include: wrong size weight or grade, poor storage, wrong delivery temperature, damaged packaging, bruising, broken or squashed items, mould, unpleasant smell or the presence of pests.

Record-keeping

To control stock effectively a number of recording procedures must be in place. Traditionally these have been paper-based systems but are increasingly being replaced by electronic systems with the ability to combine all the functions of the older systems and add further useful information. Essential parts of the stock control system of any catering establishment are described below.

- **Delivery notes** – These are sent with goods as a means of checking that everything ordered has been delivered. The delivery note should also be checked against the duplicate or matching order sheet. Delivery notes are often computer generated in the delivery vehicle at the point of delivery.
- **Invoices** – These are bills that always state 'invoice' and are sent to clients, setting out the cost of goods or services supplied. An invoice should be sent on the day the goods are despatched or as soon as possible afterwards. At least one copy of each invoice is made and used to inform accounts, stock records, etc.
- **Credit notes** – These are issued to customers, setting out allowances made for goods returned, substandard goods or adjustments made through errors of overcharging on invoices. They should also be issued when chargeable containers such as crates, boxes or sacks are returned.

- **Departmental requisition book or forms** – Requests to the stores areas from different departments, e.g. snack items for mini bars.
- **Order book or forms** – Traditionally a duplicate book completed by a storekeeper when they wanted to have goods delivered. The page from the order book or form would be checked against the delivery note. It is now more likely to be done electronically or the order given by telephone.

Also see bin cards and stores ledgers on page 58.

Seasonal demand

A number of commodities used in kitchens and restaurants will be seasonal by nature, so it is not always possible or advantageous to agree a fixed price with suppliers for them. However, seasonal and local produce should reflect a good price and the supplier should pass this on to the food business. Good menus will always reflect seasonal and locally produced food, so remain aware of these and when they are available. The supplier should also be able to advise you on seasonal produce so frequent dialogue with suppliers is advantageous.

Security

Stored stock is a valuable asset that can be worth significant amounts of money to a business, so it is absolutely essential to keep it secure. The storage area itself should be a secure place with suitable security measures on windows. Preferably there should be only one door, with a secure locking system and limited access to people entering the store. The best method will always be written requests to the store with goods issued by the storekeeper or at least by one person with responsibility for issues. Returns to the store should also be recorded. The recording systems described above should help to monitor stock, and regular stock takes show discrepancies. Action must be taken on serious or regular discrepancies.

Stock rotation

Stock rotation simply means that older stock is used before newly delivered stock. This is often referred to as 'first in–first out' (FIFO). This procedure should be followed whether it is for food with a long shelf life or for perishable foods. It is important to check that food is still within the required dates, either the Use-by date for perishable food or the best before date for food with a longer storage life. If these dates have been exceeded the food must be thrown away.

Storage capacity

There must be sufficient storage capacity for food coming into the business. Storerooms must be large enough to store deliveries in a logical and safe way, and to allow for efficient stock rotation and thorough cleaning. There must also be space and facilities to store food items off the floor. It is a legal requirement that there is enough refrigerated and frozen storage for food requiring this, and they must be running at the correct temperatures (see Unit 201, section 2, on food safety). Refrigerators and freezers should not be overcrowded.

4.2 Sustainability considerations

Provenance (local, national, international)

Food provenance means where the food comes from: where it is grown, raised or reared. The food could be local, from a nationally controlled source or have international availability. Interest in food provenance could involve supporting the economy and fair trade in one country or region.

Consumers are increasingly demanding local, regional food. Food provenance is given consideration on menus informing the customer what they are eating and where it has come from.

In the UK there are strict regulations as to how farmers must rear animals and how they are slaughtered; animals are regularly tested to ensure they are healthy and comply with these regulations. Regulations may differ from country to country.

Many factors drive this interest in food provenance. For example, ethical labels guarantee that products such as coffee were produced under fair and decent working conditions, while promoting local sustainability and fair terms of trade for farmers and workers in the developing world. Understanding the provenance of food has become an advantage to many restaurants, since it allows them to demonstrate their commitment to locally sourced food, quality in taste, carbon footprint and food ethics.

Carbon footprint

This is the total amount of greenhouse gases produced to directly and indirectly support human activities, usually expressed in equivalent tons of carbon dioxide (CO2).

Food production emits carbon dioxide greenhouse gas emissions during growing, rearing, farming, processing, packaging, transporting, storing, cooking and disposing of food. These emissions have a negative and damaging effect on the environment and contribute to the effects of global warming. Reducing carbon footprint can reduce pollution, preserve the environment and slow down global warming.

An understanding of carbon emissions from food production means taking account of all the carbon-emitting processes that occur as a result of food supply.

- **Production** – Farms generate a large proportion of the emissions from food production because of deforestation, fertiliser production and use, and livestock management.
- **Transporting and storing food** generates emissions. However, this activity also contributes to making the food industry more efficient and cost-effective by providing food where and when it is required.
- **Seasonality** – Growing food out of season, either in the UK or overseas, can be a high-carbon method of production. Seasonal and local food will have a lower carbon footprint.
- **Food waste** directly increases emissions as extra food production and expense is required to replace wasted food.
- **Fuel** is needed to store (refrigeration) and to cook food. Many kitchens will have ovens, grills, griddles and fryers on all day whether needed or not. This wasted fuel increases carbon emissions as does having refrigerator doors open unnecessarily.

A food business demonstrating that it is taking steps to lower carbon emissions can lead to enhanced brand reputation and customer loyalty because of its commitment to lowering its environmental impact. A food business can reduce its carbon emissions by:

- sourcing locally produced seasonable food wherever possible
- avoiding bottled water, especially when it has travelled a considerable distance
- using fuel economically
- reducing waste in all areas.

Sustainable sources and stock

All food businesses are now encouraged to source sustainable food and other items. Sustainable food enhances a community's environmental, economic and social well-being worldwide. The aims are to further the ecological, social and economic values of a community and region. As well as supporting food producers and their communities, supporting sustainable food ensures quality food supplies for the future.

Sustainable food:

- produces safe and healthy products in response to market demand
- ensures that consumers have access to nutritious food and to accurate information about food products
- supports the viability and diversity of rural and urban economies and communities
- enables viable livelihoods to be made from sustainable land management
- respects and operates within the biological limits of natural resources, especially soil, water and biodiversity
- achieves consistently high standards of environmental performance by reducing energy consumption, minimising resource inputs, and using renewable energy wherever possible
- ensures a safe and hygienic working environment, and high social welfare and training for all employees involved in the food chain
- achieves consistently high standards of animal health and welfare
- sustains the resources available for growing food and supplying other public benefits over time.

Source: Strategy for Sustainable Farming and Food, 2002

Minimised or alternative packaging

Food packaging amounts to almost 3 million tonnes of waste in the UK each year. Other non-food waste includes disposables such as kitchen paper, which accounts for 0.66 million tonnes per year. Much of this waste is difficult to recycle. For example, plastic contaminated with food often can't be reused, and packets such as the card, plastic and foil of fruit juice cartons are often made up of several different layers laminated together, which makes them impossible to recycle. This means that large quantities of food packaging go into landfill sites. The packaging industry argues that packaging is necessary for hygiene reasons, and has made efforts to make packaging much lighter and thinner, but the amount of packaged food is increasing all the time. Local authorities and waste disposal companies will now charge businesses on their volume and type of waste. Unnecessary waste will affect the costs and profit of a business as well as having a negative impact on the environment, so all staff must be made aware of packaging waste and how it could be minimised. In a food business it may be useful to discuss packaging with suppliers and ask what they are doing to reduce amounts of packaging used, use of recyclable packaging, returnable containers, wrapping in paper or no packaging at all where possible. Requesting minimal packaging from suppliers may have an impact – for example, does a cucumber need to be plastic wrapped? There has recently been a campaign by London restaurant owners objecting to the amounts of fish and many other products delivered in polystyrene containers that cannot be recycled. This has resulted in some fish suppliers delivering fish in reusable, returnable plastic boxes or in cardboard boxes.

Fair Trade products

Products branded 'Fair Trade' ensure that disadvantaged producers in the developing world are getting a fairer deal for products such as coffee, tea, sugar, and exotic fruit and vegetables. Many restaurants and coffee shops now promote the fact that their ingredients are Fair Trade sourced.

Products with standards such as Red Tractor, LEAF, Freedom Foods, Organic, BRC and STS guarantee food safety, and higher standards of environmental performance and animal welfare.

Impact on customer perception

Customers have become much more aware of food sustainability, reducing carbon footprint, reducing 'food miles', using less packaging or recyclable packaging, and movements such as Fair Trade. People are often committed to these things at home so may expect the restaurants they visit to do the same. When customers see these things promoted on menus or statements displayed in a restaurant, it may encourage them to become regular customers and recommend the business to others.

Impact on business

Customers have an expectation that food businesses will have concerns about carbon emissions, food miles, excess packaging and other environmental issues. They expect to see that at least some of the food is ethically sourced and comes from local suppliers. People like to think that they are supporting local industry. Customers expect they will be served tap water when they ask for it, but are they actually offered it? As well as the obvious environmental advantages of these things it is good for business too, with customers feeling comfortable with and wishing to support an 'ethical' restaurant.

TEST YOURSELF

1. When meeting with a new food supplier for the first time what are three of the questions you would ask?
2. Name three ways that food production impacts on carbon emissions.
3. Suggest three ways that food packaging could be reduced or changed for packaging that could be recycled.
4. What is meant by sustainable products, and how do they help the producers?
5. What is meant by Fair Trade products?
6. What needs to be considered in a storage area for food stock?
7. When managing or controlling stock, what are three of the documents that may be used? What could an alternative be?
8. What is meant by stock rotation?
9. List the different items that could be recycled by a kitchen and restaurant.

TAKE IT FURTHER

You are part of a partnership setting up a new 80-cover high-street restaurant based on healthy eating and ethical values.

1. What is a partnership?
2. What are the grades of kitchen staff you will need, and how many?
3. Design a menu to reflect your healthy eating and ethical values.
4. What ingredient, garnish and cooking method substitutes could you make to traditional dishes to meet your restaurant's aims?
5. Design statements for the menu describing the values and aims of the restaurant, and how you will inform customers about possible allergens.

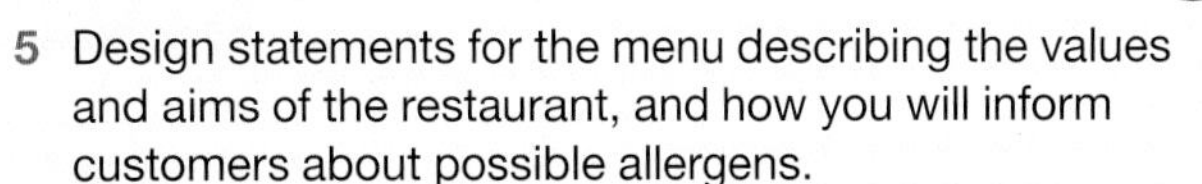

6. How will you find suitable suppliers to reflect the provenance of menu items?
7. How can you keep food and packaging waste to a minimum, and what will you be able to recycle?
8. What will you call the restaurant?

203 Tools and equipment used in professional cookery

The purpose of this chapter is to help you know the types and uses of tools and equipment commonly found in a professional kitchen. You will need to demonstrate effective knife skills across a range of commodities, and will also need to use appropriate tools and equipment for particular dishes, ensuring that correct maintenance and storage requirements are followed.

You will also learn about the various types of equipment – large and small – used in the hospitality and catering industry. Every piece of equipment has a particular purpose for which it has been specifically designed. One of the essential skills of being a chef is to be able to identify and use the correct equipment for a task, to avoid mistakes and accidents.

Learning outcomes

In this chapter, you will be able to:

1 use knives and cutting equipment throughout the food production process, including:
   - 1.1 types and characteristics of different knives and cutting equipment
   - 1.2 maintaining and storing knives and cutting equipment
   - 1.3 using knife skills and cutting equipment

2 use tools and small equipment throughout the food production process, including:
   - 2.1 types and characteristics of tools and small equipment
   - 2.2 maintaining and storing tools and small equipment
   - 2.3 using tools and small equipment

3 use large equipment throughout the food production process, including:
   - 3.1 types and characteristics of large equipment
   - 3.2 maintaining large equipment
   - 3.3 using large equipment

1 Use knives and cutting equipment throughout the food production process

1.1 Types and characteristics of different knives and cutting equipment

The professional chef will use a whole range of knives in the kitchen; each type of knife is used for a specific job and skill. It is important that knives are used safely and efficiently.

Boning knives are short-bladed knives used for boning meat. The blade is strong and rigid, with a pointed end. The inflexible blade allows the chef to get close to the bones and cut away the meat.

Butcher's saws are commonly used in butchery to saw through bones.

Carving knives and forks – A French carving knife has a long, thin blade and is known as a tranchard. A carving fork is two-pronged. It is strong enough to support meats for carving, and to lift them to and from containers.

Chopping knives are used for a variety of jobs, such as chopping, cutting, slicing and shredding vegetables, meat and fruit. These are also known as **chef's knives**.

Filleting knives are used for filleting fish (removing the flesh from the bones). They have a very flexible blade, which allows the chef to move the knife easily around the bone structure of fish.

Meat cleavers are also known as **choppers** and are usually used for chopping bones.

Paring knives (also known as **office knives**) are small, multi-purpose vegetable knives. They are used for topping and tailing vegetables, and for peeling certain fruits and vegetables.

Palette knives are flat, and used for lifting and scraping, turning and spreading. They are also useful for a variety of tasks in the pastry section.

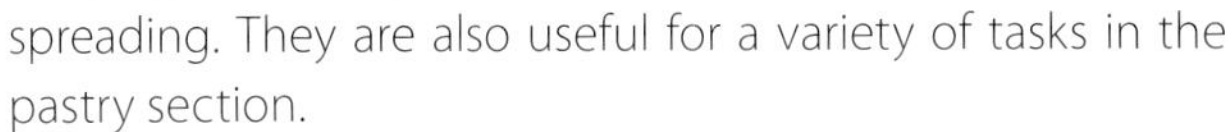

Serrated-edge carving knives are used for slicing foods. They have a long, thick serrated blade, which is used in a sawing action. These knives are not sharpened in the kitchen but have to be sent to a specialist company to be sharpened.

Turning knives have a small curved blade. They are used for shaping vegetables in a variety of ways.

Kitchen scissors are used for a number of purposes in the kitchen. Fish scissors are used for cutting fins from fish. Poultry scissors are used to portion poultry.

Peelers are used for peeling certain vegetables and fruit.

Corers are used to remove the fibrous core from fruits such as apples, pineapples and pears. They have a rounded blade, which you push down into the centre of the fruit to cut through the fruit around the core. The core stays tightly inside the corer and is removed from the fruit when you pull it out.

Sharpening equipment

A **carborundum** is used for sharpening knives.

Steels are used for sharpening knives. They are cylindrical pieces of steel with a handle at one end. To sharpen a knife, run it at an angle along the steel edge.

Whetstones are also used for sharpening knives.

1.2 Maintaining and storing knives and cutting equipment

Knives that are looked after and treated with care will give good service and will be less likely to cause injury.

Sharpening

Knives that are kept sharp are safer than blunt knives, provided that they are handled with care. This is because a sharp knife will cut efficiently and cleanly without needing too much pressure to cut through the food. A blunt knife is less easy to control; it will need more pressure and force, and is likely to slip sideways, possibly causing injury as well as poorly prepared food.

Keep knives sharp by sharpening them frequently with a steel or other sharpening tool. Make sure that you are shown how to do this safely.

If a knife has become very blunt it may need to be re-ground by someone who specialises in doing this. An electric or manually operated grinding wheel is used to replace the lost 'edge' on the knife. Arrangements can be made for mobile units to visit your premises to re-grind knives, or they can be sent away to be re-ground.

Some chefs use a sharpening stone.

Cleaning

A knife can very easily transfer harmful bacteria from one place to another, becoming a 'vehicle' for contamination. Follow a few simple rules to avoid this.

- Wash and dry knives thoroughly between tasks.
- Do not use the same cloth to clean knives between tasks, especially when you are preparing raw or high-risk foods.
- If you have used a knife on raw meat or poultry, be sure to disinfect it before using it for another task. Detergents remove the grease, but disinfectants kill harmful bacteria. To prevent cross-contamination, some kitchens will use different knives for raw and cooked food.
- When you have finished working with a knife, wash it thoroughly with hot detergent water, then rinse it, dry it and put it away. Bacteria will multiply on dirty or wet knives.

PROFESSIONAL TIP

Take great care of your knives; always keep them clean. There are a variety of knives on the market – some have handles made of easy-to-clean material.

Storage and security

Store knives carefully, preferably in a box or carrying case with compartments to keep the knives separate and easy to find. Do not just throw knives loosely into a drawer or locker.

Where possible, lock knives in a secure place when not in use to prevent theft. It is advisable to inform the local community police officer if you are carrying knives to and from your place of work.

Knives may also be kept in a knife roll, which is usually made of strong linen or plastic. However, it is not advisable to use these as they are not particularly hygienic. Magnetic strips attached to the wall are also used to store knives in a kitchen.

Age restrictions specific to the use of cutting equipment

There is an age restriction for the use of potentially dangerous equipment in the kitchen such as gravity-feed slicing machines; you must be over 18 to use them.

Safe use of knives

Knives are essential tools for all chefs, but they can cause serious injury to the user or to someone else if used incorrectly or carelessly. By following a few simple rules you should be able to avoid serious injury from knives and keep accidental cuts to an absolute minimum. Use your knives correctly at all times.

- Hold a cook's knife with your finger around the handle (thumb and index fingers on opposite sides) and well clear of the blade edge. This will sometimes vary, depending on the size and design of the knife, and the task you are carrying out.
- Grasp the knife firmly for full control.
- Always make sure that the fingers and thumb of the hand not holding the knife are well tucked in, to avoid cutting them.
- If carrying a knife in the kitchen, hold it to the side of your body, with the blade pointing downwards and backwards.
- Never run while holding a knife.
- When handing a knife to someone else, offer them the handle while you hold the top (blunt edge) of the blade.
- Keep the blade away from you when cleaning or drying knives, and never run your finger along the blade edge.
- Do not have more than one knife at a time on a chopping board. When not using a knife, place it at the side of the board with the blade pointing in. Never carry knives around on top of chopping boards because they could slide off.
- Do not let knives overhang the edge of the work surface; they could be knocked off or fall and cause injury. Never try to catch a falling knife; stand back until it reaches the floor.
- Never leave a knife on a surface with the blade pointing outwards. You or someone else could put their hand down on the blade of the knife.
- Never place knives in washing-up water; the blade will not be visible so someone can put their hands in the water and cut themselves.
- Keep the handle of the knife clean and dry. If the handle is greasy or wet it could slip in your hands during use.
- Keep knives visible, i.e. not under vegetable peelings or a dishcloth.

1.3 Using knife skills and cutting equipment

Example of boning

Carving

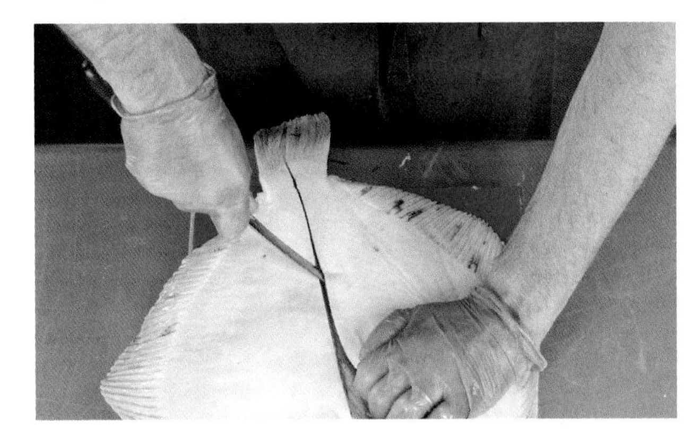

Dicing

Chopping, e.g. finely, coarsely, mirepoix

Filleting

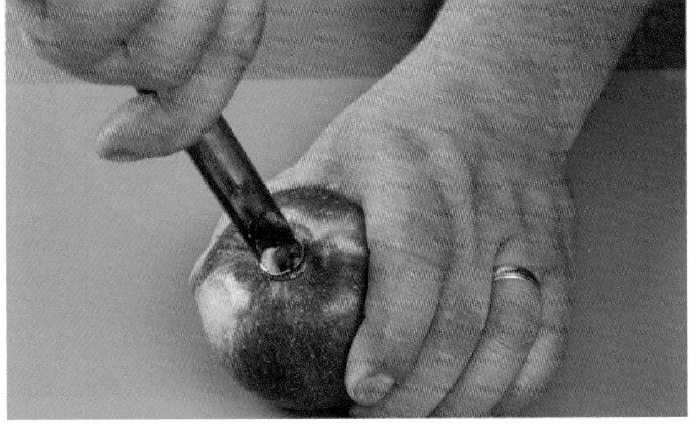

Coring

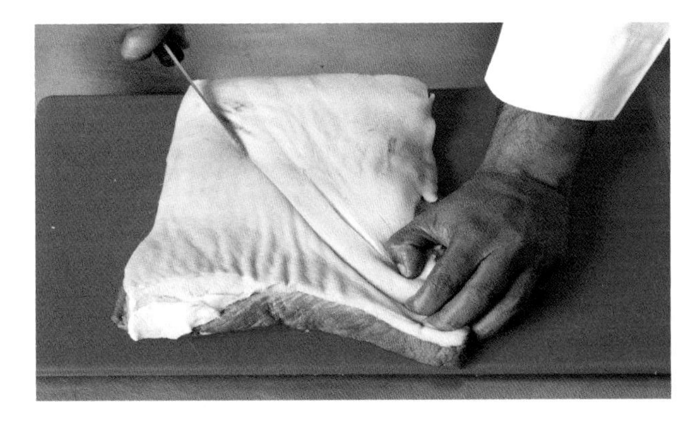

Jointing

Crushing

Marking and scoring

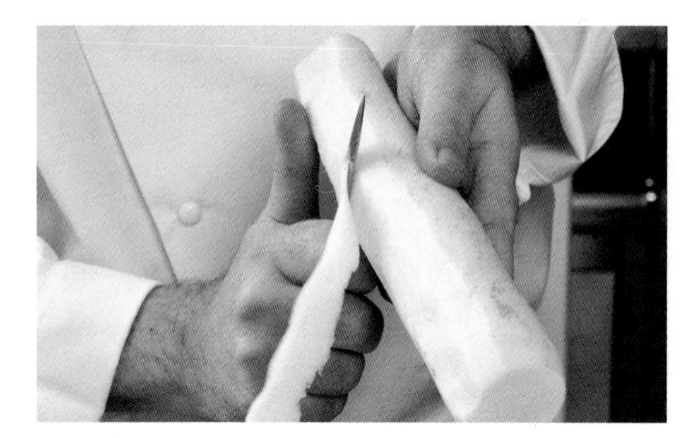
Peeling

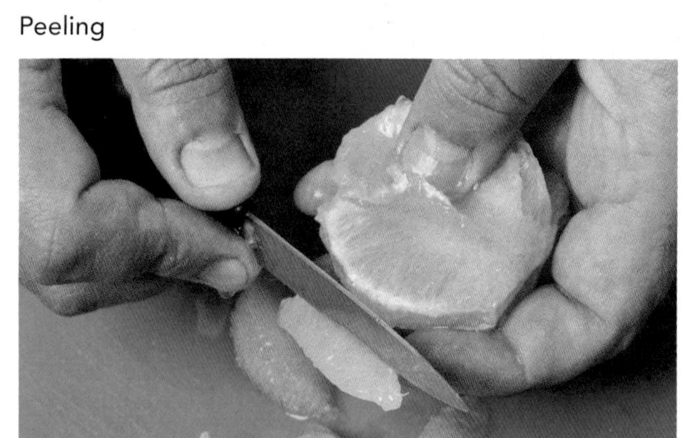
Segmenting

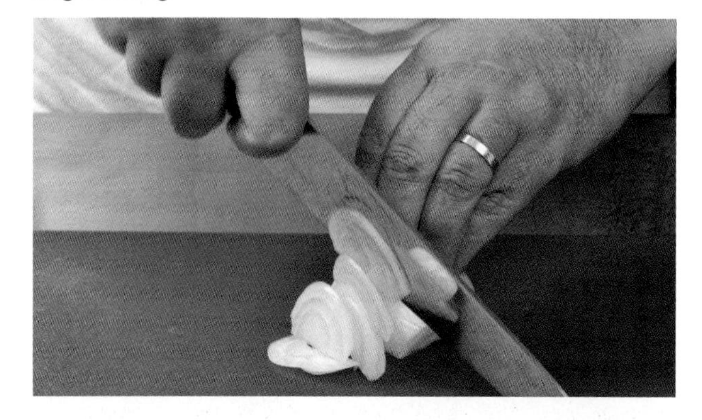
Shredding

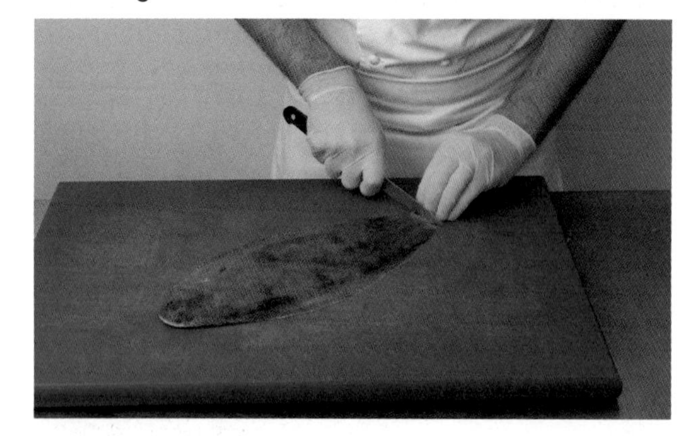
Skinning 1

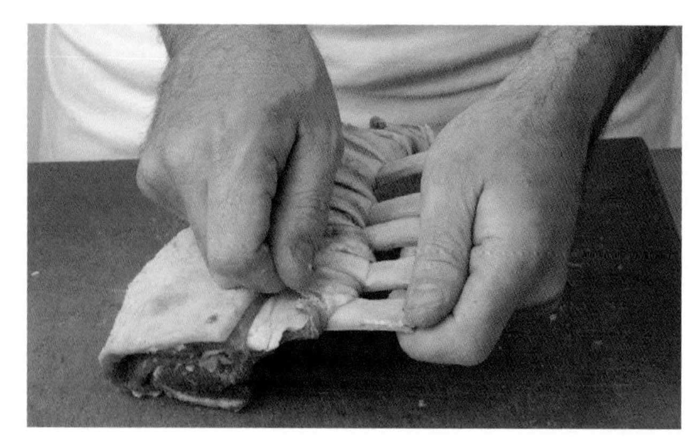
Skinning 2

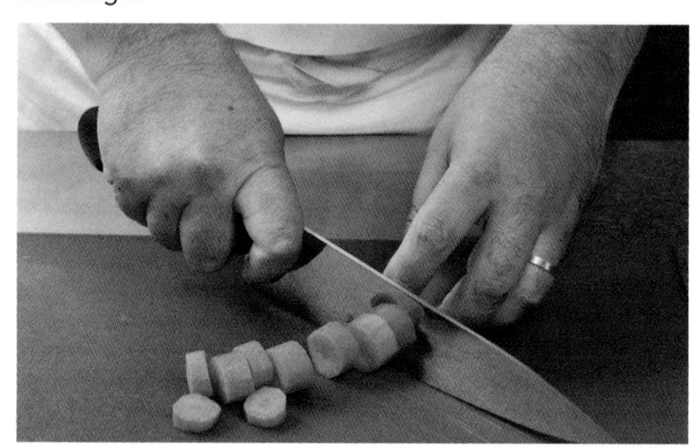
Slicing

Trimming

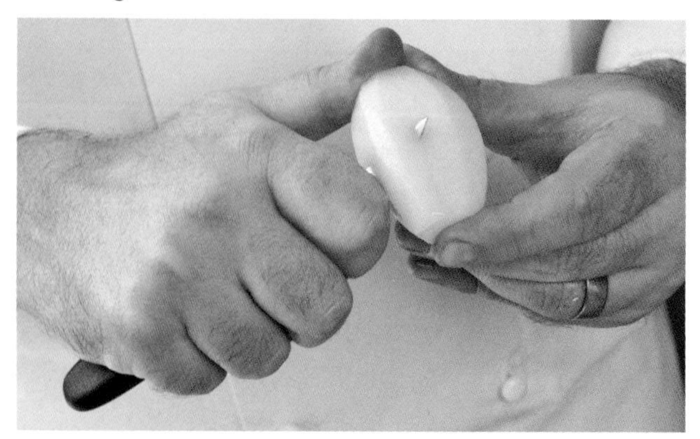
Turning/shaping

ACTIVITY

1 It is important to use knives and cutting equipment correctly to prevent accidents and injury to yourself and others. Give four other reasons why it is important to use knives and cutting equipment correctly.
2 Identify the following knives and state what they are used for:

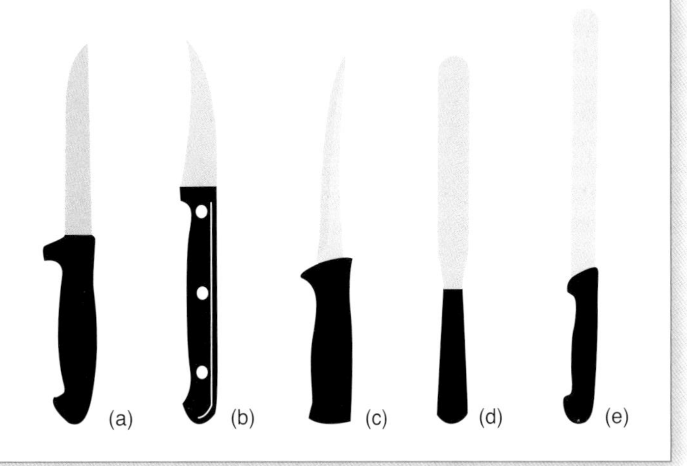

2 Use tools and small equipment throughout the food production process

Kitchen equipment can be divided into two categories, as follows.

1 **Small equipment and utensils** – for example, spoons, whisks and ladles. This also includes small mechanical equipment such as peelers, mincers and mixers.
2 **Large equipment** – for example, ovens, hobs, grills, steamers and fryers. This also includes large mechanical equipment such as refrigerators and dishwashers. You can read more about large equipment in section 3 of this chapter.

You need to know how to use a range of large and small equipment and utensils correctly and safely, and be able to identify any hazards associated with using, cleaning and storing them.

2.1 Types and characteristics of tools and small equipment

Each piece of small equipment has a specific use in the kitchen. Small equipment and utensils are made from a variety of materials, including non-stick coated metal, iron, steel and heatproof plastic. Small equipment must be looked after, cleaned, and stored safely and hygienically.

Cooking pans

Baking sheets are made in various sizes from black wrought steel. They are used for baking and pastry work.

Baking tins (sometimes called **cake tins**) are used for baking cakes, bread and sponges. The mixture is placed in the tin before cooking.

Griddle pans have raised ribs to mark the food. The griddle lines (quadrillage) give the food a chargrilled effect. Modern griddle pans have a non-stick surface.

Non-stick frying pans are coated with a material such as Teflon, which prevents the food from sticking to them. They are usually used for shallow frying.

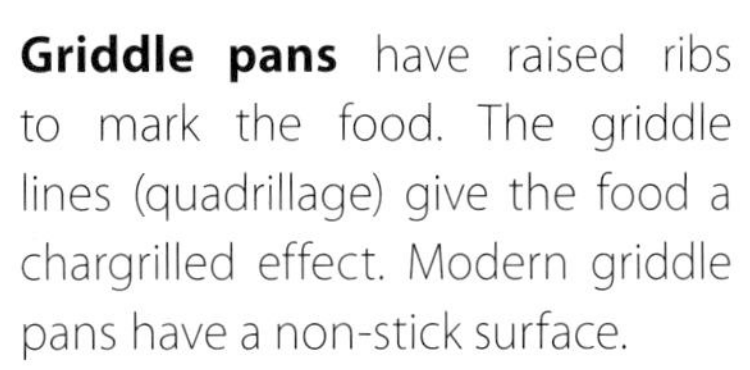

Saucepans come in various sizes and are made in a variety of materials. Some are made solely of stainless steel; others contain a mixture of metals, such as stainless steel with an aluminium layer and a thick copper coil. Saucepans are used for a variety of cooking methods, including boiling, poaching and stewing.

Sauté pans are shallow, straight-sided pans made from stainless steel or a mixture of metals. They are used for shallow frying when a sauce is made after the food is fried. They may also be used for poaching, especially for shallow-poached fish.

A **sauteuse** is a type of sauté pan with sloping sides, often used for reducing sauces and poaching.

Trays

Gastronome trays are a modular storing and serving system; they come in a variety of sizes that can be moved from refrigerator to oven.

Roasting trays are metal trays, usually made of stainless steel. They have deep sides and are used for roasting food such as meat and vegetables.

Stainless steel trays are used to store food in the refrigerator.

Woks are shallow, rounded frying pans use for stir frying and oriental cookery. They are made from material that can conduct heat quickly. Thick copper-core stainless steel is the most effective.

> **HEALTH AND SAFETY**
> - Incorrect pan storage can result in pans falling from the shelves, causing injury and damage to the equipment. Store pans upside down on clean racks. Check that handles are not loose.
> - Items stored at a great height may cause people to stretch, causing back strain. Minimise the risk by storing pans at a lower level, so people do not need to stretch for them.

Tools and small equipment

Blow torches are used, for example, to caramelise sugar on a crème brûlée or flans, or to remove skin from peppers, etc.

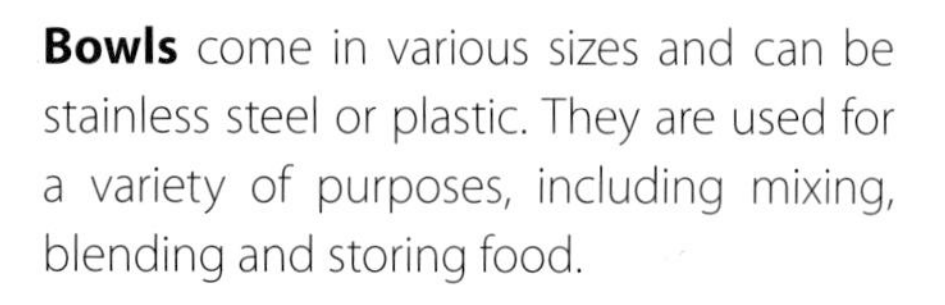

Bowls come in various sizes and can be stainless steel or plastic. They are used for a variety of purposes, including mixing, blending and storing food.

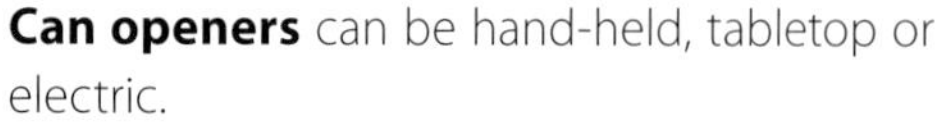

Can openers can be hand-held, tabletop or electric.

Colanders are available in a variety of sizes and usually made from stainless steel. They are used for draining liquids.

Conical strainers are usually stainless steel with large mesh. They are used for general straining and passing of liquids, soups and sauces.

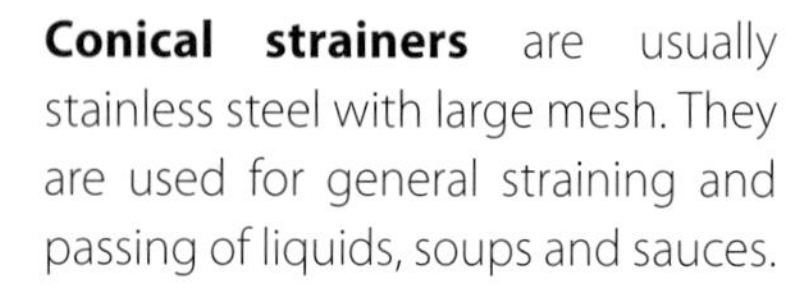

A **chinois** is a very fine mesh conical strainer.

Cooling racks are made from stainless steel mesh and are usually rectangular. Baked items are placed on cooling racks to cool. The mesh allows air to circulate, enabling the items to cool quickly.

Cutlet bats are made from metal and used to bat out meat, making it thinner.

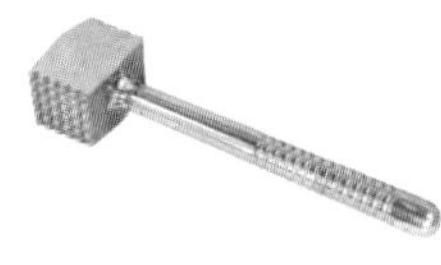

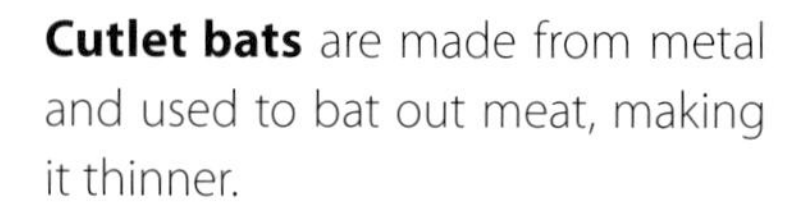

Flan rings are used to make flan cases and flans. The flan ring is lined with pastry to make the pastry case, and then filled with the flan mixture or tart filling.

Fish slices are made from stainless steel. They are used for lifting and sliding food on and off trays to serving dishes.

Food mixers are labour-saving electrical devices used for many different tasks in the kitchen. They have a range of attachments for different jobs such as mincing, cutting, blending and mixing.

Food processors are electrical machines used for many jobs in the kitchen. They usually come with a range of blades for cutting, puréeing, slicing, grating and mixing. They come in a variety of sizes.

- A **thermomix** is a type of food processor with an integrated heating system. It is able to steam, chop, whip, mix, emulsify, blend, knead and cook.
- A **pacojet** is a piece of equipment that micro-purées deep-frozen foods into ultra-fine textures such as mousses, sauces and sorbets.

Graters are made from stainless steel. They come in various sizes and are used to shred and grate food such as cheese, the zest of citrus fruits and vegetables. Graters usually have a choice of grating edges: fine, medium or large.

Gravity-feed slicers have very sharp cutting blades and must be operated with a safety guard. They are used for slicing meat so that every slice is the same thickness.

HEALTH AND SAFETY

- There is an age restriction for the use of gravity-feed slicing machines; you must be over 18 to use them.
- It is advisable to have a separate slicing machine for raw and cooked food. This is recommended by food safety officers.

Ladles come in various sizes. They are large, scoop-shaped spoons used to add liquids to cooking pots, and to serve sauces and stews.

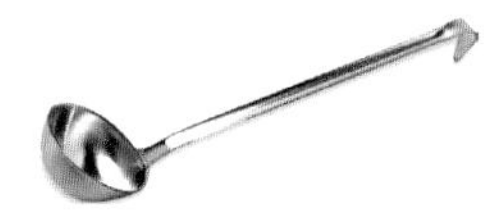

Liquidisers and blenders are pieces of mechanical equipment used to blend solid food into liquids. They can be made from glass, plastic or stainless steel.

Mashers/ricers can be manual or electric and are used for mashing vegetables.

Mandolins are specialist pieces of equipment used for slicing vegetables. The blade is made from stainless steel and is adjustable to different widths, for thick or thin slices of food. They are usually used to slice vegetables such as potatoes, courgettes, cucumbers and carrots. The blade is particularly sharp, so you should be very careful when using one. Modern mandolins have an in-built safety guard.

Measuring jugs are available in a variety of sizes. They can be made from stainless steel, glass or plastic. They are used for measuring liquids.

Mincers are standalone or attachments that fit to a mixer. They have a circular cutting blade that forces the food through a plate with different size holes depending on the requirements of the size of mince required.

Moulds come in many shapes and sizes. They are used for shaping and moulding food for presentation – for example, tartlets, mousses, custards and blancmange. Moulds can be very difficult to clean – you must make sure that all food debris is removed and that the mould is cleaned properly to prevent cross-contamination.

Mushrooms are usually made of wood or plastic and are, as their name suggests, shaped like a mushroom. They are used for passing food through a sieve.

Pastry brushes are used to brush pastry with egg wash or milk, to glaze and to brush excess flour from raw pastry.

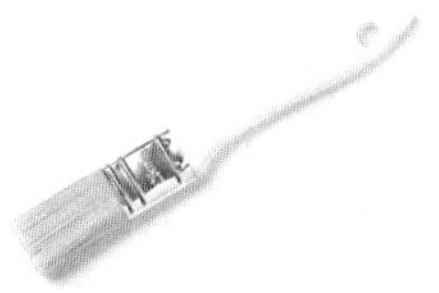

Piping bags and nozzles are used to decorate food for presentation, to fill moulds for cleanliness and accuracy. Piping bags are usually disposable for hygiene purposes. Nozzles are plastic and come in a variety of sizes; plain and star nozzles are the most common.

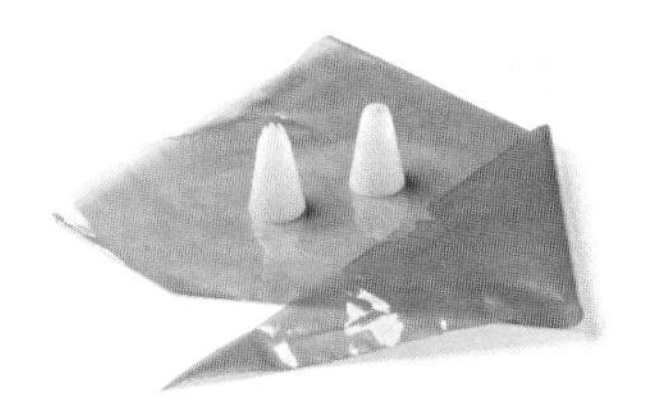

Metal pokers are used to remove the centre bullseye from the centre of the stove, and separate pokers are also used for marking fish and meat with a criss-cross effect known as quadrillage.

Rolling pins are used for rolling pastry manually. Today they are usually made from plastic.

Scales are used to weigh ingredients.

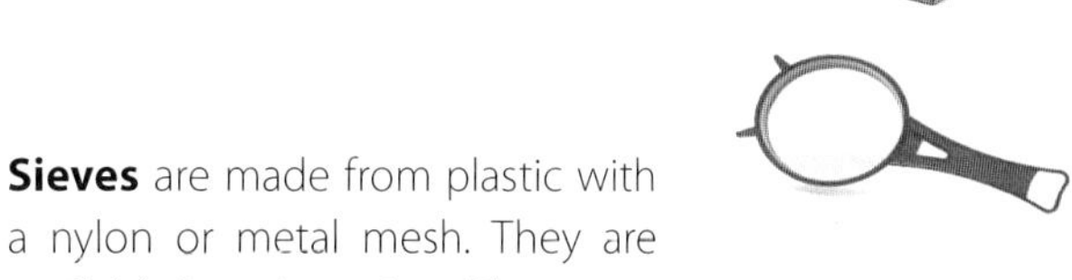

Sieves are made from plastic with a nylon or metal mesh. They are available in various sizes. They are a type of strainer and can be used to sieve dry ingredients such as flour or for purées.

Skimming spoons are made from stainless steel and have holes in them. They are used for skimming and draining. Skimming is removing fat and other unwanted substances from the top of liquids, such as stocks and soups.

Spatulas are flat spoons used for stirring and scraping.

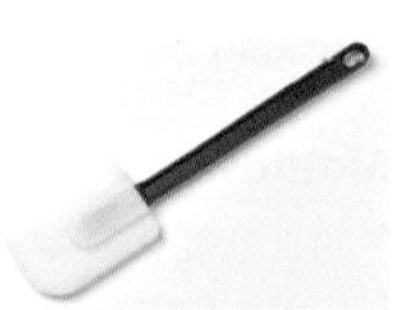

Spiders are made from stainless steel. They are used for removing food from containers, saucepans, water, etc. They are also used to remove food from a deep fat fryer.

Spoons come in a variety of sizes for serving and moving food to and from containers. They are made from stainless steel.

Temperature probes are an essential piece of equipment used in the kitchen to check temperatures of food on arrival in the kitchen from suppliers and to take the core temperature of food before serving to make sure it has reached a safe temperature.

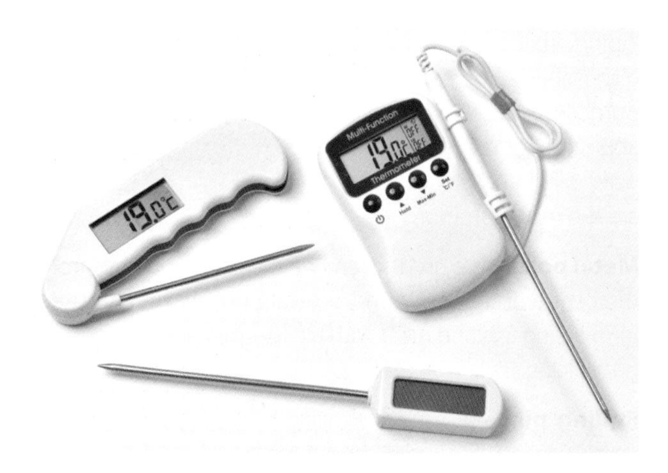

Trussing needles are used to truss poultry and game. These are not in common use today as most poultry and game is purchased already tied.

Whisks are wired and used for whisking and beating air into products – for example, whisking egg whites. Heavier wired whisks are available for whisking sauces; these are known as sauce whisks. A sauce whisk is stronger than a balloon whisk, which is lighter and has an end shaped like a balloon. A balloon whisk is used for whisking ingredients such as egg whites and cream.

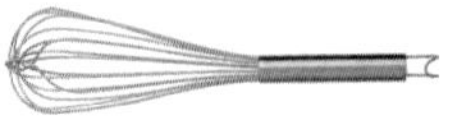

Cutting boards

These are used for chopping and slicing food on. The most popular boards are made from polyethylene or plastic. Different boards should be used for different foods, to avoid cross-contamination. The accepted UK system is shown here.

The UK system of colour coding

Cutting boards must be stored correctly in a safe and hygienic way, preferably on a rack allowing circulation of air so that after they have been thoroughly cleaned they are allowed to dry and other types of boards or equipment cannot contaminate them. Incorrect storage of boards may lead to cross-contamination and food poisoning.

Colour coded knives and equipment

In addition to coloured coded boards some kitchens will also use colour coded knives and equipment for different processes in the kitchen in order to separate raw and cooked food, to prevent cross contamination and to eliminate any risk of food poisoning. This is common practice in cook chill, cook freeze and sous vide operations. Areas of the kitchen may also be coded so that there is no crossover of equipment or staff.

In recent years a new colour code has been introduced – purple, which is used to separate foods which are listed as likely to give an allergic reaction.

Characteristics of different types of tools and equipment

- **Size** – Tools and equipment come in various sizes. Always choose the right size for the job or task to be carried out as this will make it easier and more efficient. Size is very important in portion control, and particularly when using ladles, spoons and similar equipment.
- **Shape** – Some tools and equipment are purposely designed to carry out certain tasks. For example, a sauteuse with sloping slides is better for tossing and turning food and for reducing sauces. Think about the task in hand and use the appropriately shaped equipment.
- **Length** – This is important when choosing trays and baking sheets for certain jobs, as is the length of spoon handles, particularly for jobs such as coating items with sauces, etc.
- **Materials** – When choosing and buying equipment, always consider the material that it is made of. Avoid certain materials, such as aluminium, as this can be dangerous to health, and where possible choose 18/8 stainless steel. Consider also how the materials will be cleaned. Always choose equipment that is easy to clean and will stand up to wear and tear.
- **Colour** – Avoid coloured kitchen equipment except for cutting boards and colour-coded handles for spoons, knives, etc., to prevent bacterial cross-contamination. Purple is used to mark equipment used to prevent allergy contamination.
- **Design** – The design of equipment must allow the user to carry out the function with ease and efficiency, and needs to be able to stand up to constant use. All surfaces should be smooth, there should be no sharp edges and it must be easy to clean.

2.2 Maintaining and storing tools and small equipment

Thoroughly wash all equipment, pans and utensils with hot detergent and water after use. Rinse with hot water and then dry thoroughly. Incomplete cleaning and drying can lead to build-up of mould, food contamination and cross-contamination. Always clean equipment appropriately to comply with strict hygiene standards. Where possible, store on stainless steel racks that can be easily cleaned. The racks should also be mobile and able to be locked for security reasons.

Make sure you use the right equipment for the recipe, process and service.

HEALTH AND SAFETY

Always make sure that the safety guards are in place before using mechanical equipment. Report any faulty equipment to your line manager or supervisor. Always make sure that mechanical equipment is serviced regularly, maintained in good working order and is safe to use.

2.3 Using tools and small equipment

You will need to use different tools and small equipment to prepare and cook food and to ensure the minimum amount of wastage. Choosing the correct tool can help to prevent wastage especially when portioning food.

Table 3.1 Tools and small equipment that can be used for different techniques

Technique	Equipment that can be used
Basting	Kitchen spoon, ladle
Beating	Whisk, spatula
Blanching	Saucepan, colander, blow torch
Blending	Kitchen spoon, spatula, whisk
Brushing	Pastry brush
Coating	Kitchen spoon, ladle
Cooling/chilling/refreshing	Basins, bowls, colander, blast-chiller
Cutting/shaping	Professional knives, turning knives, canale knife, parisienne spoon, cutters, moulds
Draining	Colanders, sieves
Filling	Piping bags and nozzles, spoons
Folding	Palette knife, kitchen spoons, spatula
Glazing	Blow torch, spoons, pastry brush
Lining	Rolling pin, cutters, mounds
Mashing	Ricer, sieve, mushroom
Measuring	Scales, jugs, spoons
Mixing	Whisks, spoons, spatulas
Moulding and demoulding	Moulds, basins, blow torch
Passing	Chinois, conical strainer, sieve, mushroom
Piping	Piping bags and nozzles
Portioning	Spoons, moulds, ladles, serving dishes
Pureeing	Sieves, food processors, pacojet, thermomix
Reducing	Saucepans, thermomix
Rolling	Rolling pins
Saucing	Ladles, spoons
Searing	Blow torch, poker
Serving	Serving dishes, plates, ladles, kitchen spoons
Skimming	Skimming spoon, spoons, ladles
Slicing	Carving knives, serrated knives, gravity-feed slicing machine
Straining	Chinois, conical strainers, colanders
Trussing and tying	Trussing needles, string
Turning	Small kitchen knife, turning knife
Weighing	Scales, measuring spoons
Whisking	Whisks, balloon and sauce whisks

3 Use large equipment throughout the food production process

3.1 Types and characteristics of large equipment

3.2 Maintaining large equipment

Ovens

Conventional ovens come in a wide range of types; they can be fuelled by either gas or electricity. Some have grills built in.

HEALTH AND SAFETY

With gas ovens, it is very important to light the gas once it is turned on. Gas ovens and ranges must be fitted with a flame failure device. This switches off the gas if the flame blows out, to prevent explosion.

Convection (fan-assisted) ovens have a built-in fan, which circulates hot air around the oven. This increases the temperature in all parts of the oven, making it more efficient and meaning that cooking temperatures can be lowered. For example, something that would have to be cooked at 200°C in a conventional oven might cook at 180°C in a convection oven. Convection ovens are very good for baking and roasting.

Cleaning conventional and convection ovens – Allow the equipment to cool before scrubbing it down and wiping it clean. Apply a little oil to the surface of solid tops to keep the surface in good condition.

HEALTH AND SAFETY

When cleaning, always use protective clothing and allow the equipment to cool down first to avoid accidental burns. When using a chemical oven cleaner, always wear a safety mask and thick rubber gloves.

Combination ovens can be used as an oven or steamer or both. Steam is injected into the oven when you are baking and roasting, to increase the moisture content (humidity) of the oven. These ovens are fuelled by gas or electricity. They are fully automatic, having built-in computers that can be pre-programmed to cook food for exactly the right amount of time, and are also able to keep food at the correct temperature. The latest versions monitor the internal temperatures of the food, allowing the chef to achieve the exact core temperature required and to deliver precise cooking textures. A computer system also records how often the oven is used and the temperatures used.

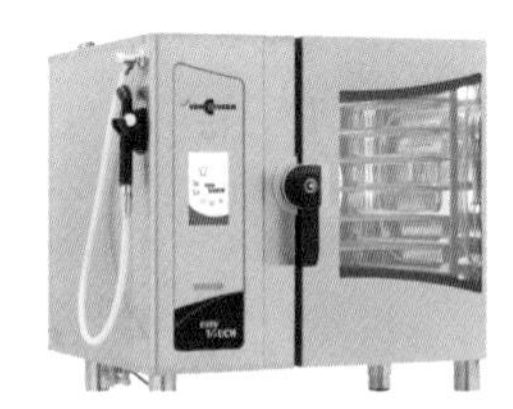

Cleaning combination ovens – Many modern models are self-cleaning, but they need to be checked regularly to make sure the cleaning programme is efficient.

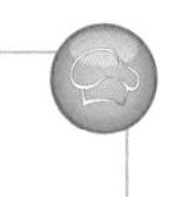

PROFESSIONAL TIP

Combination technology is changing all the time. Modern ovens are energy efficient, and time and labour saving.

HEALTH AND SAFETY

Take care when removing trays from the oven. When using a combination oven as a steamer, make sure you release the steam gently before opening the door.

Microwave ovens use high-frequency power. The energy waves disturb the molecules in food and move them, causing friction and heating the food. Microwave ovens can cook food more quickly than conventional ovens. They are often used for reheating food.

Cleaning microwave ovens – Clean up spillages immediately with hot, mild detergent water. This prevents bacteria growing and reduces the risk of contaminating other foods.

HEALTH AND SAFETY

If the door seal is damaged, do not use; report it to your employer or manager immediately. Microwave ovens should be inspected regularly.

Metal should never be used in a microwave unless it has a metal reflector. Using metal in a microwave without a metal reflector causes sparks and small explosions in the oven.

Hobs

Solid hob tops or solid-top stoves are made of solid metal with a burner. They have a single flat surface, meaning saucepans can be moved around easily during cooking. The middle of the hob has intense heat; the side is not so hot and is used to simmer. Solid-top hobs may be gas or electric. Gas-operated hobs have removable rings in the centre, which can be removed to expose the flame and allow the chef to place the saucepan directly on to the flame. This intense heat allows the food to cook faster or liquid to reduce quickly.

Cleaning solid-top hobs – Remove all food debris, clean with hot detergent water, dry and lightly oil.

> **HEALTH AND SAFETY**
> Solid-top hobs have a pilot light and a flame-failure device that switches off the gas for safety. However, they still require regular safety checks by a qualified gas fitter.

Open range hobs are stoves where the flame is exposed; the saucepans are placed on metal bars over the flame. It is more difficult to move the saucepans around on this type of hob than on solid-top hobs. To simmer, the flame has to be reduced using a switch that controls each flame.

Cleaning open range hobs – Remove the metal bars, wash in hot detergent water and dry. Clean the stove surface with hot detergent water after removing any food debris; a light abrasive may be required for any baked-on food. Dry and replace metal bars.

> **HEALTH AND SAFETY**
> Similar to solid-top hobs, these stoves are fitted with a flame-failure device, but require regular safety checks by a qualified gas fitter.

Induction hobs have burners called induction coils. A coil will heat up only when a pan with a metal base (such as a stainless steel pan) is in direct contact with the hob. When the pan is removed from the hob it turns off straight away and cools down quickly. The hob will feel slightly warm after it is turned off. Water boils rapidly on an induction hob and, overall, food cooks more quickly than on other types of hob.

Cleaning induction hobs – Induction hobs are very easy to clean and usually require only a wipe down with mild detergent water.

> **HEALTH AND SAFETY**
> Induction hobs are much safer than conventional hobs because they stay relatively cool even when cooking. There is very little chance of burning from direct contact with the hob.

Steamers

- **Atmospheric steamer** – Operates at normal atmospheric pressure (the same pressure as outside the steamer), creating steam at just above 100°C. These are often normal saucepans with a metal basket in them.
- **Pressure steamer** – A good way to cook delicate food and foods cooked in a pouch. Some pressure steamers cook at high pressure and some at low pressure. In low-pressure steamers the temperature of the steam is 70°C and so food is cooked slowly. In high-pressure steamers the temperature of the steam is 120°C and so food is cooked faster.
- **Dual steamer** – This can switch between low and high pressure. At low pressure they cook in the same way as pressure steamers. At high pressure the food is cooked more quickly than in atmospheric steamers and pressure steamers.

All steamers are available in a variety of sizes.

In addition, combination ovens can be used to combine steaming and conventional oven cooking to get the benefits of both.

Cleaning steamers – Steamers have to be cleaned regularly. The inside of the steamer, trays and runners should be washed in hot detergent water, then rinsed and dried. Door controls should be lightly greased occasionally and the door left slightly open to allow air to circulate when the steamer is not in use. If water is held in the steamer then it must be changed regularly. The water chamber should be drained and cleaned before fresh water is added.

HEALTH AND SAFETY

The main safety hazard associated with steamers is scalding. Take care when opening steamer doors: open the door slowly to allow the steam to escape gradually from the oven, then carefully remove the food items.

Before use, check that the steamer is clean and safe to use. Any faults must be reported immediately.

Pans

Boiling pans can be powered by gas or electricity, and can be supplied with indirect heat by using a water jacket or by direct heat. For delicate sauces/custards, etc., indirect heat would be used. Boiling pans come in sizes from 60 litres up to 540 litres and are ideal for small restaurants for large-volume production cooking. These boiling pans can be supplied with easy-to-use mechanical controls or electronic digital controls for precise cooking control. These days they are tilted for ease of operation and safety.

Cleaning boiling pans – Remove all food debris and clean with hot detergent water. Rinse with clean water.

HEALTH AND SAFETY

Do not overfill the boiling pan. Take special care when tilting. Ideally the pan should be sited with drainage. Turn off the power before cleaning.

Bratt pans are heavy-duty commercial cooking appliances that can perform up to eight cooking functions: braising, boiling, steaming, poaching, stewing, roasting, deep fat frying and shallow frying. Because they are so versatile they can replace numerous other pieces of heavy kitchen equipment. Bratt pans are deep, rectangular cooking pots with a counterbalanced pull-down lid. The heat source to the base of the pan is either gas or electric. They all have a tilting feature, operated electrically or by a hand-driven mechanism. Bratt pans are typically used in mass catering establishments such as schools, hospitals or large staff restaurants for producing large volumes of food. They are used in hotels for banqueting. Although bratt pans are generally large appliances, they can save vast amounts of space in comparison to individual appliances that can do limited kitchen tasks.

Cleaning bratt pans – Cleaning is easy in comparison to similar-sized machines. As all the cooking is done in the large pan, you can simply tilt the pan using either a hand crank or electric motor, depending on the model. As bratt pans usually have a central spout, any remaining food is easily removed ready for cleaning. Use hot water and detergent. Rinse thoroughly.

HEALTH AND SAFETY

Take special care when tilting the bratt pan. Before cleaning, switch the power off and allow to cool down.

Deep fat fryers

A deep fat fryer has a container with enough oil in it to cover the food. The oil is heated to very hot temperatures. A cool zone, which is a chamber at the base of the cooking pan, collects odd bits of food such as breadcrumbs or batter from fish when it is being fried. Some fryers are computerised; these can be programmed to heat the oil to the correct temperature and cook the food for the right amount of time.

Cleaning a deep fat fryer – When frying, remove all the food debris immediately and keep the oil as clean as possible. You will need to remove the oil to clean the fryer. Make sure the fryer is switched off and the oil is cool before removing it and put suitable containers in place to drain the oil into. Replace with clean oil.

HEALTH AND SAFETY

Deep fat fryers are possibly the most dangerous piece of equipment in the kitchen. Many kitchen fires have been started through careless use of a deep fat fryer. Take care not to splash the oil when placing items of food in the fryer as this can cause serious burns and eye injuries. Avoid placing wet food into the fryer. Never throw food items in the deep fat fryer from a height: place the food in carefully. When changing the oil, always allow it to cool first.

Grills

A **salamander** (also known as an **overhead grill**) is heated from above by gas or electricity. Most salamanders have more than one set of heating elements or jets, and it is not always necessary to have them all fully turned on.

Cleaning salamanders – Salamanders have a tray to catch grease and food debris. This needs to be emptied and cleaned thoroughly with hot detergent water. Soda is very useful for removing grease.

> **HEALTH AND SAFETY**
> Take care when placing food under and removing food from the salamander. Wear appropriate protective clothing when cleaning a salamander.

The heat source for **under-fired or under-heated grills** is underneath the grill. Under-fired grills are used to cook food quickly, so they need to reach a high temperature. This type of grill makes criss-cross marks on the food, known as **quadrillage**.

Cleaning under-fired grills – When the bars are cool, they should be removed and washed in hot water containing a grease solvent (detergent). They should then be rinsed, dried and replaced in the grill. If fire bricks are used for lining the grill, take care with these as they break easily.

> **HEALTH AND SAFETY**
> Take care when placing food on the grill, moving it around on the grill and removing it – always use tongs. Be extra careful when brushing the food with oil and do not allow the oil to drip on the flame.

Contact grills are sometimes called **double-sided grills** or **infragrills**. They have two heating surfaces, which face each other. The food is placed on one surface and is then covered by the second. They cook certain foods, such as toast in a toaster, very quickly.

Quadrillage

Cleaning contact grills – Turn off the electricity when cleaning and avoid using water. Lightly scrape clean.

> **HEALTH AND SAFETY**
> Always allow the grills and griddles to cool down before cleaning to prevent burns. Take great care when placing the food on or in the grill, especially open flame and barbecue grills.

Bain-marie

Bain-marie means 'water bath'. These are open wells of water for keeping food hot. They are available in many designs, some of which are built into hot cupboards and some into serving controls. They are heated by steam, gas or electricity. Water baths are also used for the gentle cooking of foods in a vacuum bag.

Cleaning bains-marie – Turn off the heat after use. Drain the water away and clean the bain-marie inside and out with hot detergent water. Then rinse and dry it. If it has a drain-off tap, this should be closed.

> **HEALTH AND SAFETY**
> It is important to never allow the bain-marie to run dry when the heat is turned on. Check the temperature regularly: never allow it to differ from the recipe and safety requirements.

Hot cupboards

Commonly referred to as a hotplate, a hot cupboard is used for heating plates and serving dishes, and for keeping food hot. You must make sure that the temperature in the hot cupboard is kept at around 63–70°C so that the food is not too hot or too cold. Hot cupboards may be heated by gas, steam or electricity.

Cleaning hot cupboards – Hot cupboards must be emptied and cleaned after each service.

HEALTH AND SAFETY

Take care when taking plates, dishes and food in and out of hot cupboards, to avoid burns and scalds.

Proving cabinets

Proving cabinets are used for proving yeast products, such as bread dough. They provide a warm and moist atmosphere that allows the yeast to grow, causing the dough to rise (prove). The most suitable temperature for this is 37°C. Proving cabinets have a drain to collect the excess water as the moist air cools.

Refrigerators and chill rooms

Refrigerators and chill rooms keep food chilled at between 1°C and 5°C. These cold conditions slow down the growth of bacteria and spoilage enzymes that make food 'go off'. They are used to store a whole range of products.

Cleaning refrigerators and chill rooms – Chill rooms and refrigerators must be tidied once a day and cleaned out once a week. Clean with hot water and suitable cleaning chemicals – diluted bicarbonate of soda is most suitable.

HEALTH AND SAFETY

The way that food is stored in chill rooms and refrigerators is very important. There must not be cross-contamination between different foods, as this spreads bacteria. All food must be covered and labelled with its use by date.

The internal temperature of chill rooms and refrigerators must be checked at least twice a day.

Vacuum packaging machine

These are used in the sous vide process and for packaging and storing food, to prolong shelf life and prevent discoloration. Sous vide is a combination of vacuum sealing food in plastic pouches, tightly controlled en papillotte (cooking in a paper bag) using steam or hot water, and rapid chilling. It is a form of cook-chill food production that can be used by almost any type of catering operation.

Vacuum pressures are as important as cooking temperatures with regard to weight loss and heat absorption. The highest temperature used in sous vide cooking is 100°C, and 1000 millibars is the minimum amount of vacuum pressure used.

As there is no oxidation or discoloration involved, this method is ideal for conserving fruits, such as apples and pears (e.g. pears in red wine, fruits in syrup). When preparing meats in sauces the meat is pre-blanched then added to the completed sauce.

Cleaning vacuum packaging machines – Vacuum packaging machines must be cleaned carefully, removing all debris, and sanitised. It is advisable to have separate vacuum packing machines for raw and cooked food.

Water baths

Water baths are used to cook delicate foods at lower temperatures for longer periods of time, to improve yields and texture. They are used in conjunction with the sous vide process.

Freezers

Freezers are used to store food between -18°C and -20°C. Food in the freezer does not last indefinitely, but the low temperature slows down the growth of bacteria and means that the food will last longer.

Cleaning freezers – Most freezers today are frost-free, which means that they do not need to be defrosted. Tidy the freezer at least once a week. Clean it out every three to six months using a mild cleaning fluid, mild detergent or diluted bicarbonate of soda.

HEALTH AND SAFETY

As in chill rooms, all food stored in a freezer must be covered and date labelled.

Blast-chillers are high-powered and well-ventilated pieces of refrigeration equipment that quickly and safely reduce the temperature of both cooked and fresh food products. Normally, the blast-chilling function will reduce cooked food temperatures from +70°C down to +3°C within a period of 90 minutes. This is in line with government Food Standards Agency regulations and Hazard Analysis and Critical Control Points (HACCP) standards (see Unit 201). The rate at which the temperature is reduced is important because it influences the outcome of the overall cooling process by carefully reducing the ability for bacteria to grow. Most blast-chillers offer two methods of blast-chilling.

1. **Soft chilling** – This produces an air temperature of between +3°C and -2°C to reduce the temperature inside the cabinet. Using a powerful ventilation system, the temperature of the food can quickly but gently be lowered so as not to damage the surface of the food. This method is ideal for unpacked, delicate, thin or small products such as vegetables, rice and lightly fried food or dairy products such as custard tarts, flans and quiches.
2. **Hard chilling** – This produces an air temperature as low as -20°C. This ensures the air temperature inside the cabinet drops quickly to +3°C to enable the core food temperature to pass through the danger zone as quickly as possible.

Blast freezers are high-powered pieces of refrigeration equipment that quickly and safely reduce the temperature of both fresh and cooked products down to a negative temperature. The air temperature entering the cabinet at the beginning of the blast freezing cycle can range from -30°C to -40°C. It is essential that the freezing function reduces the food temperature down from +70°C to -18°C within a period of 240 minutes. This ensures compliance with HACCP standards.

How to choose equipment

Think carefully about what the equipment is going to be used for and for how long. There is a wide variety of equipment on the market and you must learn to assess its durability and usefulness. Consider the material equipment is made from: stainless steel, for example, is very durable and is a good choice if you are looking for long-lasting, hard-wearing equipment.

Also consider how easy equipment is to clean. Equipment that is more difficult to clean is less likely to be cleaned properly; harsh abrasives may have to be used, which may result in damage to the equipment.

When choosing equipment it is also important to know the size and design of the equipment you will need to do the job. If you are producing a large quantity of food at one time, for example, you will need larger pans than if you are cooking smaller quantities or fewer meals.

The Food Safety (General Food Hygiene) Regulations 1995, and subsequent regulations (2006, 2013), require all articles, fittings and equipment with which food comes into contact to be kept clean and to be constructed and maintained so as to minimise risk of contamination. Equipment must also be installed in such a way that the surrounding area can be cleaned.

The following equipment is preferable:

- tubular machinery frames
- stainless steel table legs
- drain cocks and holes instead of pockets and crevices that could trap liquid
- dials fitted to machines having adequate clearance to facilitate cleaning.

Where possible, equipment should be mobile so that it can be removed for cleaning – for example, it could be mounted on castors, with brakes on all the wheels.

Cooking equipment is the key to catering success and quality. In terms of food safety it controls the most critical step in the food production process. A mistake at the cooking stage, such as the undercooking of raw food, could result in a mass food-poisoning incident.

Kitchen equipment is expensive, so choosing the right equipment is important. The following points should be considered before each item is purchased or hired.

- **Size** of the equipment in relation to available space.
- **Weight** – can the floor support the weight?
- **Fuel supply** – is the existing fuel supply sufficient for the new equipment? Always look at the overall energy requirement and choose equipment that is energy saving.
- **Drainage** – where necessary, are there adequate facilities?
- **Water** – where necessary, is it to hand?
- **Use** – if it is a specialist piece of equipment for certain foods or products, will it be used enough to justify the expense and investment?
- **Capacity** – can it cook the quantities of food required efficiently?
- **Time** – can it cook the given quantities of food in the time available?
- **Ease** – is it easy to handle, control and use properly?
- **Maintenance** – is it easy to clean and maintain?
- **Attachments** – is it necessary to use additional equipment or attachments?
- **Extraction** – does it require extraction facilities for fumes or steam?
- **Noise** – does it have an acceptable noise level?
- **Construction** – is it well made, safe, hygienic and energy efficient, and are all handles, knobs and switches sturdy and heat resistant?
- **Appearance** – if equipment is to be on view to customers, does it look good and fit in with the overall design?
- **Spare parts** – are replacement parts easily obtainable?

3.3 Using large equipment

You will need to choose the right equipment for the method and process to achieve the exact yield to prevent wastage.

Table 3.2 Large equipment that can be used for different techniques

Technique	Equipment that can be used
Baking	Convection ovens, combination ovens
Boiling	Boiling pans, saucepans
Braising	Bratt pans, convention and combination ovens
Chilling	Blast-chillers
Cold holding	Refrigerators, refrigerated display cabinets
Freezing	Freezers
Frying	Deep fat fryers, frying pans, bratt pans
Grilling	Contact grills, salamanders, griddles
Hot holding	Bains-marie, hot cupboards
Microwaving	Microwave ovens
Poaching	Water baths, steamers, sauté pans
Roasting	Ovens, combination and convection
Steaming	Atmospheric steamers, low-pressure and high-pressure steamers
Stewing	Bratt pans, combination and convection ovens
Storing	Refrigerators, freezers, hot cupboards, refrigerator display cabinets

ACTIVITY

1 When a combination oven is set to introduce steam into the cooking process, what safety precautions should you take when placing food into and removing it from the oven?
2 When lifting a heavy drum of cooking oil from the floor to fill a fryer, you should bend your knees and keep your back straight. What other safety precautions should you observe?
3 How should you clean an open range hob?
4 Describe what a bain-marie is used for.
5 Describe how a microwave cooks food.

TEST YOURSELF

1 Name a piece of equipment that saves energy.
2 Describe the various processes that a combination oven can be used for.
3 What is the purpose of a cool zone in a deep fat fryer?
4 Why should you not use blunt knives?
5 How can a professional knife be sharpened?
6 What is the legal age at which someone can use a gravity-feed slicing machine?
7 What piece of equipment would you use to purée a soup?
8 What would you use a mandolin for?
9 How would you clean a deep fat fryer?
10 What health and safety points do you need to consider when using a bain-marie?

204 Boiling, poaching and steaming

The purpose of this chapter is to help you develop skills, knowledge and understanding of the processes involved in preparing and cooking food by boiling, poaching or steaming to produce a variety of dishes.

In this chapter, you will be able to:

Learning outcomes

1 produce boiled products, including:
  - **1.1** selecting food items for boiling
  - **1.2** applying preparation methods for boiling
  - **1.3** applying techniques to produce boiled products
  - **1.4** applying finishing methods for boiled products

2 produce poached products, including:
  - **2.1** selecting food items for poaching
  - **2.2** applying preparation methods for poaching
  - **2.3** applying techniques to produce poached products
  - **2.4** applying finishing methods for poached products

3 produce steamed products, including:
  - **3.1** selecting food items for steaming
  - **3.2** applying preparation methods for steaming
  - **3.3** applying techniques to produce steamed products
  - **3.4** applying finishing methods for steamed products

Recipes included in this chapter

Boiling	
1	Suffolk pork collar daube cooked in cyder
2	White stock
3	Brown stock
4	Fish stock
5	Split pea soup
6	Mutton broth
7	Leek and potato soup
8	Sweet potato soup
9	Tomato soup
10	Garden marrow soup
11	Velouté
12	Béchamel (basic white sauce)
13	Roast gravy
14	Thickened roast gravy
15	Boiled eggs
16	Farfalle with chives and bacon
17	Plain boiled rice
18	Boiled chicken with rice and suprême sauce
19	Chicken à la king
20	Pease pudding
21	Boiled bacon
22	Pastry cream
Poaching	
23	Mulled cider poached pear with shortbread
24	Poached eggs
25	Poached salmon
26	Poached pears in red wine
Steaming	
27	'Tiny Tip' raspberry steamed sponge pudding
28	Steamed fish with garlic and spring onion
29	Steamed steak pudding
30	Steamed sponge pudding
31	Boiled/steamed cauliflower
32	Boiled/steamed broccoli
33	Boiled/steamed spinach
34	Boiled/steamed potatoes
35	Plain steamed rice

1 Produce boiled products

Process

Boiling is when food is covered in liquid, which is then heated up until the liquid starts to bubble vigorously. At this point it is boiling. Usually the heat is then turned down so that the liquid is just bubbling gently. In the kitchen it is often referred to as simmering.

PROFESSIONAL TIP

Boiling is an economical way of cooking lots of food as it does not use too much fuel.

Purpose

Boiling is a healthy method of cookery as it does not use any fat and, when done properly, will keep the flavour and nutritional value of the food. Boiling will:

- make food easy to digest and pleasant to eat, giving an agreeable flavour
- make food safe to eat
- give food a good texture – tender, slightly firm and crisp (depending on the food)
- help to retain colour, freshness and therefore the appearance of food items, when completed correctly.

1.1 Selecting food items for boiling

Some of the foods that can be cooked by boiling are listed below.

- **Vegetables** – Some are cooked quickly by placing in boiling liquid – for example, green vegetables. Others start in cold water and are brought to the boil, such as root vegetables.
- **Eggs** are placed into boiling water. Time is adjusted depending upon what the egg is for – for example, a soft-boiled egg for breakfast service takes 3–5 minutes depending on the customer request.
- **Pasta** – Either fresh or convenience products.
- **Pulses** – Some are soaked or blanched before boiling, as in dried marrowfat peas (for mushy peas to serve with fish and chips).

Boiling

- **Rice and grains** – including couscous and quinoa, as well as varieties of rice.
- **Meat and poultry** can also be boiled.
- **Stocks, soups and sauces** are often started by boiling and then simmered to finish.
- Some dishes contain a **mixture of ingredients** – for example, a good stock will have vegetables and bones/meat. Cooking time will vary depending on the ingredients used.

1.2 Applying preparation methods for boiling

Liquids used when boiling

There are four main liquids used when boiling foods:

1. water
2. milk
3. infused liquids
4. stock (fresh or convenience product).

The amount or type of liquid used depends on the type of food being boiled. It also influences the flavour and finish of a dish, or could be used to add to the final sauce that may be offered with some dishes – for example, pork collar daube.

- When you put vegetables into boiling liquid, always make sure that there is enough liquid in the pot and that it is boiling before you add the food. The liquid should just cover the vegetables but not boil over during cooking.
- When boiling meat, skim the surface of the liquid regularly during the cooking; this will remove impurities and help enhance the finished dish.
- When using a convenience stock or sauce mix you should ensure that it is reconstituted with the right amount of liquid, being careful not to allow too much to evaporate during cooking as this will impair the flavour and possible finish of the dish
- You should simmer rather than boil vigorously whenever possible. This will mean that less water evaporates, so the amount of liquid will stay more or less the same and the food will not shrink too much.

Methods of boiling

There are two ways of boiling.

1. Place the food in boiling liquid. The liquid will stop boiling when you put the food in, so heat it up to bring it back to boiling. Then reduce the heat so that the liquid just bubbles gently (this is known as simmering) and boils the food.
2. Cover food with cold liquid. Heat it up and bring it to the boil, then reduce the heat to allow the food to simmer.

HEALTH AND SAFETY

- When you place food into boiling water, you should lower it into the water gently to prevent splashing and scalding.
- Make sure that the handles on pots of boiling liquids are turned in when on stoves, so that sleeves and hands do not catch them. When removing the lid from the cooking pot, tilt it away from your face to allow the steam to escape safely. If you open it towards you the hot steam may burn your face.

Temperature and time control

For both methods of boiling, the temperature must be controlled so that the liquid is brought to the boil and then adjusted so that it goes to a gentle boil (simmer) until the food is cooked.

The time taken to cook food by boiling depends on the food being cooked.

- Stocks, soups and sauces must only simmer.
- Pasta should not be overcooked but left slightly firm (called al dente).
- Meat and poultry should be well cooked and tender.
- Vegetables should not be overcooked but left slightly crisp.

Equipment

Saucepans of various sizes can be used for boiling. Always choose pans that are the correct size for the item to be boiled – neither too small nor too large. Ensuring that the cooking pot is large enough for the water to cover the food without spilling over the edge once the water starts to boil will reduce the risk of being splashed by boiling water.

HEALTH AND SAFETY

Check the cleanliness and condition of the pan before use so as not to cause cross-contamination.

1.3 Applying techniques to produce boiled products

There are a number of techniques associated with boiling that help the chef to prepare dishes correctly.

- **Soaking** – Dried pulses and beans are pre-soaked prior to the cooking process to soften them.
- **Cutting** – The trimming, dicing, slicing and shredding of ingredients to ensure even size and shape to aid cooking. Trimmings could be used to make stocks and soups.
- **Blanching** – Food is cooked and then cooled rapidly to stop the cooking process. This is known as refreshing food; it is a good method to help retain colour in vegetables.
- **Skimming** – Scum or impurities often appear as foam or froth on the surface of the cooking liquid. To remove these, stir gently from the centre with a ladle to move the foam or froth to the edge of the pan; it can be collected by the edge of the ladle and placed into a bowl to be discarded.
- **Draining** – This is the process of removing food from the cooking liquid.
- **Chilling** – Reducing temperature to a holding or storage temperature.
- **Reheating** – Bringing previously cooked food to the required temperature for serving.
- **Holding for service** – Holding at a temperature above 63°C.

Products associated with boiling

Stock

Stock is important in several cooking methods. It is the basis of all meat sauces, gravies, soups and purées, as well as a cooking liquid in its own right.

There are three main types of stock:

1. white stock is made from bones, vegetables and herbs
2. brown stock is the same as white stock, except the bones are browned in a pan or in the oven before adding the rest of the ingredients
3. vegetable stock is made from vegetables and herbs, without any bones.

Recipes for making stocks are included in the recipe section.

When making stock:

- use only fresh bones and vegetables
- continually remove scum and fat from the surface of the stock as it cooks
- always simmer gently
- never add salt
- if the stock is going to be kept, strain and cool it quickly then store it in a refrigerator.

Convenience stocks are available in chilled, frozen, powder and condensed forms. It is important to taste these to check that you are satisfied with their quality before using them.

Soups

Stocks can be used to make a large variety of soups. A vast range of fresh vegetables and dried pulses (peas and beans) can be added to soups. Grains, pasta, and many herbs and spices can also be used.

There are a variety of ready-prepared soups on the market, including soups in powdered and condensed form. If you have to make use of a convenience product, always taste and assess it first. In some situations, you can combine a freshly prepared soup with a suitable convenience product.

Sauces

A sauce is a liquid that has been thickened, either by a roux, cornflour or arrowroot (a roux is a combination of fat and flour cooked gently over a low heat for a short time). Sauces that will be used for coating foods (for example, jus-lié – thickened gravy) should be as thin as possible and should coat the food only lightly.

Some types of accompaniment that are called sauces are not really sauces (for example, apple sauce, mint sauce, horseradish sauce). Recipes for several of this type of 'sauce', which are served with meat or poultry, are included in the recipe section.

For further products that can be prepared by boiling, see the recipe section later in this chapter.

1.4 Applying finishing methods for boiled products

For examples of finishing methods for boiled products, see the quality points and recipe sections later in this chapter, which covers examples of the following:

- finishing
- consistency and texture
- flavour, aroma and taste
- appearance and presentation
- portion size
- garnish.

2 Produce poached products

Process

Poaching is when food is cooked in a liquid that is very hot but not boiling. It should be just below boiling point. This process is often used for lighter or delicate food items, such as fish or fruits.

Purpose

The purpose of poaching is to cook food so that:

- it is very tender, and easy to eat and digest
- the flavour of the dish is enhanced
- the nutritional content is retained.

2.1 Selecting food items for poaching

The range of foods that can be cooked by poaching includes the following.

- **Poultry** – Normally the breast would be covered with stock and a cartouche, and slowly poached. Used when preparing chicken à la king.
- **Eggs** are poached in acidulated water for breakfast or as part of a garnish or accompaniment for other dishes – for example, haddock Monte Carlo.
- **Fish** – Fish fillets, darnes or suprêmes of fish can be either shallow or deep poached in stock or cooking liquor.
- **Fruit** – Whole or pieces of fruit poached in a stock syrup or wine.

2.2 Applying preparation methods for poaching

Liquids used when poaching

The same liquids used for boiling foods can be used for poaching, with a few additions.

- **Water** – Eggs are usually poached in water, with a little vinegar added.
- **Milk** – Fish fillets, such as smoked haddock, may be poached in milk.
- **Stock** – The stock should be suited to the food – for example, fish fillets can be poached in fish stock and chicken breast fillets in chicken stock. You can also poach poultry and fish in a rich vegetable stock.
- **Wine** – Fruit, such as pears, may be poached in wine.
- **Stock syrup** – This is sugar based and normally used for poaching fruits.
- **Infused liquids** – Cooking liquor may be flavoured with seasoning, spice, herbs or wine.

PROFESSIONAL TIP

Sometimes a tasty sauce can be made with the cooking liquid – for example, a parsley or other sauce can be made from the milk in which fish is poached.

HEALTH AND SAFETY
Although poaching liquids are not quite as dangerous as boiling liquids, they are still very hot and can cause serious burns or scalds. Be aware of pans of hot liquids – when you lower food into the poaching liquid, you should do so carefully to prevent splashes.

Methods of poaching

For most foods, the poaching liquid is heated first. When it reaches the right temperature, lower the prepared food into the barely simmering liquid and allow it to cook in the gentle heat.

There are two ways of poaching.

1. **Shallow poaching** – Cook the food in only a small amount of liquid and cover it with greased greaseproof paper. Never allow the liquid to boil – keep it at a temperature as near to boiling as possible without actually boiling. To prevent the liquid from boiling, bring it to the boil on top of the stove, take it off the direct heat and then place the food in the water. Complete the cooking in a moderately hot oven (approximately 180°C). Foods poached using this method include cuts of fish and chicken.
2. **Deep poaching** – This can be used to cook eggs. Place eggs in approximately 8 cm of gently simmering water. You can also deep poach whole fish (such as salmon), slices of fish on the bone (such as turbot), filleted cod and salmon, and whole chicken, as well as whole fruits. All of these should be covered with the poaching liquid.

Poaching

Equipment

A poaching pan should be used for this method of cooking. A spider, fish slice or slotted spoon can be used to remove poached items from the poaching liquid.

2.3 Applying techniques to produce poached products

There are a number of techniques associated with poaching that help the chef to prepare the dishes correctly.

- **Cutting:** trimming and shaping food so it cooks efficiently and looks attractive.
- **Tying:** food items are tied so that they stay in shape during the cooking process.
- **Folding:** foods such as fillets of flat fish, which are shallow poached, are folded to balance the thickness of the flesh, to make an even cooking time and to enhance presentation.
- **Reducing cooking liquid:** with some dishes the liquid is strained and then reduced by boiling. This will then be used as the base for a sauce to accompany the dish.
- **Straining:** removing food from cooking liquid and draining. This will enhance presentation as no poaching liquid weeps from the food item when served.
- **Holding for service:** holding at a temperature above 63°C.

Temperature and time control

The temperature must be controlled so that the cooking liquid does not become too cool or too hot. Poaching is cooking at just below simmering point.

It is important to time the cooking correctly so that food is neither undercooked nor overcooked. If it is undercooked it will not be pleasant to eat and can sometimes be dangerous (for example, undercooked chicken). If it is overcooked, it will break up and lose some of its nutrients.

The time and temperature needed to cook the food correctly will vary slightly for different types of food, as well as the size and shape if more than one item is cooked this way.

The cooking process should be monitored. Cooking too quickly will cause the liquid to evaporate and the dish to dry out, affecting the texture of the dish. Cooking too slowly might mean that the dish is not ready in time for service. Both will affect the overall finished product.

2.4 Applying finishing methods for poached products

For examples of finishing methods for poached products, see the quality points and recipe sections later in this chapter, which cover examples of the following:

- finishing
- consistency and texture
- flavour, aroma and taste
- appearance and presentation
- portion size
- garnish.

3 Produce steamed products

Process

Steaming is another method of cooking using moist heat. Food is cooked under pressure in the steam produced by a boiling liquid (rather than placing the food itself in the boiling liquid).

Purpose

Steaming:

- cooks food in a way that keeps it as nutritious as possible (most of the nutrients remain in the food)
- changes the texture of food and makes it tender and edible – the texture will vary according to the type of food, type of steamer and level of heat
- makes some foods lighter and easy to digest.

Liquids used when steaming

The following liquids can all be used to create a steam in which to cook food items:

- water
- stock (fresh or convenience)
- infused liquids.

These liquids will add flavour and moisture to the dish.

> **PROFESSIONAL TIP**
> The natural juices that result from steaming fish, for example, can be served with the fish or used to make the accompanying sauce.

3.1 Selecting food items for steaming

The range of foods that can be cooked by steaming include the following.

- **Meat:** for example, in a steak and kidney pudding, where the meat encased in pastry is cooked in a steamer.
- **Poultry:** normally the breast, although small joints or whole birds could be steamed and then finished with sauce and/or garnish.
- **Fish:** small whole fish or folded fillets, steamed over an infused liquid to add a little flavour to the finished dish.
- **Vegetables:** used to blanch and then quickly regenerate for service; quicker than boiling, and helps to retain nutrients and colour to improve appearance, maintaining quality.
- **Rice** cooked over infused liquid will produce a drier end grain for service.
- **Savoury and sweet puddings:** the combination of ingredients, and the size and shape of the pudding, will influence the overall cooking time.

3.2 Applying preparation methods for steaming

There are two main methods of steaming.

1. **Atmospheric steaming** – This is a low-pressure steaming method in which steam is produced by placing water in the bottom of a saucepan and bringing it to a rapid boil. Food is placed in a container above the boiling water. The steam from the boiling water heats the container and cooks the food inside it. This could be done in a combi oven.
2. **High-pressure steaming** – This is done in high-pressure steamers such as pressure cookers or a commercial steaming unit. The high pressure in the steamer produces higher temperatures and forces steam through the food, which makes the food cook faster.

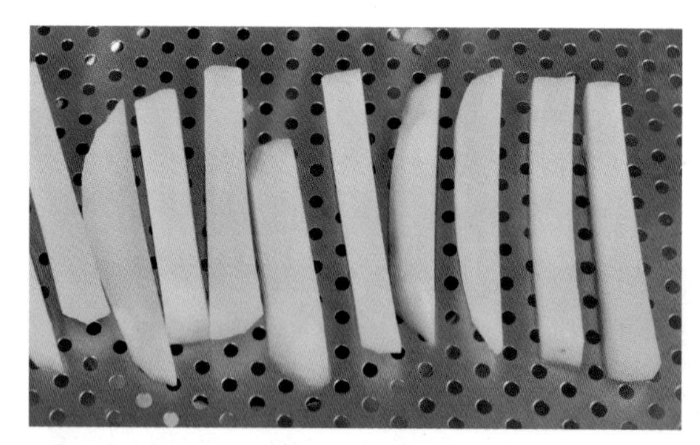

Steaming

> **PROFESSIONAL TIP**
> High-pressure steaming enables food to be cooked or reheated quickly. It is often used for 'batch' cooking, where small quantities of vegetables are cooked frequently throughout the service. This means the vegetables are always freshly cooked, so they keep their colour, flavour and nutritional content.

There are a number of techniques associated with steaming that help the chef to prepare the dishes correctly.

- **Preparation of containers** – Ensure that the container being used to steam is fit for purpose (in good condition and the correct size).

- **Greasing** – Lightly coat the inside of a mould to help provide a non-stick surface to allow puddings to be removed easily when cooked.
- **Creaming** – This is the mixing of fat and sugar to incorporate air.
- **Mixing and folding** – This is incorporating ingredients gently so as not to lose the volume.
- **Moulding/lining** – This could be lining with pastry and/or placing food into a cooking mould. The food will take on the shape of the mould when cooked.
- **Traying up** – This is placing individual moulds on to a tray so multiple items can be steamed at the same time.
- **Covering/waterproofing** – This refers to covering the food with greaseproof paper or foil to ensure that steam does not come into contact with the food during cooking, and also seals in the flavours.
- **Loading** – Placing moulds into the steamer.

3.3 Applying techniques to produce steamed products

Temperature and time control

When using steamers it is important to make sure that the food is not undercooked or overcooked, and therefore that the correct temperature and cooking time is used.

Food cooks much faster in high-pressure steamers, which means there is a great danger of the food overcooking very quickly. When you are using a high-pressure steamer, wait until the pressure gauge shows that it has reached the correct pressure, then open the door very carefully to allow the steam to escape before you place the food in the steamer. This way you will be sure that the necessary cooking temperature has been reached.

Individual sponge puddings, for example, will cook in less time than when cooking in a large pudding basin to be portioned when cooked.

HEALTH AND SAFETY

Boiling water is used in the bottom of steamers, so the same safety points apply to steaming as to boiling. Steam is extremely hot and can cause serious burns and scalds. To avoid injuring yourself:

- make sure you know how to use steamers properly, and use them with great care
- check the pressure in high-pressure steamers continually and allow the pressure to return to the correct level before opening doors or removing pressure cooker lids
- allow time for the pressure to return to normal before opening commercial steamers; stand well away from the door as you open it, to avoid the full impact of the escaping steam.

3.4 Applying finishing methods for steamed products

For examples of finishing methods for steamed products, see the quality points and recipe sections below, which cover examples of the following:

- finishing
- consistency and texture
- flavour, aroma and taste
- appearance and presentation
- portion size
- garnish.

Quality points for boiling, poaching and steaming foods

To ensure the quality of finished dishes there are a number of things that a chef should do to ensure the dish meets the customer's expectations.

- **Selection of products** – Ensure that products are fresh, have a good appearance, smell as expected and are at the appropriate temperature.
- **Preparation** – Foods should be trimmed, shaped and sized according to dish requirements, ensuring that trimming is kept to a minimum and other uses are considered, e.g. for use in soups, stocks or purées.
- **Cooking process** – The temperature and cooking time should be checked, as should the amount of liquid to be used. These elements will impact on the flavour, colour, texture and taste of the dish.
- **Blanching and refreshing** – Associated with wet cooking, these methods are where foods are part cooked and then chilled in cold water to hold colour, nutrients and flavour. Chefs then finish to order in the kitchen.
- **Finishing of the final dish** – This is where the chef gets to make final adjustments to a dish, including checking the service temperature. Consistency, appearance, portion size, seasoning and garnish, if required, should all be considered.
- **Consistency of the sauce or cooking liquor** – This can be corrected by reducing or adding a thickener.
- **Flavour and taste** – This should be checked and the seasoning adjusted if necessary.
- **Appearance** – Check the colour, glace and the way the dish is presented.
- **Portion size** – Consider whether the dish is set for individual or multiple portions. Is the dish balanced with all ingredients and any garnishes – for example, button onions, croutons.
- **Garnish** – Consider whether this is required. A garnish may be something as simple as a sprinkling of chopped herbs such as parsley.

TEST YOURSELF

1. Briefly describe the process for the following methods of cooking:
   a. poaching
   b. steaming
   c. boiling.
2. What is the purpose of poaching food?
3. List three vegetables that are cooked in boiling water.
4. What is the term for removing scum or foam from the top of a boiling liquid? How should you do this?
5. List three types of food that could be steamed.
6. List three cooking liquids that could be used as a sauce in the finished dish.
7. List five safety points for chefs to consider when cooking by boiling, poaching or steaming.
8. List four foods that can be cooked by poaching, and indicate whether each is deep or shallow poached.
9. Describe one method of boiling.
10. What would you use to steam a pudding? Why are puddings for steaming covered?

Boiling recipes

1 Suffolk pork collar daube cooked in cyder

Energy	Calories	Fat	Saturated fat	Carbohydrates	Sugar	Protein	Fibre	Sodium
2807 kJ	670 kcal	31.4 g	6.8 g	19.1 g	18.8 g	62.0 g	5.4 g	595.0 g

* Using lean pork and chicken stock

Ingredient	4 portions	10 portions
Olive oil	75 ml	200 ml
Pork collar, cleaned of excess fat, cut into portions and tied	1 kg	2½ kg
Carrots	4	10
Shallots	5	12
Leeks, small	2	5
Fresh parsley, sprigs	2	5
Black peppercorns	8	20
Semi-sweet cyder	1 litre	2½ litres
Chicken stock or light pork stock	1 litre	2½ litres

Mise en place

1. Prepare the vegetables into mirepoix.
2. Remove excess fat from the pork collar. Cut it into portions and tie it. Season the meat.

Cooking

1. Heat the oil in a large pan and seal the meat all over.
2. Add the vegetables, herbs, peppercorns, cyder and stock to the pan with the sealed pork. Bring up to the simmer.
3. Cover and cook in the oven until the pork is cooked through, about 2 hours.
4. Remove the pork from the cooking liquor, set aside, cool and refrigerate. Strain and chill the stock overnight. (This recipe could also be prepared and served straight away.)

To serve

1. Take the stock from the fridge, remove the fat from the surface and decant the stock from the container, leaving the sediment behind.
2. Untie the pork, place in a tray and cover with 300 ml of stock.
3. Cover with foil and place in the oven at 180°C for about 15 minutes until the pork is heated through.
4. Reduce the remaining stock to 450 ml and set aside.
5. Heat some vegetables ready for serving.
6. Divide the pork between four plates, garnish with the vegetables and spoon over the reduced stock. Finish with picked herbs.

2 White stock

Energy	Calories	Fat	Saturated fat	Carbohydrates	Sugar	Protein	Fibre	Sodium
11 kJ	3 kcal	0.0 g	0.0 g	0.4 g	0.4 g	0.1 g	0.2 g	2.9 g

Ingredient	To make 4½ litres	To make 10 litres
Raw, meaty bones	1 kg	2½ kg
Water	5 litres	10½ litres
Onion, carrot, celery, leek	400 g	1½ kg
Bouquet garni	1	1

Mise en place

1. Chop the bones into small pieces and remove any fat or marrow.
2. Wash and peel the vegetables.
3. Prepare a bouquet garni.

Cooking

1. Place the bones in a large pot, cover with cold water and bring to the boil.
2. As soon as the water comes to the boil, take pot to the sink and drain away the water.
3. Wash the bones and clean the pot.
4. Return the bones to the pot, cover them with water and bring them back to the boil again.
5. Reduce the heat so that the water is simmering gently.
6. Skim the surface to remove any scum as and when required. Also wipe round the top and inside of the pot.
7. After 2–3 hours add the vegetables and bouquet garni.
8. Simmer for 3–4 hours, skimming regularly.
9. When the cooking is finished, skim the stock again and strain it.

Storage

If you are going to keep the stock, cool it quickly, pour it into a suitable container and put it in the fridge.

VARIATION

Chicken stock can be made in the same way, using either chicken carcasses and/or winglets, or an old boiling fowl.

- Simmer the carcasses and/or winglets for 1 hour, then add the vegetables and simmer for a further hour.
- Allow the boiling fowl to three-quarters cook before adding the vegetables. The time will vary according to the age of the bird.

3 Brown stock

Energy	Calories	Fat	Saturated fat	Carbohydrates	Sugar	Protein	Fibre	Sodium
13 kJ	3 kcal	0.3 g	0.1 g	0.0 g	0.0 g	0.0 g	0.0 g	0.4 g

Ingredient	To make 1 litre	To make 3 litres
Raw, meaty bones	250 g	750 g
Water	1¼ litres	3¾litres
Onion, carrot, celery, leek	100 g	300 g
Fat or oil, a little for frying		
Bouquet garni	1	1

Mise en place

Chop the bones into small pieces.

Cooking

1. Brown the chopped bones well on all sides. You can do this by frying them in a little fat or oil in a frying pan, or by roasting them in a hot oven.
2. Strain off any fat and place the bones in a large pot.
3. If there is any sediment in the bottom of the frying pan or roasting tray, brown this and then deglaze (swill out) the pan with ½ litre of boiling water.
4. Simmer for a few minutes and then add this liquid to the bones.
5. Cover the bones with cold water and bring it to the boil.
6. Reduce the heat so that the water is simmering gently.
7. Simmer for 2–3 hours, skimming the surface to remove any scum as and when required.
8. Fry the vegetables in a little fat or oil until brown. Drain off any fat and add the vegetables to the bones with the bouquet garni.
9. Simmer for 3–4 hours, skimming regularly.
10. When the cooking is finished, skim the stock again and strain it.

Storage

If you are going to keep the stock, cool it quickly, pour it into a suitable container and put it in the fridge.

VARIATION

You could add some squashed tomatoes or washed mushroom trimmings to this stock.

4 Fish stock

Energy	Calories	Fat	Saturated fat	Carbohydrates	Sugar	Protein	Fibre	Sodium
1523 kJ	371 kcal	25.0 g	3.7 g	3.2 g	2.1 g	0.9 g	1.6 g	15.0 g

Ingredient	To make 1 litre	To make 3 litres
Oil, butter, margarine	10 g	30 g
Onions	50 g	150 g
Fresh white fish bones	500 g	1½ kg
Lemon juice	¼	1
Bay leaf	1	1
Parsley stalks	2	6
Water	1 litre	3 litres

Mise en place

1. Slice the onions.
2. Wash the fish bones thoroughly.

Storage

If you are going to keep the stock, cool it quickly, pour it into a suitable container and put it in the fridge.

Cooking the stock for longer than 20 minutes will spoil the flavour.

Cooking

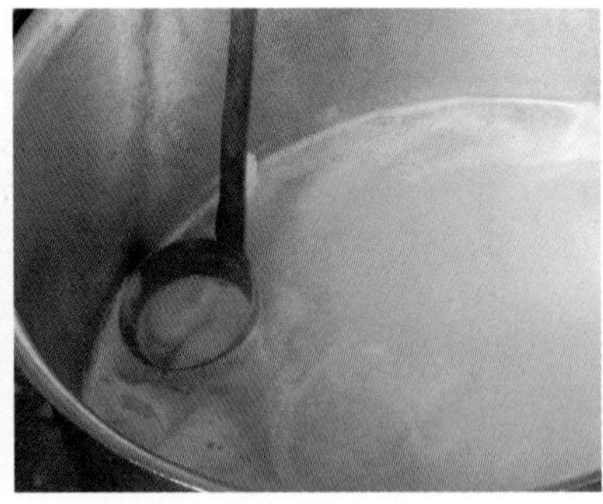

1. Place the oil, butter or margarine in a thick-bottomed pan.
2. Add the onions, fish bones, lemon juice, bay leaf and parsley stalks.
3. Cover the ingredients with oiled greaseproof paper and a tight-fitting lid, and sweat them gently without colouring for 5 minutes.
4. Add the water and bring it to the boil.
5. Reduce the heat so that the water is simmering gently.
6. Simmer for 20 minutes, skimming regularly.
7. Strain the stock.

5 Split pea soup

Energy	Calories	Fat	Saturated fat	Carbohydrates	Sugar	Protein	Fibre	Sodium
1218 kJ	289 kcal	11.8 g	6.7 g	31.9 g	3.3 g	12.2 g	4.4 g	308.0 g

* Using half teaspoon salt, white vegetable stock, unsalted butter

Ingredient	4 portions	10 portions
Split peas	200 g	500 g
White stock or water	1½ litres	3¾ litres
Onions, chopped	50 g	125 g
Carrots, chopped	50 g	125 g
Bouquet garni	1	2
Knuckle of ham or bacon (optional)		
Salt		
Stale bread sliced (to make croutons)	1 slice	2½ slices
Butter, margarine or oil	50 g	125 g

Mise en place

1 Check and wash the peas. If pre-soaked, change the water.
2 Wash, peel and chop the onions and carrots.
3 Prepare a bouquet garni.
4 Prepare the croutons.

Cooking

1 Place the peas in a thick-bottomed pan.
2 Add the stock or water. Bring to the boil and skim.
3 Add the remainder of the ingredients and a little salt.
4 Simmer until tender, skimming when necessary.
5 Remove the bouquet garni and ham.
6 Liquidise the soup and pass it through a chinois.
7 Return the soup to a clean pan and bring it back to the boil.
8 Taste and correct the seasoning and consistency. If too thick, dilute with stock.

VARIATION

Any type of pulse can be made into soup – for example, split pea (yellow or green), haricot beans, lentils.

Some pulses may need to be soaked overnight in cold water.

SERVING SUGGESTION

Serve with fried or toasted croutons.

VARIATION

Add either of the following:

- a chopped fresh herb from parsley, chervil, tarragon, coriander, chives
- a spice or a combination, such as garam masala.

ACTIVITY

Name as many types of pulse as you can (there are at least 21).

6 Mutton broth

Energy	Calories	Fat	Saturated fat	Carbohydrates	Sugar	Protein	Fibre	Sodium
835 kJ	199 kcal	8.4 g	3.5 g	8.9 g	3.1 g	21.5 g	1.9 g	87.0 g

* Using lean lambg. Used 60g each of the vegetables (to make up 300g in total). Used water

Ingredient	4 portions	10 portions
Scrag end of mutton, off the bone	400 g	1 kg
Mutton or lamb stock or water	800 ml	2 litres
Barley	30 g	80 g
Carrot, turnip, leek, celery, onion	300 g	750 g
Bouquet garni	1	2
Parsley, chopped		

Mise en place

1 Trim off any fat from the meat.
2 Wash the barley.
3 Wash and peel the vegetables and cut into small neat squares (brunoise).
4 Prepare a bouquet garni.

VARIATION

Instead of chopped parsley, you could use basil and oregano if you prefer.

Cooking

1 Place the meat in a saucepan and add cold water.
2 Heat this to a fast boil.
3 As soon as the water starts to boil, remove the pan from the heat. Lift out the meat and wash it under cold running water.

4 Pour away the cooking water and clean the pan.
5 Replace the meat and cover with cold water or stock. Bring to the boil and skim.
6 Add the barley to the pan and then reduce the heat and simmer for one hour.

7 Add the vegetables, the bouquet garni and seasoning.

8 Continue simmering for 30 minutes or until the meat is tender. Skim off any fat or scum as necessary.

9 Once cooked, remove the meat from the pan and allow it to cool.

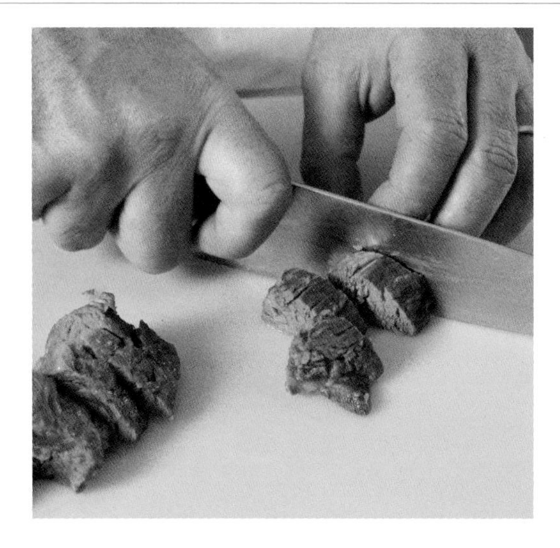

10 Cut the meat into neat cubes the same size as the vegetables. Return the meat to the broth.

11 Skim off any fat, taste and correct the seasoning.

SERVING SUGGESTION

This is a traditional, rustic recipe, which may be served as a substantial dish. Add fresh chopped parsley and serve.

ACTIVITY

Suggest a different broth of your own choice.

VARIATION

For a more delicate dish, the vegetables and meat may be diced smaller.

- For **Scotch broth** use lean beef and beef stock in place of mutton.
- For **chicken broth** use chicken and well-flavoured chicken stock. Add washed rice 12–15 minutes before the broth is cooked. Leave out the barley.

7 Leek and potato soup

Energy	Calories	Fat	Saturated fat	Carbohydrates	Sugar	Protein	Fibre	Sodium
463 kJ	111 kcal	5.7 g	3.4 g	11.6 g	2.9 g	2.6 g	3.3 g	250.0 g

* Using unsalted butter, half teaspoon salt

Ingredient	4 portions	10 portions
Butter, margarine or oil	25 g	60 g
Leeks	400 g	1½ kg
White stock	750 ml	2 litres
Potatoes	200 g	½ kg
Bouquet garni	1	2
Salt		

Mise en place

1 Wash and trim the leeks, and cut the white and light green part into ½ cm squares (paysanne).

2 Wash and peel the potatoes and cut into ½ cm squares 2 mm thick.

3 Prepare a bouquet garni.

Cooking

1 Melt the fat in a saucepan. Add the leeks, cover with a lid and cook slowly without colouring until soft.

2 Add the stock, potatoes, bouquet garni and a little salt.

3 Simmer for approximately 15 minutes.

4 Remove the bouquet garni. Liquidise the soup and pass through a chinois, then taste and correct the seasoning before serving.

8 Sweet potato soup

Energy	Calories	Fat	Saturated fat	Carbohydrates	Sugar	Protein	Fibre	Sodium
1154 kJ	272 kcal	1.1 g	0.3 g	60.0 g	22.8 g	4.9 g	9.4 g	981.0 g

* Using half teaspoon salt, vegetable stock

Ingredient	4 portions	10 portions
Onions, peeled and diced	1	3
Sweet potatoes, peeled and diced	1 kg	2½ kg
Red peppers, deseeded and diced	2	5
Garlic cloves, chopped	2	5
Vegetable or chicken stock	1 litre	2½ litres
Salt and pepper to season		

Mise en place

1 Remove the seeds from the peppers and dice into evenly sized pieces.
2 Peel and dice the sweet potato.
3 Peel and dice the onions and chop the garlic.

Cooking

1 Sweat the onions until soft and translucent.

2 Add the sweet potato, peppers and garlic, and cook gently for 10–15 minutes on a low heat.

3 Add the stock and simmer for approximately 40 minutes.
4 Purée the vegetables either in the pan with a stick blender or in a liquidiser.

5 Pass through a conical strainer.
6 Return to the pan and season to taste.

9 Tomato soup

Energy	Calories	Fat	Saturated fat	Carbohydrates	Sugar	Protein	Fibre	Sodium
811 kJ	193 kcal	10.8 g	6.6 g	20.4 g	11.2 g	3.5 g	4.8 g	26.6 g

* Using unsalted butter, not including bacon trimmings

Ingredient	4 portions	10 portions
Butter, margarine or oil	50 g	125 g
Bacon trimmings (optional)	25 g	60 g
Onion and carrot, washed, peeled and roughly chopped	100 g of each	250 g of each
Flour	50 g	125 g
Tomato purée	100 g	250 g
Large tomatoes, chopped	2	5
Stock	1½ litres	3½ litres
Bouquet garni	1	2

Mise en place

1 Peel, wash and roughly chop the vegetables.
2 Prepare a bouquet garni.
3 Prepare the croutons.

VARIATION

A slightly sweet/sharp flavour can be added to the soup by preparing what is known as a gastric (gastrique). In a thick-bottomed pan, reduce 100 ml of malt vinegar and 35 g caster sugar until it is a light caramel colour. Mix this into the completed soup.

Some tomato purée can be stronger than others, so you may have to add a little more or less when making this soup.

Cooking

1 Melt the fat in a thick-bottomed pan.

2 Add the bacon, carrots and onions, and lightly brown these.

3 Mix in the flour and cook to a sandy texture.

4 Mix in the tomato purée, then remove the pan from the heat and allow the mixture to cool.

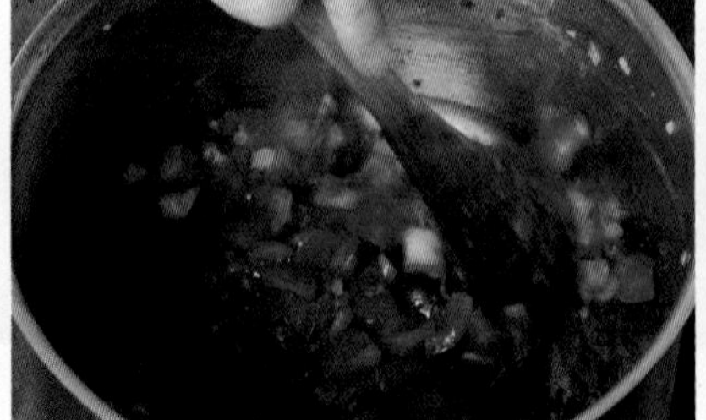

5 Return the pan to the heat and add the chopped tomatoes.

6 Mix well.

7 Gradually mix in the hot stock. Stir it until it is boiling.

8 Add the bouquet garni and a little salt and simmer for 1 hour.

9 Skim the soup and remove the bouquet garni.

10 Liquidise the soup, then pass through a medium-mesh conical strainer.

11 Return the soup to a clean pan and reheat it.

12 Taste the soup and check seasoning and consistency.

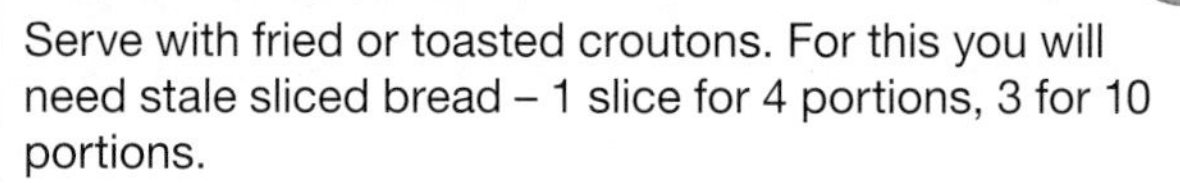

SERVING SUGGESTION

Serve with fried or toasted croutons. For this you will need stale sliced bread – 1 slice for 4 portions, 3 for 10 portions.

VARIATION

Try adding:

- the juice and lightly grated peel of 1–2 oranges
- cooked rice
- a chopped fresh herb, such as chives.

ACTIVITY

1. Prepare, cook and taste the recipe for tomato soup with and without a gastric. Discuss and assess the two versions.
2. Name and prepare a variation of your own.
3. Review the basic recipe for tomato soup and adjust to meet dietary requirements for a low-fat vegetarian customer.

10 Garden marrow soup

Energy	Calories	Fat	Saturated fat	Carbohydrates	Sugar	Protein	Fibre	Sodium
1145 kJ	277 kcal	25.0 g	3.7 g	5.4 g	4.9 g	6.8 g	1.8 g	522.0 g

* With 1/4 teaspoon of salt

Ingredient	4 portions	10 portions
Onions, peeled and roughly diced	1	2
Olive oil	90 ml	225 ml
Marrow (large), cut into cubes	1	2½
Mild curry powder	½ tbsp	2½ tbsp
Chicken or vegetable stock	1 litre	2½ litres

Mise en place

1. Peel and roughly dice the onion.
2. Peel and cube the marrow.

Cooking

1. Sweat the onion in the olive oil until translucent.
2. Add the cubed marrow and fry gently.
3. Stir in the curry powder.
4. Add the stock and simmer for approximately 40 minutes.
5. Purée the soup either in the pan with a stick blender or in a liquidiser.
6. Pass through a chinois or conical strainer. Season with salt and pepper.
7. Adjust the consistency if necessary by adding a little water.

VARIATION

Courgette may be used instead of marrow. Courgettes are available all year round.

11 Velouté

Energy	Calories	Fat	Saturated fat	Carbohydrates	Sugar	Protein	Fibre
4594 kJ	1094 kcal	82.6 g	35.4 g	79.1 g	1.6 g	13.3 g	3.6 g

* Using hard margarine, for 1 litre. Using sunflower oil instead, this recipe provides, for 1 litre: 5304 kJ/1263 kcal Energy; 101.5 g Fat; 13.3 g Sat Fat; 78.9 g Carb; 1.5 g Sugar; 13.2 g

Ingredient	4 portions	10 portions
Margarine, butter or oil	100 g	250 g
Flour	100 g	250 g
Stock, chicken, fish	1 litre	2½ litres

This is a basic white sauce made from white stock and a blond roux.

Cooking

1 Melt the fat in a thick-bottomed pan.
2 Mix in the flour.
3 Cook out to a sandy texture over a gentle heat, allowing the lightest shade of colour (blond roux).
4 Remove the pan from the heat to allow the roux to cool.
5 Return the pan to the stove and, over a low heat, gradually add the hot stock.
6 Mix until smooth and simmering.
7 Cook gently for 1 hour and pass through a fine conical strainer.

Storage

To prevent a skin from forming, brush the surface with melted butter. When ready to use, stir this into the sauce. Alternatively, cover the sauce with a circle of oiled greaseproof paper or baking parchment. You are advised not to use clingfilm for this purpose.

VARIATION

A velouté-based sauce can be used for egg, fish, chicken and mutton.

Sauce	Served with	Additions per ½ litre
Caper	Boiled leg of mutton or lamb	2 tbsp capers
Aurora	Poached eggs, chicken	1 tsp tomato purée 60 ml cream or natural yoghurt 2–3 drops of lemon juice
Mushroom	Poached chicken	100 g sliced button mushrooms lightly cooked in a little fat or oil

ACTIVITY

Suggest an alternative of your choice. Prepare, taste, discuss and assess it.

12 Béchamel (basic white sauce)

Energy	Calories	Fat	Saturated fat	Carbohydrates	Sugar	Protein	Fibre	Sodium
5859 kJ	1440 kcal	91.0 g	57.0 g	107.0 g	41.0 g	40.0 g	3.6 g	396.0 g

* Using semi-skimmed milk, unsalted butter

Ingredient	1 litre	2½ litres
Onion	½	1
Clove	1	1
Bay leaf	1	2
Milk, warmed	1 litre	2½ litres
Margarine, butter or oil	100 g	250 g
Flour	100 g	250 g

Mise en place

Push a clove into an onion, with the sharp end going into the onion, leaving the round end studding the outside of the onion.

Cooking

1 Add the studded onion and a bay leaf to the milk. Simmer, allowing it to infuse, for 5 minutes.

2 Melt the fat in a thick-bottomed pan.

3 Mix in the flour with a wooden spoon.

4 Cook for a few minutes, stirring frequently. When making white roux you should not allow the mixture to colour.

5 Remove the pan from the heat to allow the roux to cool.

6 Return the pan to the stove over a low heat. Gradually ladle the milk into the roux – stir the mixture back to a smooth paste each time you add a ladleful of milk.

7 Continue adding the milk, one ladleful at a time.

8 Allow the mixture to simmer gently for 30 minutes, stirring frequently.

9 Remove from the heat and pass the sauce through a conical strainer.

Storage

To prevent a skin from forming, brush the surface with melted butter. When ready to use, stir this into the sauce. Alternatively, cover the sauce with a circle of oiled greaseproof paper or baking parchment. You are advised not to use clingfilm for this purpose.

ACTIVITY

1 As a group, make all six of these sauces. Taste, discuss and assess them.

2 Suggest a variation of your own, using béchamel and a dish with which it might be served.

VARIATION

Béchamel is a basic white sauce that can be used as the base for many other sauces. The suggestions below are for half a litre of béchamel, which is enough for 8 to 12 portions of sauce.

Sauce	Served with	Additions per ½ litre
Egg	Poached or steamed fish	2 diced hard-boiled eggs
Cheese	Poached fish or vegetables	50 g grated cheddar cheese
Onion	Roast lamb or mutton	100 g chopped onions cooked without colouring, either by boiling or sweating in fat
Parsley	Poached fish or boiled ham	1 tsp chopped parsley
Cream	Poached fish or vegetables	Add cream or natural yoghurt to give the consistency of double cream
Mustard	Grilled herrings	Add diluted English or continental mustard to give a spicy sauce

13 Roast gravy

Energy	Calories	Fat	Saturated fat	Carbohydrates	Sugar	Protein	Fibre	Sodium
309 kJ	74 kcal	3.9 g	1.5 g	3.3 g	2.7 g		1.3 g	0.1 g

Ingredient	4 portions	10 portions
Raw meat bones	200 g	500 g
Brown stock or water	500 ml	1½ litres
Onions	50 g	125 g
Carrots	50 g	125 g
Celery	25 g	60 g

Roast gravy is traditionally made from the residue that roast joints leave in their roasting pans, but can also be made with raw bones if you need a larger quantity, as in this recipe.

Mise en place

1 Chop the bones into small pieces.

2 Wash, peel and roughly chop the vegetables.

Cooking

1 Brown the bones in a little fat in a roasting tray in the oven or in a heavy frying pan on the stove.

2 Drain off the fat and place bones in a saucepan.

3 Deglaze the tray or pan with stock or water to ensure that all the tasty brown residue is not wasted.

4 Pour the deglaze liquid into the saucepan with the bones and cover the bones with stock or water.

5 Bring to the boil, skim and allow to simmer.

6 Lightly fry the vegetables in a little fat in a frying pan or add them to the bones when these are partly browned.

7 Simmer for 1½ –2 hours and strain.

8 Skim off any fat that settles on the surface.

VARIATION

If your roast gravy does not have enough flavour when tasted, add a little of a suitable convenience product to help. Many convenience gravy products are available, but you should taste and assess these before using them.

14 Thickened roast gravy

Energy	Calories	Fat	Saturated fat	Carbohydrates	Sugar	Protein	Fibre	Sodium
753 kJ	185 kcal	6.1 g	3.9 g	29.9 g	4.1 g	2.6 g	1.4 g	1,935.0 g

* Using cornflour

Ingredient	Amount per ½ litre of gravy
Gravy	
Tomato purée	1 tsp
Mushroom trimmings	1 heaped tsp
Thyme	small pinch
Arrowroot or cornflour	1 heaped tsp

You can make a light brown sauce by lightly thickening a well-flavoured roast gravy with arrowroot or cornflour dissolved in water.

Cooking

1 Simmer the required amount of gravy in a thick-bottomed pan.
2 Add the tomato purée, mushroom trimmings and thyme.
3 Dilute the arrowroot or cornflour in a basin with a little cold water and gradually add this to the simmering gravy, stirring continuously until it re-boils.
4 Simmer for 5–10 minutes and pass through a fine-mesh chinois.

VARIATION

- This basic sauce can be used for a number of variations; it is more commonly known as jus-lié and is used in many other sauces as a base.
- Rosemary or lavender can be used in place of thyme.

15 Boiled eggs

Energy	Calories	Fat	Saturated fat	Carbohydrates	Sugar	Protein	Fibre	Sodium
339 kJ	82 kca	5.5 g	1.5 g	0.0 g	0.0 g	8.0 g	0.0 g	86.0 g

* 1 large egg per portion

Ingredient
Allow 1 or 2 eggs per portion

Cooking soft-boiled eggs

1 Place the eggs in a saucepan. Cover with cold water and bring to the boil.
2 Simmer for 2–2½ minutes.
3 Remove from the water and serve in egg cups.

Cooking medium-soft eggs

1 Place the eggs carefully into a pan of boiling water.
2 Re-boil, simmer for 4–5 minutes and remove.

Cooking hard-boiled eggs

1 Place the eggs carefully into a pan of boiling water.
2 Re-boil and simmer for 8–10 minutes.
3 Refresh until cold under running water.

16 Farfalle with chives and bacon

Energy	Calories	Fat	Saturated fat	Carbohydrates	Sugar	Protein	Fibre	Sodium
2652 kJ	631 kcal	27.9 g	13.3 g	69.0 g	3.4 g	24.5 g	5.0 g	726.0 g

* Using unsalted butter

Ingredient	4 portions	10 portions
Farfalle	400 g	1 kg
Streaky bacon rashers	10	25
Butter or oil	50 g	125 g
Fresh chives	2 tbsp	5 tbsp
Parmesan	50 g	125 g

Mise en place

1. Grill the bacon until crisp then cut into small pieces.
2. Chop the chives.
3. Grate the Parmesan.

Cooking

1. Cook the pasta in lightly salted boiling water until al dente (firm to the bite).
2. Drain the pasta and place in a warm bowl.
3. Mix in the butter, chives, bacon and Parmesan.
4. Taste, correct the seasoning and serve.

17 Plain boiled rice

Energy	Calories	Fat	Saturated fat	Carbohydrates	Sugar	Protein	Fibre
37 kJ	90 kcal	0.1 g	0.0 g	20.0 g	0.0 g	1.9 g	0.0 g

Ingredient	4 portions	10 portions
Basmati rice or similar long-grain rice, dry weight	100 g	250 g

Mise en place

Pick and wash the rice. (Picking the rice means checking that there is nothing in it that should not be there!)

Cooking

1. Place the washed rice in a saucepan.
2. Add to plenty of lightly salted boiling water.
3. Stir to the boil then simmer gently until tender (approximately 12–15 minutes).
4. Pour into a sieve and rinse well, first under cold running water then very hot water.
5. Drain off all water and leave the rice in a sieve placed over a bowl and covered with a clean tea cloth.

HEALTH AND SAFETY

Once rice is cooked, it should be kept at a temperature above 65°C, but for no longer than 2 hours. If it is kept at a lower temperature than this, or for longer than 2 hours, the spores of a bacterium found in the soil may change back to bacteria and could result in food poisoning.

Avoid storing and reheating cooked rice unless it has it has been done in strict hygiene and temperature-controlled conditions.

18 Boiled chicken with rice and suprême sauce

Energy	Calories	Fat	Saturated fat	Carbohydrates	Sugar	Protein	Fibre	Sodium
3510 kJ	836 kcal	35.3 g	19.9 g	52.0 g	1.4 g	74.0 g	1.9 g	842.0 g

* Using single dairy cream for the sauce, 1 g salt added for cooking the chicken. Using unsalted butter

Ingredient	4 portions	10 portions
Boiling fowl, 2–2½ kg	1	2–3
Onion	50 g	125 g
Cloves		
Carrot	50 g	125 g
Celery	50 g	125 g
Bouquet garni	50 g	125 g
Salt, pinch		
Sauce		
Butter, margarine or oil	75 g	180 g
Flour	75 g	180 g
Chicken stock	1 litre	1½ litres
Cream or non-dairy cream	4 tbsp	10 tbsp
Lemon juice, a few drops		
Braised rice		
Onion	50 g	125 g
Butter, margarine or oil	50 g	125 g
Rice, long grain	200 g	500 g
Chicken stock	500 ml	1¼ litres

Mise en place

1 Wash and peel the carrot and celery. Leave them whole.

2 Peel the onions for the chicken and stud with one clove per onion.

3 Prepare a bouquet garni.

4 Peel and chop the onion for the rice.

5 Wash the chicken and truss it. Trussing is a way of tying the chicken to hold and improve its shape so that it is easier to carve.

Cooking

1 Place the prepared chicken into a saucepan. Cover it with cold water. Bring to the boil and skim.

2 Add the peeled whole vegetables, bouquet garni and a little salt.

3 Simmer gently until cooked (approximately 1–1½ hours).

4 While the chicken is cooking, prepare the suprême sauce as per the velouté recipe (recipe 11), and the braised rice as per the recipe on page 140.

5 Cook the velouté for 30–45 minutes.

6 Once the sauce is cooked, taste it and correct the seasoning.

7 Pass it through a fine chinois and mix in the cream.

8 To check that the chicken is cooked, insert a two-pronged fork between a drumstick and a thigh and remove the chicken from the stock. Hold it over a plate and allow the juices to come out. There should be no trace of blood in the juices. Also pierce the drumstick with a trussing needle or a skewer, which should easily slide in as far as the bone.

SERVING SUGGESTION

1 Remove the legs and cut each leg into two (drumstick and thigh).
2 Remove the breasts and cut each one in two.
3 A portion for one person is one piece of leg and one piece of breast.
4 Place the rice and chicken portions carefully on plates. The chicken can be placed on top of the rice or beside it. Coat the chicken with the sauce.

The skin may be removed before the chicken is served.

VARIATION

This dish can be prepared using suprêmes (breasts) of chicken, instead of whole birds. In that case, poach the chicken in stock instead of water.

19 Chicken à la king

Energy	Calories	Fat	Saturated fat	Carbohydrates	Sugar	Protein	Fibre
1,226 kJ	292 kcal	16.7 g	7.8 g	3.2 g	0.8 g	30.4 g	0.9 g

Using butter or hard margarine.

Ingredient	4 portions	10 portions
Button mushrooms	100 g	250 g
Butter or oil	25 g	60 g
Red pepper, skinned	50 g	125 g
Chicken, poached or steamed	400 g	1.25 kg
Sherry	30 ml	75 ml
Chicken velouté	125 ml	150 ml
Cream or non-dairy cream	30 ml	75 ml

To poach chicken breast, place in a pan and half cover with chicken stock, cover with cartouche, place lid on pan and poach for 10–15 minutes until cooked and firm to the touch.

Use a velouté with a good chicken flavour, to create the best sauce.

Cooking

1. Wash, peel and slice the mushrooms.
2. Cook them without colour in the butter or oil.
3. If using raw pepper, discard the seeds, cut the pepper into dice and cook with the mushrooms.
4. Cut the chicken into small, neat slices.
5. Add the chicken to the mushrooms and pepper.
6. Drain off the fat. Add the sherry.
7. Add the velouté and bring to the boil.
8. Finish with the cream and correct the seasoning.
9. Place in a serving dish and decorate with small strips of cooked pepper.

Slice the mushrooms and dice the red pepper

Neatly slice the cooked chicken

Add the velouté during cooking

VARIATION

- Try adding 1 or 2 egg yolks to form a liaison with the cream, mixed into the boiling mixture at the last possible moment and immediately removed from the heat.
- Chicken à la king may be served in a border of golden-brown duchess potato, or a pilaf of rice (see page 140) may be offered as an accompaniment. It is suitable for a hot buffet dish.

HEALTHY EATING TIPS

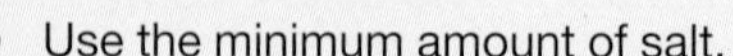

- Use the minimum amount of salt.
- Remove the skin from the cooked chicken.
- Try reducing or omitting the cream used to finish the sauce.
- Serve with plenty of rice and vegetables or salad.

20 Pease pudding

Energy	Calories	Fat	Saturated fat	Carbohydrates	Sugar	Protein	Fibre	Sodium
1101 kJ	262 kcal	11.8 g	6.8 g	26.0 g	1.2 g	11.4 g	3.3 g	132.0 g

* Using salted butter and no other salt added

Ingredient	4 people	10 people
Yellow split peas (dried), soaked	200 g	500 g
Water	½ litre	1¼ litre
Onion, studded with a clove	50 g	125 g
Carrot	50 g	125 g
Bacon trimmings	50 g	125 g
Butter or margarine	50 g	125 g
Salt		

Mise en place

1. Soak the split peas overnight and then drain.
2. Peel the onion and then push a clove into it, sharp end first, so the round end is on the outside of the onion.

Cooking

1. Place all ingredients except the butter in a thick-bottomed saucepan. Cover with a tight-fitting lid.
2. Bring to the boil and skim the water.
3. Allow the peas to cook, preferably in an oven at 180–200°C, for 2 hours.
4. Remove the onion, carrot and bacon and either pass the peas through a sieve or use a food processor.
5. Return the peas to a clean pan and mix in the butter. Taste and correct the consistency, which should be firm.

21 Boiled bacon

Energy	Calories	Fat	Saturated fat	Carbohydrates	Sugar	Protein	Fibre
1543 kJ	367 kcal	30.5 g	12.2 g	0.0 g	0.0 g	23.1 g	0.0 g

* Using 113 g per portion

Ingredient

You can use a hock, collar or gammon joint for this recipe

Mise en place

1 Prepare the joint as follows.
  - Hock: cook it whole, or bone it and tie it with string.
  - Collar: remove the bone and tie the joint with string.
  - Gammon: cook it whole or cut it into two or three pieces and tie it with string if necessary.

2 Depending on how salty the bacon joint is, you may need to soak it in cold water for 2–3 hours (or longer) before cooking.

Cooking

1 Place the joint in a suitably sized pan and cover with water.

2 Bring to the boil, skim and simmer gently. The cooking time will depend on the size of the joint: simmer for approximately 25 minutes per ½ kg plus another 25 minutes.

3 Remove the pan from the heat and allow the joint to cool in the liquid.

4 Remove the rind and brown skin and any excess fat.

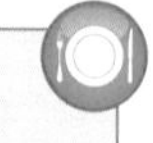

SERVING SUGGESTION

Carve into thick slices and serve with a little of the cooking liquor.

It can be accompanied by a traditional dish of puréed peas, known as pease pudding (see recipe 20), and a suitable sauce, such as parsley or mustard.

22 Pastry cream

Energy	Calories	Fat	Saturated fat	Carbohydrates	Sugar	Protein	Fibre	Sodium
5736 kJ	1357 kcal	42.0 g	18.1 g	217.0 g	154.0 g	35.7 g	3.1 g	293.0 g

* Using whole milk

Left to right: pastry cream, crème diplomate and crème chiboust

Ingredient	Approx. 1 litre
Vanilla pod (can be replaced with a few drops of vanilla arome)	1
Milk	1 litre
Eggs	4
Caster sugar	200 g
Flour (strong)	100 g
Custard powder	30 g

Cooking

1 Split open the vanilla pod and scrape out the seeds. Place the pod and seeds in a heavy stainless steel pan, add the milk and place on the heat.

2 Whisk the eggs and sugar together.

3 Sieve the flour and custard powder on to paper and then add to the eggs. Whisk them all together to form a liaison.

4 When the milk has boiled, pour about one-third of it into the egg mixture and whisk in.

5 Bring the rest of the milk back to the boil, then pour in the liaison. Whisk hard until the mixture comes back to the boil again.

6 Simmer gently for 5 minutes.

7 Pour into a sterilised tray and stand on a wire rack. Stir occasionally to help the mixture cool quickly.

8 When cold, store in a plastic container in the fridge. Use within three days.

VARIATION

The recipes below are based on the recipe for crème pâtissière, with additional ingredients:

- **Crème mousseline:** beat in 100 g of soft butter (a pomade). The butter content is usually about 20 per cent of the volume but this can be raised to 50 per cent depending on its intended use.
- **Crème diplomate:** when the pastry cream is chilled, fold in an equal quantity of whipped double cream.
- **Crème chiboust:** when the pastry cream mixture has cooled slightly, fold in an equal quantity of Italian meringue (recipe 42).

Additional flavourings can also be added to crème pâtissière, crème diplomat or crème chiboust.

PROFESSIONAL TIP

At step 4, the microwave may be used effectively. Pour the mixture into a plastic bowl and cook in the microwave for 30-second periods, stirring in between, until the mixture boils and thickens.

Poaching recipes

23 Mulled cider poached pear with shortbread

Energy	Calories	Fat	Saturated fat	Carbohydrates	Sugar	Protein	Fibre	Sodium
5013 kJ	1195 kcal	60.0 g	33.4 g	145.0 g	89.0 g	9.4 g	8.3 g	22.2 g

* Using 'dry' cider rather than sweet

Ingredient	4 portions	10 portions
Mulled cider poached pears		
Northamptonshire cider	500 ml	1¼ litres
Root ginger	50 g	125 g
Orange zest	½ orange	1½ oranges
Lemon zest	½ lemon	1½ lemons
Granulated sugar	200 g	500 g
Pears	4	10
Shortbread		
Unsalted butter	250 g	625 g
Caster sugar	75 g	190 g
Soft flour	250 g	625 g
Ground rice	50 g	125 g
Crushed hazelnuts	50 g	125 g

Mise en place

1 Peel and slice the ginger.
2 Grate the orange and lemon zest.
3 Finely chop the hazelnuts.

Regional recipe contributed by Mike Coppock, formerly Curriculum Manager, Hospitality and Catering, at Northampton College.

Northamptonshire cider is made by David and Elizabeth Bates at Welland Valley Vineyard in Marston Trussell.

Northampton College sources local pears from Sima Johnston at Windmill Orchards, Sulgrave.

Cooking

Cooking the pears

1 Bring to the boil the cider, ginger, zest and sugar, then remove from the heat.
2 Peel the pears whole and core out the centre without damaging the outside, remove the stalks if damaged.
3 Place all the pears into the hot syrup at the same time, making sure there is sufficient to just cover them.
4 Place a disc of silicone paper over the top and use a small plate to hold the pears under the surface.
5 Return to the heat, bring up to a gentle simmer. Cooking time depends on the ripeness of the pears. They are ready when the blade of a knife sinks easily into them (possibly 25 to 30 minutes).
6 Remove the pears from the syrup and allow to cool. The syrup can be reduced to make a sauce for accompanying the dessert.

Making the shortbread

1 Cream together the butter and sugar until just mixed but not lightened.
2 Gently add the flour, ground rice and hazelnuts then bring the ingredients together to form a smooth paste. Allow to chill for 15–20 minutes.
3 Roll out on a lightly floured surface to 5 mm thickness.
4 Cut into desired shape and place on to a tray with baking parchment, leaving a gap between each one.
5 Bake at 180°C for 20 minutes until golden brown (the edges should be golden leaving the centre of the shortbread paler in colour).
6 While still warm, cut through the shortbread to portion, remove from the tins and allow to cool.

SERVING SUGGESTION
Serve the pears and shortbread plated together with a vanilla-flavoured whipped cream.

24 Poached eggs

Energy	Calories	Fat	Saturated fat	Carbohydrates	Sugar	Protein	Fibre	Sodium
339 kJ	82 kcal	5.5 g	1.5 g	0.0 g	0.0 g	8.0 g	0.0 g	86.0 g

* 1 large egg per portion

Ingredient
Allow 1 or 2 eggs per portion
Malt vinegar – 1 tbsp per litre of water

Use only top-quality fresh eggs for poaching because they have thick whites, which help them to stick together in the simmering water.

Using vinegar (an acid) helps to set the egg white and also makes it more tender and white.

Poached eggs may be cooled, stored and then reheated (in hot, acidulated water).

Cooking

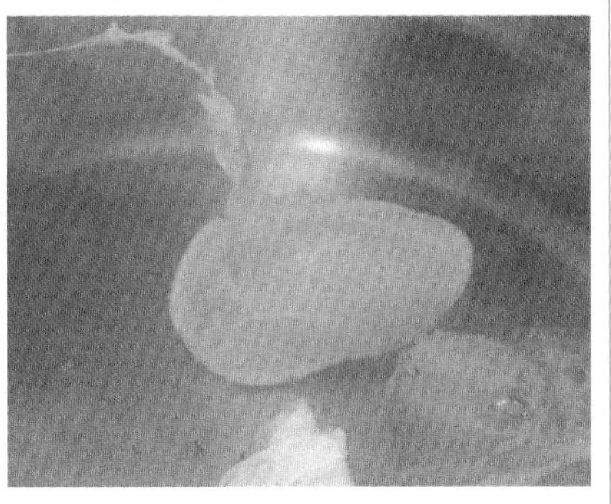

1 Heat a shallow pan of water at least 8 cm deep.

2 Add 1 tablespoon of malt vinegar per litre of water.

3 Break the eggs into small pots.

4 Carefully tip the eggs into the gently simmering water.

5 You will see each egg form a ball shape.

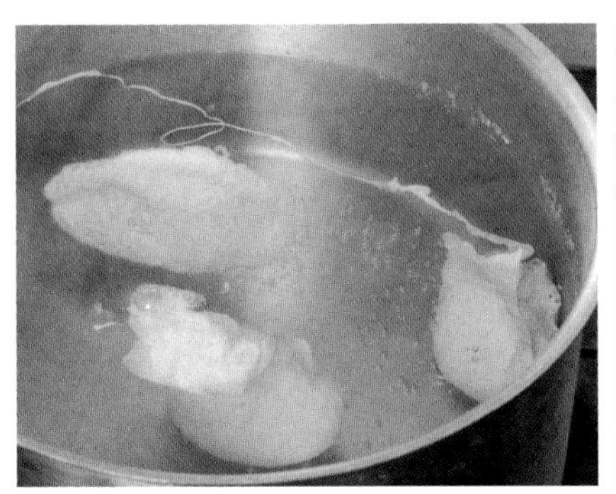

6 Cook for approximately 3–3½ minutes, until lightly set.

7 Remove carefully using a perforated spoon. Place into ice water to stop the cooking process, then place on a clean, dry cloth to drain off any water.

SERVING SUGGESTION

Serve on hot buttered toast.

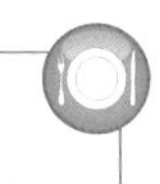

ACTIVITY

Poach two eggs: one as fresh as possible, the other stale and out of its 'best before' date. Assess the results.

25 Poached salmon

Energy	Calories	Fat	Saturated fat	Carbohydrates	Sugar	Protein	Fibre	Sodium
1369 kJ	329 kcal	24.3 g	6.8 g	0.9 g	0.5 g	26.7 g	0.5 g	224.0 g

* Using unsalted butter

Ingredient	4 portions	10 portions
Salmon fillets (100–150 g)	4	10
Butter or margarine	25 g	60 g
Salt		
Fish stock	Sufficient to come halfway up the fish – this will depend on the size and type of cooking vessel	

Mise en place

1. Wash and dry the fish fillets.
2. Grease an ovenproof dish with butter.

Cooking

1. Arrange the washed and dried fish fillets in the ovenproof dish and season lightly.
2. Cover with buttered greaseproof paper.
3. Add sufficient fish stock to come halfway up the fish.
4. Cook in a moderate oven at 170°C for approximately 10 minutes. The cooking time will vary according to the thickness of the fillets. Fish should not be overcooked.
5. When cooked, remove the fillets, drain well, and keep warm and covered with greaseproof paper.
6. Strain off the cooking liquor into a small pan. Place on a hot stove and allow to reduce by half. Strain.

SERVING SUGGESTION

Serve with a little of the cooking liquid spooned over the fish.

VARIATION

- Enrich the cooking liquid to give a light sauce. When the cooking liquid has been reduced, gradually add 25 g of softened butter, mixing well until combined. Taste and correct the seasoning.
- Add chopped fresh herbs to the sauce, such as chives, parsley, dill or fennel.
- When the salmon is prepared for cooking, sprinkle a few finely cut slices of white button mushrooms on the top before covering with the buttered greaseproof paper. When the fish is finally presented for serving, add a light sprinkle of freshly chopped parsley.

ACTIVITY

In groups, prepare, cook and serve five variations of poached salmon. Then taste, assess and discuss the findings.

26 Poached pears in red wine

Energy	Calories	Fat	Saturated fat	Carbohydrates	Sugar	Protein	Fibre	Sodium
833 kJ	196 kcal	0.1 g	0.0 g	39.0 g	39.1 g	0.5 g	3.9 g	6.6 g

Ingredient	4 portions	10 portions
Water	100 ml	250 ml
Red wine	300 ml	50 ml
Granulated sugar	125 g	300 g
Lemon zest	1	2
Cinnamon stick	1	3
Pears (firm e.g. William/Comice)	4	10

Poaching of fruits is completed in flavoured liquids – that is, stock syrup or wines with the addition of spices to enhance the flavour of the fruits. The fruit can be cooked whole or in pieces, depending on how it is going to be used.

Mise en place

Grate the lemon zest.

Cooking

1 Place the water, wine and sugar in a saucepan and heat gently to dissolve the sugar.

2 Add the zest of lemon and cinnamon.

3 Peel the pears neatly without removing the stalks.

4 Place upright in the pan, ensuring they are fully covered with liquor, cover with greaseproof paper and lid.

5 Bring to the boil and simmer until the pears are cooked – they should be tinged red and tender when pricked with a skewer.

6 Pears can be removed from the syrup to cool, or cooled quickly in liquid to store.

7 Reduce some of the cooking liquor to make a sauce or glaze to serve with the pears.

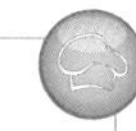

PROFESSIONAL TIP

When peeling white fruit, like pears, you can place them into acidulated water to stop them oxidising and going brown.

Steaming recipes

27 'Tiny Tip' raspberry steamed sponge pudding

Energy	Calories	Fat	Saturated fat	Carbohydrates	Sugar	Protein	Fibre	Sodium
1751 kJ	416 kcal	17.7 g	10.5 g	60.0 g	36.6 g	5.7 g	1.3 g	35.3 g

* Using unsalted butter, semi-skimmed milk

Ingredient	4 portions	10 portions
Lemon juice	1 dessertspoon	2½ dessertspoons
'Tiny Tip' raspberry jam	100 g	250 g
Butter	75 g	185 g
Caster sugar	75 g	185 g
Lemon zest	pinch	pinch
Vanilla essence		
Egg, beaten	75 g	185 g
Self-raising flour	125 g	310 g
Milk	30 ml	75 ml

This regional recipe was supplied by Chris Barker, formerly of the Colchester Institute. 'Tiny Tip' raspberry jam is made by the well-known local firm Wilkin & Sons of Tiptree Jam.

Mise en place

Prepare an individual pudding mould for each portion.

Cooking

1. Mix together the lemon juice and jam. Divide the mixture evenly between the pudding moulds.
2. Cream together the butter, sugar, lemon zest and vanilla until light and white.
3. Gradually add the egg.
4. Fold in the flour.
5. Add milk to form a dropping consistency.
6. Divide the mixture evenly into the moulds, seal them and steam until cooked.
7. Serve with crème Anglaise or custard.

28 Steamed fish with garlic and spring onion

Energy	Calories	Fat	Saturated fat	Carbohydrates	Sugar	Protein	Fibre
468 kJ	112 kcal	3.5 g	0.7 g	1.2 g	0.4 g	18.7 g	0.1 g

* Using 2 cloves of garlic

Ingredient	4 portions	10 portions
White fish fillets, e.g. plaice, lemon sole	400 g	1½ kg
Salt		
Ginger, peeled and freshly chopped	1 tbsp	2½ tbsp
Spring onions, finely chopped	2 tbsp	5 tbsp
Garlic, peeled and thinly sliced (optional)	1 clove	2 cloves
Light oil	1 tbsp	2½ tbsp
Light soy sauce	1 tbsp	2½ tbsp

Mise en place

1. Peel and chop the ginger.
2. Peel and thinly slice the garlic.
3. Chop the spring onions.
4. Wash and dry the fish well.

ACTIVITY

Suggest two or three variations, then prepare, cook, serve, taste, assess and discuss them.

Cooking

1. Rub the fish lightly with salt on both sides.
2. Put the fish on to plates or dishes. Sprinkle the ginger evenly on top.
3. Put the plates into a steamer, cover tightly and steam gently until just cooked (5–15 minutes, according to the thickness of the fish). Do not overcook.

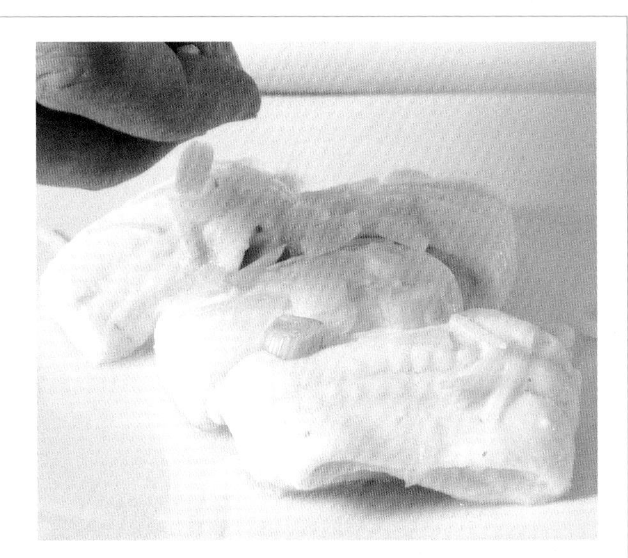

4. Remove the plates and sprinkle on the spring onions.

5 Brown the garlic slices in hot oil in a small frying pan, if required.

6 Sprinkle the garlic slices and soy sauce over the fish.

29 Steamed steak pudding

Energy	Calories	Fat	Saturated fat	Carbohydrates	Sugar	Protein	Fibre	Sodium
2164 kJ	516 kcal	25.9 g	14.1 g	42.0 g	1.6 g	27.5 g	2.6 g	517.0 g

* Using 1/4 teaspoon salt in the recipe for 4 portions. Including 75 g onion in the recipe

Ingredient	4 portions	10 portions
Suet paste		
Flour, soft or self-raising	200 g	500 g
Baking powder	10 g	25 g
Salt	pinch	pinch
Prepared beef suet	100 g	250 g
Water	125 ml approx.	300 ml
Filling		
Prepared stewing beef – chuck steak	400 g	1½ kg
Worcester sauce	3–4 drops	8–10 drops
Parsley, chopped	1 tsp	2½ tsp
Onion, chopped (optional)	50–100 g	200 g
Salt		

If you would like to thicken the gravy in the pudding, lightly toss the meat in flour at the beginning.

Mise en place

1. Cut the meat into 2 cm strips and then into squares.
2. Peel and chop the onion.
3. Grease a half-litre basin.

Cooking

1. Sieve the flour, baking powder and salt together.
2. Add the suet, then make a well in the mixture and add the water.
3. Mix lightly to a fairly stiff paste.
4. Lightly flour the rolling surface and rolling pin.
5. Roll out three-quarters of the suet paste and use this to line a greased half-litre basin.

6 Mix all of the filling ingredients except the water. Season lightly with salt.
7 Place in the lined basin and add the water so that the basin is filled to within 1 cm of the top.
8 Moisten the edge of the paste at the top of the basin. Roll out the remaining paste, cover the filling with this and seal firmly.
9 Cover with greased greaseproof paper or foil, or a pudding cloth tied securely with string.
10 Cook in a steamer for at least 3½ hours.

SERVING SUGGESTION
When serving, offer extra thickened gravy separately.

30 Steamed sponge pudding

Energy	Calories	Fat	Saturated fat	Carbohydrates	Sugar	Protein	Fibre	Sodium
1748 kJ	418 kcal	23.8 g	14.0 g	46.0 g	26.8 g	6.4 g	1.0 g	229.0 g

* Using unsalted butter and 30 ml semi-skimmed milk

Ingredient	6 portions	12 portions
Butter or margarine	100 g	200 g
Caster or soft brown sugar	100 g	200 g
Eggs, medium, well beaten	2	4
Flour	150 g	300 g
Baking powder	10 g	20 g
Milk	a few drops	several drops
Flavouring		

Flavourings for the pudding

- For vanilla sponge pudding, add a few drops of vanilla essence.
- For jam sponge pudding, add a good measure of jam to the moulds before putting in the mixture. When cooked and turned out there should be an appetising cap of jam on top.
- For fruit sponge pudding, add dried fruit to the mixture – raisins, sultanas, currants or a mixture.

SERVING SUGGESTION
Turn the puddings out of the moulds to serve accompanied with a suitable sauce, such as jam, lemon, chocolate or custard.

Atmospheric steaming video, http://bit.ly/YDBMdF

Cooking

1 Cream the fat and sugar in a bowl until almost white.

2 Gradually add the eggs, mixing vigorously.

3 Sieve the flour and baking powder. Lightly fold this into the mixture and add a little milk if necessary. It should be of dropping consistency (this means that if you lift a spoonful of the mixture and turn the spoon on its side, the mixture will drop off).

4 Place the mixture in a greased pudding basin or individual moulds.

5 Make a fold across the middle of the foil cover; the fold will allow the foil to expand during cooking.

6 Cover the basin securely with greaseproof paper, then tie the foil cover over the top. Steam for 1–1½ hrs.

31 Boiled/steamed cauliflower

Energy	Calories	Fat	Saturated fat	Carbohydrates	Sugar	Protein	Fibre	Sodium
184 kJ	43 kcal	0.6 g	0.1 g	4.5 g	4.1 g	3.6 g	2.6 g	10.1 g

Ingredient	4 portions	10 portions
Cauliflower, prepared	1 medium sized	2 large

VARIATION

All vegetables that can be boiled can also be steamed. The vegetables are prepared in the same way for boiling and steaming. To steam vegetables, place them in steamer trays and salt lightly. Steam them under pressure for as short a time as possible. The shorter the time they are cooked for, the more nutritional value and colour they will keep.

Mise en place

1. Remove the outer leaves and discard.
2. Trim the stem.
3. Hollow out the stem using a potato peeler or cut into florets and wash.

Cooking

1. Place the cauliflower in lightly salted water. Bring the water to the boil.
2. Boil or steam for approximately 10–15 minutes if you have left the cauliflower whole, or 3–5 minutes if you are using florets. Do not overcook.
3. Drain well. If you have cooked it whole, cut it into four even portions before serving.

SERVING SUGGESTION

- Serve plain or lightly coated with melted butter.
- Serve with a cream sauce (see page 100).
- Place the portioned cauliflower on a tray or dish. Coat it with cream sauce and sprinkle with grated Cheddar or Parmesan cheese. Lightly brown the topping under the salamander or in a hot oven.

32 Boiled/steamed broccoli

Energy	Calories	Fat	Saturated fat	Carbohydrates	Sugar	Protein	Fibre	Sodium
183 kJ	43 kcal	0.8 g	0.2 g	3.0 g	2.4 g	5.4 g	5.0 g	11.3 g

Ingredient	4 portions	10 portions
Broccoli, prepared	½ kg	1¼ kg

Mise en place

Break the broccoli into florets, removing the main stem.

Cooking

1. Place the broccoli in lightly salted water. Bring the water to the boil.
2. Boil or steam for approximately ½–1 minute. This should leave the broccoli slightly crisp and not mushy. Do not overcook – as they are in florets they require very little cooking.
3. Drain well.

33 Boiled/steamed spinach

Energy	Calories	Fat	Saturated fat	Carbohydrates	Sugar	Protein	Fibre	Sodium
345 kJ	80 kcal	3.0 g	0.4 g	1.0 g	0.0 g	13.0 g	5.0 g	150.0 g

* Using baby spinach

Ingredient	4 portions	10 portions
Spinach	2 kg	5 kg

Mise en place

1. Remove the stems from fully grown spinach. You do not need to remove them from young or baby spinach.
2. Wash the leaves carefully in deep water, several times if the spinach feels gritty. When washing, lift the spinach out of the deep water into a colander with your hands.

Cooking

1. Place the spinach into a saucepan and season lightly with salt. If you are cooking the spinach immediately after washing it there should be no need for extra water. If it is dry add a little water.
2. Cover it with a lid and cook for 1–3 minutes (according to its age) over a fierce heat.
3. Tip it into a colander over the sink and press it several times to remove all the water.
4. Squeeze the spinach into portion-sized balls ready for service.

Boil green, leafy vegetables like spinach in the smallest possible amount of lightly salted boiling water until slightly crisp. Do not let them go mushy.

SERVING SUGGESTION

- Reheat the spinach in a steamer. Use a two-pronged fork to separate the leaves loosely.
- Alternatively, you could heat the spinach in a thick-bottomed pan containing 25 g butter per portion.

VARIATION

- Make spinach purée by passing the cooked spinach through a sieve or mouli (vegetable puréeing mill), or using a food processor. Reheat in 25 g butter per portion.
- You can halve the amount of butter you use and add a tablespoonful of cream instead.

34 Boiled/steamed potatoes

Energy	Calories	Fat	Saturated fat	Carbohydrates	Sugar	Protein	Fibre	Sodium
628 kJ	148 kcal	0.2 g	0.1 g	32.2 g	1.6 g	3.4 g	3.6 g	3.6 g

* Based on 5 portions

Ingredient
1 kg of old potatoes will yield 4–6 portions

Mise en place

1. Wash, peel and re-wash the potatoes.
2. Cut into evenly sized pieces, 2–3 pieces per portion.

Cooking

1. Place the potatoes in a pan of lightly salted cold water and bring it to the boil.
2. Cook carefully for approximately 15–20 minutes.
3. Drain well and serve.

To boil potatoes or other root vegetables, just cover them with lightly salted cold water. Bring the water to the boil and cook until the vegetables are slightly firm. Do not let them go mushy. The one exception to this is potatoes that you are boiling to mash, which should be allowed to cook until they are a bit softer.

VARIATION

- You can steam the potatoes rather than boiling them.
- Brush 10 g melted butter per portion on to the potatoes.
- Sprinkle lightly with freshly chopped parsley.

35 Plain steamed rice

Energy	Calories	Fat	Saturated fat	Carbohydrates	Sugar	Protein	Fibre
1277 kJ	305 kcal	1.4 g	0.0 g	63.7 g	0.0 g	7.1 g	0.0 g

Ingredient	4 portions	10 portions
Basmati rice or similar long-grain rice, dry weight	100 g	250 g

Mise en place

Wash the rice.

Cooking

1. Place the rice in a saucepan. Add cold water until the water level is $2\frac{1}{2}$ cm above the rice.
2. Bring to the boil over a fierce heat until most of the water has evaporated.
3. Turn down the heat as low as possible. Cover the pan with a lid and allow the rice to complete cooking in the steam.
4. Once cooked, the rice should be allowed to stand in the covered pan for 10 minutes.

HEALTH AND SAFETY

Make sure you follow the health and safety points on reheating and storing rice (see recipe 17).

205 Stewing and braising

The purpose of this chapter is to help you develop skills, knowledge and understanding of the processes involved in preparing and cooking food by stewing or braising to produce a variety of dishes.

Learning outcomes

In this chapter, you will be able to:

1 produce stewed products, including:
- 1.1 selecting food items for stewing
- 1.2 applying preparation methods for stewing
- 1.3 applying techniques to produce stewed products
- 1.4 applying finishing methods for stewed products

2 produce braised products, including:
- 2.1 selecting food items for braising
- 2.2 applying preparation methods for braising
- 2.3 applying techniques to produce braised products
- 2.4 applying finishing methods for braised products

Recipes included in this chapter

Stewing	
1	Stewed fruits
2	Traditional scouse
3	Brown lamb or mutton stew (navarin)
4	Irish stew
5	Beef goulash
6	Beef olives
7	Vegetable casserole with herb dumplings

Braising	
8	Braised belly pork
9	Braised lamb shanks
10	Traditional braised beef
11	Braised chicken leg forestière
12	Braised rice (pilaf)
13	Braised mushrooms 'east–west'

1 Produce stewed products

Stewing is a slow, gentle, moist-heat method of cooking in which the food is completely covered by a liquid. Both the food and the sauce are served together. Stews are cooked on top of the stove. When stews are cooked in the oven they are called casseroles.

The purpose of stewing is to achieve the following.

- **Make food tender and palatable** – Stewing is an ideal method for cheaper cuts of meat and poultry as they often have more flavour than more tender cuts of meat, which tend to dry out in stews due to the long cooking times.
- **Keep the nutritional value of food** – During stewing, meat and vegetable juices that escape from the food during cooking stay in the liquid. This means that any vitamins and minerals are not lost, but are served up in the tasty and nutritious sauce.
- **Give a rich, deep flavour to the food** – Because it is a gentle cooking method, the food does not shrink much and keeps its flavour.

1.1 Selecting food items for stewing

Foods that are often braised include those listed below.

- **Fruit** – Stewed fruit associated with hard fruits sometimes finished with dried fruits used in pies, crumbles or served on its own.
- **Meat** (beef, lamb and pork) – As in a traditional stew and dumplings, often associated with dice or small cuts of meat, can be white or brown style.
- **Poultry** (chicken and turkey) – Trimmed pieces of meat on or off the bone that is cooked in stock in a covered pan as in a chicken **fricassée**.
- **Vegetables** – Trimmed vegetables that are cooked in a liquid, a traditional stew is ratatouille.

1.2 Applying preparation methods for stewing

Meat dishes may require the meat to be sealed first. This can be done to various degrees.

- **Blanching and refreshing** – The meat is placed in cold water and brought to the boil; it is then refreshed in running cold water.
- **Cutting** – This is the trimming, dicing and chopping of ingredients to an even size and shape to aid the cooking process.
- **Searing without colour** – Meat or chicken is placed in moderately hot fat or oil to start to cook the surface of the meat.
- **Browning or searing with colour** – Meat is placed in hot fat or oil to seal and colour the meat.
- **Selecting and preparing cooking liquids/liquor** – This will include choosing fresh or convenient liquids.

Liquids used for stewing

Liquid, other than stock, could include the following.

- **Stock syrup:** a water and sugar base, which could be infused with herbs and spices for cooking fruits in.
- **Wine:** the alcohol cooks off to leave a rich flavoured sauce to cook the meat in.
- **Beer and cider:** used in the same way as wine, but often associated with regional dishes; these add flavour to the dish.
- **Sauce:** this includes ready-made sauces – for example, **velouté** – or even convenience sauces such as a curry sauce; sauces are used to stew vegetables in for a vegetable curry.

Liquids are added to stews at various points through the cooking process depending on the recipe. Some are thickened during the cooking process; others are thickened once the main ingredient is cooked, as in a **blanquette**.

If stews and casseroles are cooked correctly, very little liquid will evaporate, leaving plenty of sauce to serve up as part of the stew. The amount of liquid used should be enough to cover the food items to keep them moist throughout the process. Consistency should be monitored to ensure that there is sufficient liquid/sauce for each portion of the finished dish.

1.3 Applying techniques to produce stewed products

There are a number of techniques associated with stewing that help the chef to prepare the dishes correctly.

- **Skimming** – This refers to removing scum or impurities that appear as foam or froth on the surface of the cooking liquid. Stir gently from the centre with a ladle to move impurities to the edge of the pan. Collect them with the edge of the ladle and place them in a bowl to be discarded.
- **Reduction** – With some dishes the liquid is strained and then reduced by boiling. The liquid will then be used as the base for a sauce to accompany the dish.
- **Straining** – Removing food from the cooking liquid and draining.
- **Blanching** – This means to set food by quickly heating and then chilling, or to seal meat before adding to cooking liquor.
- **Reheating** – This is where items are added back to a sauce or finished to order. It is important that the serving temperature is checked.
- **Temperature control** – Good stews are cooked slowly, so it is important to control the temperature properly. The liquid must barely simmer. Use a tight-fitting lid to keep in the steam. This helps to keep the temperature correct and reduces evaporation.

Stewing

Methods of cooking

Stews can be cooked on a hob or in an oven, depending on the recipe and foods being cooked.

When cooked on a hob, meat and vegetables are placed in a saucepan and covered with liquid (water or stock). The liquid is brought to the boil then turned down to a low simmer. This is then covered with a lid to ensure the food is left to cook slowly.

A stew may also be cooked in the oven, when it is referred to as a casserole. In both methods it is important to not allow the cooking liquor to evaporate too much. There should also be sufficient room for the liquid to move within the pan to ensure that the stew is cooked evenly.

Trimming and the size of cuts to be used need to be even to ensure an even cooking time. The trimmings need to be kept to a minimum with other uses considered to help control waste. The fresher the ingredients, the less trimming is required.

PROFESSIONAL TIP

Time required will vary according to the type and quality of foods to be stewed. As a guide, red meat will need longer than poultry and some vegetables will take longer than fruits.

HEALTH AND SAFETY

Place large stews on stovetops carefully to avoid splashes and spills. When you lift the lid from a pan, lift it away from you to avoid burning yourself on the steam.

Thickening sauces

All stews should have a thickened consistency. This comes from thickening agents.

- Unpassed ingredients can cause thickening – for example, in an Irish stew all of the vegetables are left in the stew and help to make it the right consistency.
- Flour can be added to the sauce – for example, for brown lamb stew (**navarin**) you will cook the meat, then mix flour with the meat, browning the flour before adding the cooking liquid.
- In fricassées (white stews), the cooking liquid is thickened using a roux (flour and butter mixture).
- Egg yolks and cream can also be used to thicken white stews, such as blanquette.

However, stews should not be over-thickened and the sauce should stay light. Make sure you use the correct amount of thickening agents and adjust the consistency during cooking if necessary by adding more liquid or more thickening agent.

PROFESSIONAL TIP

Do not overcook stews as this causes too much liquid to evaporate. The food also breaks up, loses its colour and spoils the flavour.

1.4 Applying finishing methods for stewed products

Finishing of the final dish is where the chef gets to make final adjustments to a dish.

When finishing dishes, it is important to consider the following points.

- **Consistency** – It is important to check the consistency of a sauce or cooking liquor, and to correct it by reducing or adding a thickener.
- **Flavour and taste** – Check and adjust the seasoning, if necessary.
- **Appearance** – The colour, glace and the way the dish is presented all need to be considered.
- **Portion size** – Think about whether the dish is set for individual or multiple portions, and if the dish is balanced, with all ingredients.
- **Garnish** – The appearance of a finished dish should be appealing. If required, garnish the dish; this may be a simple sprinkling of chopped herbs such as parsley.
- **Temperature** – Ensure food is served at the correct temperature.

KEY TERMS

Blanquette: A white stew; the sauce is made by thickening the cooking liquor at the end of the cooking process

Fricassée: A white stew; the sauce is thickened as part of the cooking process

Navarin: A brown lamb stew; the sauce is thickened as part of the cooking process

2 Produce braised products

Braising is a moist-heat method used for cooking larger pieces of food. The food is only half covered with liquid and can be cooked on the stovetop or in the oven. The food is cooked very slowly in a pan with a tightly fitted lid, using very low temperatures. A combination of steaming and stewing cooks the food. Food is usually cooked in very large pieces and carved before serving.

The purpose of braising food is:

- to enhance the flavour – cooking foods in the braising liquid helps to retain the maximum flavour
- to change the texture to make the food more tender and edible – braising breaks down the tissue fibres in certain foods, which softens them and makes them tender; this means that tougher, less expensive cuts of meat and poultry can be used.

2.1 Selecting food items for braising

Foods that are often braised include the following.

- **Meat** (beef, lamb and pork) – Normally pieces of butcher's meat or joints; lamb shank is a traditional braised dish.
- **Poultry** – Whole small birds or joints are often braised and finished with an appropriate garnish.
- **Rice** – Pilaf is a braised rice dish that is used in a lot of kitchens.
- **Vegetables** – Whole or reshaped as a dish or garnish; for example, braised onion or cabbage.

2.2 Applying preparation methods for braising

Good preparation and trimming of ingredients helps to ensure that all elements are cooked evenly to meet both the recipe specification and customer expectations.

Meat dishes may require the meat to be sealed first.

- **Cutting** – This is the trimming, dicing and chopping of ingredients to an even size and shape to aid the cooking process.
- **Sealing without colour** – Meat or chicken is placed in moderately hot fat or oil to start to cook the surface of the meat.
- **Browning or sealing with colour** – Meat is placed in hot fat or oil to seal and colour the meat.
- **Selecting and preparing cooking liquids/liquor** – This will include choosing fresh or convenient liquids.

Liquids used when braising foods

These include:

- stock, including fresh and convenience stocks
- wine
- beer and cider
- water
- sauce.

Always use the correct amount of these liquids to achieve the requirements of the finished dish.

2.3 Applying techniques to produce braised products

There are a number of techniques associated with braising that help the chef to prepare the dishes correctly.

- **Skimming** – This refers to removing scum or impurities that appear as foam or froth on the surface of the cooking liquid. Stir gently from the centre with a ladle to move impurities to the edge of the pan. Collect them with the edge of the ladle and place them in a bowl to be discarded.
- **Basting** – This is spooning the cooking liquid over food items during the cooking process, to help keep them moist and glaze them to enhance the presentation of the finished dish.
- **Reduction** – With some dishes the liquid is strained and then reduced by boiling. The liquid will then be used as the base for a sauce to accompany the dish.
- **Straining** – Removing food from the cooking liquid and draining.
- **Reheating** – This is where items are added back to a sauce or finished to order. It is important that the serving temperature is checked.
- **Temperature control** – The temperature should be controlled so that the liquid is barely simmering.

Techniques to produce different types of braised products

There are two methods of braising.

1. **Brown braising** is used, for example, for joints and portion-sized cuts of meat. Meat must be sealed and browned first (use the same method as given for stewing, above). The sealed and browned meat is then placed over browned vegetables (**mirepoix**). During the cooking process, the vegetables prevent the meat from touching the base of the pan. If it does come into contact with the pan, the meat may become tough and dry.
2. **White braising** is used, for example, for vegetables. First blanch the vegetables and then place them in a braising pan with mirepoix and white stock. Add the liquid to the braising pan so that it half covers the food being braised. Once you have added the liquid, place a heavy, tight-fitting lid on the cooking pan. The lid keeps the moisture in the pan and around the food, and creates steam. This prevents the food from becoming dry and tough.

HEALTH AND SAFETY

Use heavy, dry oven cloths whenever you remove the pot from the oven or lift the lid. When you lift the lid from the pan, lift it away from you to avoid burning yourself on the steam. The contents can become extremely hot, so take great care to prevent splashing when you stir them.

The length of time required to cook individual dishes will depend on the item being braised, its size, shape and the type of food. For example, if lamb shanks are cooked too quickly the meat can detach from the bone before it is tender enough for the customer to enjoy.

The following is a guide to braising correctly.

- Cook the food slowly. The liquid must barely simmer.
- Use a tight-fitting lid to reduce evaporation and maintain the temperature.
- The time needed for braising will vary according to the quality of the food.
- The ideal oven temperature for braising is approximately 160 °C.

Once food has been braised the liquid is normally strained from the food. For foods other than vegetables this is then normally made into a sauce by reducing or thickening.

When braising a joint of meat to be served whole, remove the lid three-quarters of the way through cooking and baste the joint frequently to glaze it – this makes it look attractive when it is served.

To ensure the quality of finished dishes there are a number of things that a chef should do to ensure the dish meets the customer's expectations. Remind yourself of these by looking back at the stewing section, above.

2.4 Applying finishing methods for braised products

Finishing of the final dish is where the chef gets to make final adjustments. When finishing dishes, it is important to consider the consistency, flavour and taste, appearance, portion size, garnish/appearance and temperature.

Braising

Quality checks when producing stewed and braised goods

To ensure the quality of finished dishes there are a number of things that help a chef when preparing food for stewing.

- **Selection of products** – Ensure that products are fresh, have a good appearance, smell as expected and are at the appropriate temperature.
- **Preparation** – Foods should be trimmed, shaped and sized according to dish requirements, ensuring that trimming is kept to a minimum and other uses are considered, e.g. for use in soups, stocks or purées.
- **Cooking process** – The temperature and cooking time should be checked, as should the amount of liquid to be used. These elements will impact on the flavour, colour, texture and taste of the dish; do not allow the stew to cook too quickly – the liquid should just be moving gently and not rapidly boiling away.
- **Blanching and refreshing** associated with wet cooking methods is where foods are partly cooked and then chilled in cold water to hold colour, nutrients and flavour. Chefs then finish to order in the kitchen.

Equipment for stewing and braising

- Saucepans, sauté pans and, where large numbers of portions are being cooked, bratt pans are all considered to be traditional types of equipment for stewing and braising. These should be clean and in good repair, with no loose handles and with correctly fitting lids.
- A number of kitchens now use non-traditional equipment to stew and braise foods; this includes slow cookers and steamers.
- Casserole dishes are usually deep, round, ovenproof dishes with handles and a tight-fitting lid. They can be made of glass, metal (cast iron), ceramic or any other heatproof material. They are available in various sizes, some of which are then used to serve the food at the table. Always make sure you use the appropriate size and type of dish for the food that you are cooking.

TEST YOURSELF

1 Briefly describe the process for the following methods of cooking:
   a stewing
   b braising.
2 What is the purpose of stewing?
3 List three cooking liquids that could be used as a sauce in the finished dish.
4 List three types of stew.
5 List five safety points that chefs should consider when cooking by stewing or braising.
6 What is the term for removing scum or foam from the top of a boiling liquid? Why do we do this?
7 List four foods that can be cooked by braising.
8 List three types of food that could be stewed.
9 What is a mirepoix?
10 List two pieces of equipment that are traditionally used for stewing and braising.

Stewing recipes

1 Stewed fruits

Energy	Calories	Fat	Saturated fat	Carbohydrates	Sugar	Protein	Fibre	Sodium
377	88	0.3	0.03	22.1	22.1	6.7	3.2	2.9

Based on 100g each of apple, plum, pear, rhubard and strawberries, to make 4 portions (analysed as per portion)

Ingredient	4 portions	10 portions
Seasonal fruits – rhubarb, apricots, apples, plums, strawberries, pears	500 g	1¼ kg
Caster sugar	50 g (75 g for rhubarb)	125 g (190 g for rhubarb)
Water	30 ml	75 ml
For rhubarb, add some fresh grated ginger to bring out the flavour (optional)	2 cm piece	5 cm piece

Mise en place

1. Peel the fruit if necessary. Hull the strawberries (remove the tops).
2. Chop up all the fruit to even sizes, discarding any stones.

Hulling a strawberry

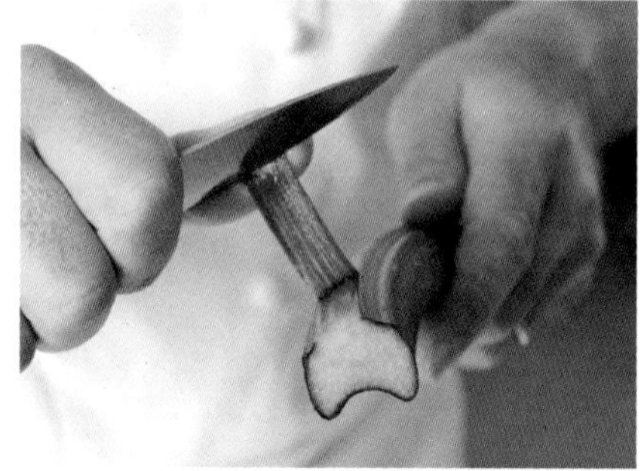

Peeling rhubarb

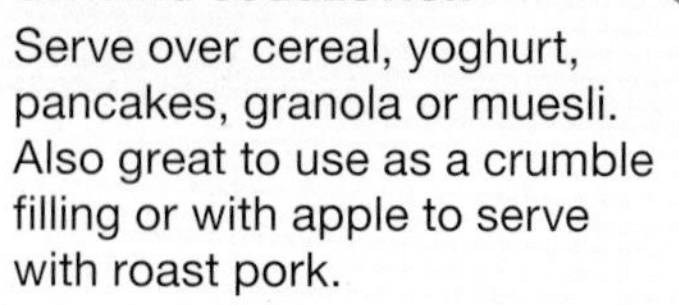

SERVING SUGGESTION

Serve over cereal, yoghurt, pancakes, granola or muesli. Also great to use as a crumble filling or with apple to serve with roast pork.

PROFESSIONAL TIP

When you are stewing fruit it is best to decide how much sugar to add by tasting the fruit. If your fruit is really ripe and sweet, you'll need less than suggested in the recipe above.

Cooking

1. Place the fruit in a pan and add the sugar.
2. Add water and cook on a medium heat with the lid on.

3. Once the fruit has softened, remove the lid and let the liquid reduce – you want to end up with a fairly thick consistency.

2 Traditional scouse

Energy	Calories	Fat	Saturated fat	Carbohydrates	Sugar	Protein	Fibre	Sodium
1806	432	24.5	11.3	22.2	12.5	30	3.9	737

Added 1/4 teaspoon of salt

Ingredient	4 portions	10 portions
Salted butter	10 g	25 g
Lamb shoulder	500 g	1¼ kg
Onions	1	3
Garlic cloves	1	2–3
Carrots	1	3
Tomato purée	1 tbsp	2½ tbsp
Black treacle	1 tbsp	2½ tbsp
Chicken stock	1 litre	2½ litres
Bouquet garni (black peppercorns, bay leaf, parsley, thyme)		
Celeriac	¼	¾
Potatoes	1	3
Worcester sauce	1 tbsp	2½ tbsp
Ground white pepper and sea salt		

Contributed by Paul Robinson, Curriculum Leader, Hospitality at Grimsby Institute of Further and Higher Education.

This recipe is based on the traditional lamb dish called scouse, which was brought to England by Scandinavian sailors and then changed by the people of Liverpool.

Mise en place

1. Remove the bone and fat from the lamb.
2. Cut the lamb into cubes of equal size (2 cm square) with minimal waste.
3. Wash, peel, then re-wash the vegetables. Cut the carrots and potatoes into macédoine, the celeriac into jardinière, and the onions and garlic into brunoise.

Cooking

1. Melt the butter in a thick-bottomed deep pan and seal the meat until it starts to brown.
2. In the same pan soften the onions for a few minutes with the garlic, then add the carrots.
3. Add the tomato purée, black treacle and stir, then pour in the stock and bring to the boil.
4. Once the liquid starts to boil turn back the heat and allow it to simmer with the bouquet garni.
5. Simmer for 40 minutes until the meat is almost tender then add the celeriac and potato.
6. Add the Worcester sauce and continue to simmer gently until the meat is tender.
7. Once the potato starts to break down reduce the sauce, then remove the bouquet garni.
8. Finish the stew by skimming any excess fat that has risen to the surface.
9. Check the consistency of sauce then adjust the flavour (season), present and garnish.

3 Brown lamb or mutton stew (navarin)

Energy	Calories	Fat	Saturated fat	Carbohydrates	Sugar	Protein	Fibre
1320 kJ	314 kcal	18.7 g	6.2 g	9.4 g	3.2 g	27.9 g	1.3 g

* Using sunflower oil

Ingredient	4 portions	10 portions
Stewing lamb – shoulder, neck end, breast	500 g	1½ kg
Salt		
Oil	2 tbsp	5 tbsp
Onion, roughly chopped	100 g	250 g
Carrot, roughly chopped	100 g	250 g
Flour, white or wholemeal	25 g	60 g
Tomato purée	1 level tbsp	2½ level tbsp
Brown stock, mutton stock or water	500 ml	1¼ litres
Bouquet garni	1	1
Garlic clove (optional)	1	2–3
Parsley, chopped for garnishing		

Mise en place

1. Trim the meat of any excess fat and bone, and cut into even pieces.
2. Peel and roughly chop the onion and carrot.
3. Prepare a bouquet garni.

Cooking

1. Season the meat lightly with salt. Heat the oil in a frying pan and fry the meat quickly until just coloured.

2. Add the onion and carrot, and continue frying until well browned.
3. Drain off any surplus fat and discard.

4. Mix in the flour with a wooden spoon and cook on a low heat, stirring continuously, for 3–4 minutes.

5. Mix in the tomato purée, then allow the meat mixture to cool slightly.
6. Put it back on the heat and gradually add the stock and stir to the boil.

7. Add the bouquet garni and garlic. Skim and cover with a lid.
8. Simmer gently, in a moderate oven at 180°C or on the side of the stove, for approximately 1½–2 hours.

9. When cooked, pick out the meat and put it into a clean pan.
10. Taste and correct the sauce and pass it through a strainer on to the meat.

SERVING SUGGESTION
Serve lightly sprinkled with chopped parsley.

VARIATION
- Either separately or in with the stew, cook a garnish of small neat vegetables, such as carrots, turnips, button onions, potatoes, peas. If cooking them with the stew, add them approximately 30 minutes before the meat is cooked.
- Brown beef stew can be made by using this recipe and substituting prepared stewing beef cut into 2 cm pieces in place of the lamb.

ACTIVITY

As a group, prepare, cook, serve, taste and assess the recipe using:

1. an ordinary brown stock (page 89)
2. a well-flavoured lamb or mutton brown stock
3. water.

4 Irish stew

Energy	Calories	Fat	Saturated fat	Carbohydrates	Sugar	Protein	Fibre
1544 kJ	378 kcal	25.1 g	9.9 g	7.2 g	5.9 g	29.6 g	20.6 g

Ingredient	4 portions	10 portions
Stewing lamb, shoulder, neck end, breast	500 g	1½ kg
Water or white stock	400 g	1 kg
Salt		
Bouquet garni	1	1
Potatoes	100 g	250 g
Onions	100 g	250 g
Celery	100 g	250 g
Savoy cabbage	100 g	250 g
Leeks	100 g	250 g
Button onions (optional), whole	100 g	250 g

Mise en place

1. Trim the meat of any excess fat and bone, and cut into even pieces.
2. Peel and wash the vegetables.

Cooking

1. Place the meat in a shallow saucepan, cover with water and bring to the boil (blanch).
2. Refresh by placing the meat under running water until meat is clean, then return it to the cleaned pan.
3. Cover with water or white stock, season lightly with salt and add the bouquet garni.
4. Skim, cover with a lid and allow to simmer for three-quarters of an hour.
5. Peel and wash the vegetables and cut into neat, small pieces and add to the meat.
6. Simmer for 30 minutes, skimming frequently.
7. Add the button onions, if using, and simmer for a further 20–30 minutes.
8. Skim, taste and correct the seasoning.

SERVING SUGGESTION
Serve lightly sprinkled with chopped parsley. You could also accompany it with Worcester sauce and/or pickled red cabbage.

Offer a good soda bread as an accompaniment, to make a filling meal.

5 Beef goulash

Energy	Calories	Fat	Saturated fat	Carbohydrates	Sugar	Protein	Fibre
1625 kJ	389 kcal	20.4 g	6.0 g	26.1 g	3.9 g	26.9 g	1.7 g

Ingredient	4 portions	10 portions
Lard or oil	35 g	100 g
Prepared stewing beef	500 g	1½ kg
Salt		
Onions, chopped	100 g	250 g
Paprika	10–25 g	25–60 g
Flour	25 g	60 g
Tomato purée	25 g	60 g
Stock or water	750 ml	2 litres

Mise en place

1. Trim the meat and cut it into 2 cm square pieces.
2. Peel and chop the onion.

Cooking

1. Heat the fat in a thick-bottomed pan, season the meat lightly with salt and quickly fry it until lightly coloured.
2. Add the onions, cover with a lid and cook gently for 3–4 minutes until the onions are soft.
3. Mix in the paprika and flour using a wooden spoon.
4. Allow to cook out on top of the stove or in an oven for 2–3 minutes.
5. Mix in the tomato purée and then gradually add the stock, mixing well.
6. Bring to the boil, skim, taste, correct seasoning and cover.
7. Simmer, preferably in the oven, for approximately 1½–2 hours, until the meat is tender.
8. Skim, taste and correct the seasoning again.

VARIATION

Add a little cream or yoghurt at the last moment.

6 Beef olives

Energy	Calories	Fat	Saturated fat	Carbohydrates	Sugar	Protein	Fibre
1134 kJ	271 kcal	13.1 g	2.6 g	13.6 g	5.0 g	25.4 g	1.5 g

* Using 625 ml stock

Ingredient	4 portions	10 portions
Stuffing		
White or wholemeal breadcrumbs	50 g	125 g
Parsley, chopped	1 tbsp	3 tbsp
Thyme	small pinch	pinch
Suet, prepared and chopped	5 g	25 g
Onion, finely chopped and lightly sweated in oil	25 g	60 g
Salt		
Egg	½	1
Olives		
Lean beef, topside	400 g	1¼ kg
Salt		
Dripping or oil	35 g	100 g
Onion, chopped	100 g	250 g
Carrot, chopped	100 g	250 g
Flour	25 g	60 g
Tomato purée	25 g	60 g
Brown stock (boiling)	500–700 ml	1¼–1½ litres
Bouquet garni		

Mise en place

1. Cut the meat into four thin slices across the grain and, using a meat bat, carefully thin out the slices.
2. Trim the slices to approximately 10 x 8 cm and chop the trimmings.
3. Peel and chop the onions and carrots.
4. Prepare a bouquet garni.
5. Prepare and chop the suet.

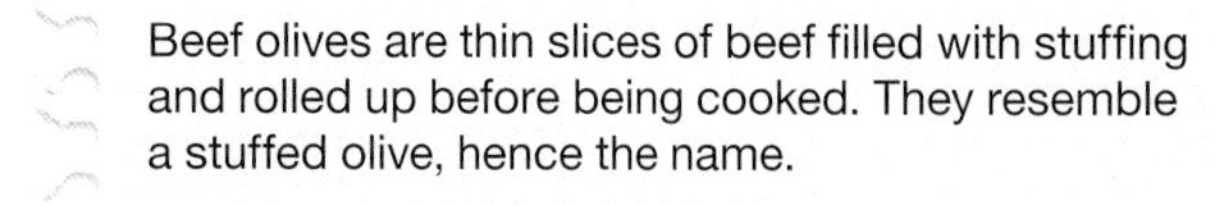

Beef olives are thin slices of beef filled with stuffing and rolled up before being cooked. They resemble a stuffed olive, hence the name.

Cooking

1. Combine all the stuffing ingredients.
2. Add the meat trimmings and make sure the stuffing is mixed thoroughly.
3. Season the meat lightly with salt.
4. Spread a quarter of the stuffing down the centre of each slice. Neatly roll up each slice and tie with string.
5. In a thick-bottomed pan, heat the dripping or oil and fry the rolls until a light golden brown on all sides.
6. Add the chopped onions and carrots halfway through.
7. Place the olives and vegetables into a suitable ovenproof pan or casserole.
8. Drain off any remaining fat into a clean pan and if necessary add more to make it up to 25 ml. Mix in the flour and, stirring continuously, brown lightly.
9. Mix in the tomato purée, then cool and mix in the boiling stock.
10. Bring to the boil, skim and pour on to the olives.
11. Add the bouquet garni, cover and simmer gently, preferably in a moderate oven at 160°C, for approximately 1½–2 hours.
12. Once cooked, take out the meat and cut off the strings.
13. Skim, taste and correct the sauce, then pass it through a fine strainer on to the meat and serve.

ACTIVITY

As a group, use four variations to the stuffing of your choice. Prepare one without salting the meat then taste, assess and discuss.

7 Vegetable casserole with herb dumplings

Energy	Calories	Fat	Saturated fat	Carbohydrates	Sugar	Protein	Fibre	Sodium
2094	500	24.6	9	59	11.2	9.5	8.2	1189

Ingredient	4 portions	10 portions
Casserole		
Vegetable oil	2 tbsp	5 tbsp
Onion, chopped	50 g	125 g
Garlic cloves, crushed	2	5
Carrots	100 g	250 g
Parsnip	100 g	250 g
Swede	100 g	250 g
Turnip	100 g	250 g
Jerusalem artichokes	60 g	150 g
Fresh thyme	1 tsp	2½ tsp
Fresh parsley	1 tsp	2½ tsp
Button mushrooms	100 g	250 g
Vegetable stock	1 litre	2½ litre
Yeast extract (e.g. Marmite)	1 tsp	2½ tsp
Ground pepper		
Dumplings		
Plain flour	200 g	500 g
Baking powder	10 g	25 g
Vegetable suet	100 g	250 g
Herbs, freshly chopped:		
• Parsley	1 tsp	2½ tsp
• Chervil	1 tsp	2½ tsp
• Tarragon	1 tsp	2½ tsp
• Oregano	1 tsp	2½ tsp
• Rosemary	1 tsp	2½ tsp
• Basil	1 tsp	2½ tsp
English mustard powder	2 tsp	4 tsp
Water	60 ml	180 ml

Mise en place

1. Peel and chop the onion.
2. Peel the carrots, parsnip, swede, turnip and Jerusalem artichokes, and cut into ½ cm pieces.
3. Clean the mushrooms and cut into quarters.
4. Chop all of the fresh herbs.

Cooking

1 In vegetable oil, shallow fry the onion, garlic, carrots, parsnips, swede, turnip and artichoke for 5–10 minutes. Stir continuously.

2 Sprinkle with the fresh herbs. Add the mushrooms and cook for a further 5 minutes.

3 Add the vegetable stock and yeast extract, and season with ground pepper. Simmer until the vegetables are tender.

4 Prepare the dumplings by sifting the flour with the baking powder.

5 Mix in the shredded suet.

6 Dilute the mustard powder in half of the water and add this and the herbs. Mix well.

7 Add the mustard and the remaining water to the flour and suet, and mix to a soft dough.

8 Knead and form into small dumplings.

9 Cook the dumplings in the casserole or separately in vegetable stock, for 10–15 minutes.

SERVING SUGGESTION

Serve the casserole with the dumplings in a suitable dish.

Braising recipes

8 Braised belly pork

Energy	Calories	Fat	Saturated fat	Carbohydrates	Sugar	Protein	Fibre	Sodium
1628 kJ	392 kcal	28.2 g	9.3 g	10.5 g	8.3 g	24.3 g	0.4 g	443.0 g

* Including 1 tbsp vegetable oil to sear the meat

Ingredient	4 portions	10 portions
Belly pork, boned and skinned	500 g	1¼ kg
Marinade		
Ginger, finely chopped	10 g	25 g
Red chilli, chopped	½	1
Garlic cloves	1	2
Soy sauce	15 ml	40 ml
Five spice powder	½ tsp	1 tsp
Honey	1 tbsp	2 tbsp
Tomato ketchup	1 tbsp	2 tbsp
Oranges, zest and juice	½	1
Worcester sauce	1–2 tsp	5 tsp
Arrowroot	5 g	12 g
Small amount of oil to seal		

Regional recipe contributed by Iain Middleton, Team leader for Hospitality and Catering at New College Stamford, Lincolnshire.

Mise en place

1. Bone and skin the pork belly, unless this has already been done by the butcher.
2. Mix together the ingredients for the marinade. Marinade the pork overnight.

Cooking

1. Remove the pork from the marinade and drain well.
2. Sear the meat on all sides in small amount of oil in a shallow pan.
3. Place in braising pan.
4. Add marinade to pan and enough water or white stock to come halfway up meat and bring to simmer.
5. Cover with tight-fitting lid or foil and braise in oven at 160°C for 2½ hours (or until tender).
6. Drain off meat and allow to rest.
7. Reduce cooking liquor or thicken with a little arrowroot dispersed in cold water.
8. Slice the pork and serve on a plate with the sauce and garnish.

SERVING SUGGESTION

Serve with fondant potatoes and braised red cabbage.

To make crackling, cut rind into thin strips, place on tray, salt, cover with silicone paper and another tray, and bake in oven at 190°C until crispy.

9 Braised lamb shanks

Energy	Calories	Fat	Saturated fat	Carbohydrates	Sugar	Protein	Fibre	Sodium
1700 kJ	408 kcal	20.3 g	5.3 g	22.4 g	10.3 g	33.3 g	5.3 g	487.0 g

* Using 500 g lean lamb

Ingredient	4 portions	10 portions
Lamb shanks	4	10
Oil	3 tbsp	7 tbsp
Red onions	50 g	125 g
Garlic cloves	2	5
Plum tomatoes (canned)	400 g	1 kg
Lamb stock	250 ml	625 ml
Flageolet beans (canned)	400 g	1 kg
Honey, clear	1 tbsp	2½ tbsp
Rosemary, fresh	1 tbsp	2½ tbsp
Salt		

Mise en place

1. Peel and finely chop the onions.
2. Peel and crush the garlic.
3. Drain and chop the tomatoes.
4. Rinse and drain the beans.
5. Chop the rosemary.

Cooking

1. Lightly season the shanks.
2. Heat the oil in a suitable braising pan.
3. Quickly fry the shanks on all sides until golden brown. Remove from the pan and set aside.
4. Add the chopped onion and garlic to the pan (if there is insufficient oil, add a little more). Allow to sweat gently over a moderate heat until soft.
5. Stir in the tomatoes and stock.
6. Place the shanks back in the pan.
7. Bring to the boil, then reduce the heat so that the cooking is at a gentle simmer. Cover and put in the oven at 160°C for 1 hour.
8. Check the shanks to see that they are cooked by using a two-pronged fork, which should slide in as far as the bone in the thickest part of the shank.
9. Remove the shanks and stir in the beans, honey and rosemary.
10. Replace the shanks and reheat to a gentle simmer. Skim, taste the liquid and correct the seasoning.

SERVING SUGGESTION

Serve in an earthenware dish sprinkled with freshly chopped parsley.

ACTIVITY

You can make many variations to this recipe, using different beans, additional vegetables, different herbs, and so on.

1. Create your own recipe, then prepare, cook, taste, assess and discuss it.
2. Suggest what accompaniments you would like to serve with the shanks.

10 Traditional braised beef

Energy	Calories	Fat	Saturated fat	Carbohydrates	Sugar	Protein	Fibre	Sodium
1315 kJ	313 kcal	12.8 g	2.6 g	12.6 g	8.1 g	35.7 g	1.8 g	612.0 g

* Using topside, vegetable oil, added 1/4 teaspoon salt (in recipe for 4 portions). Using 1000 ml of beef stock to account for the 500 ml brown stock plus 250 ml demi-glace

Ingredient	4 portions	10 portions
Lean beef (topside or thick flank)	500 g	1½ kg
Dripping or oil	25 g	60 g
Onions	100 g	250 g
Carrots	100 g	250 g
Brown stock	500 ml	1¼ litres
Salt, pepper		
Bouquet garni		
Tomato purée	25 g	60 g
Demi-glace or jus-lié	250 ml	625 ml

Mise en place

1. Preheat the oven to 150–180°C.
2. Wash, peel and slice the onions and carrots. Lightly fry them.
3. Trim and tie the joint.

About one-third of the meat weight gives you the weight of vegetables needed.

Braised beef video, http://bit.ly/10llYyU

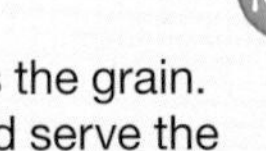

SERVING SUGGESTION

Remove the string and carve slices across the grain. Pour some of the sauce over the slices and serve the remainder of the sauce in a sauceboat.

Serve with plenty of potatoes and vegetables, or with pasta.

Cooking

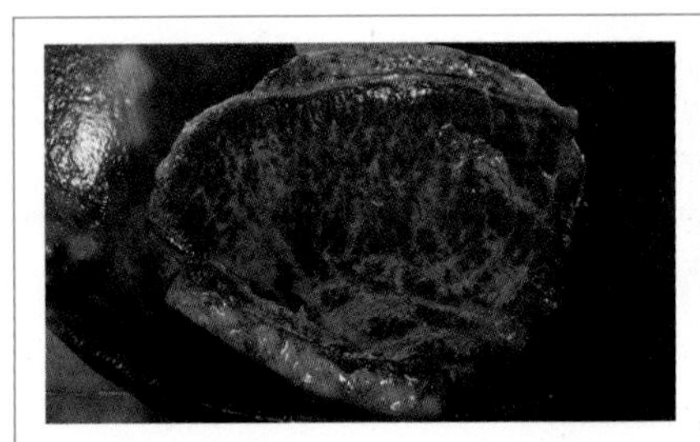

1. Season the meat and colour quickly on all sides in hot fat to seal the joint.
2. Place the lightly fried vegetables into a small braising pan (any pan with a tight-fitting lid that may be placed in the oven) or in a casserole.
3. Place the joint in with the vegetables.

4. Add the stock, which should come two-thirds of the way up the meat, and season lightly.
5. Add the bouquet garni and tomato purée and, if available, add a few mushroom trimmings.
6. Bring to the boil, skim and cover with a lid; cook in a moderate oven at 150–180°C.
7. After approximately 1½ hours' cooking, remove the meat.
8. Add the demi-glace or jus-lié, re-boil, skim and strain.

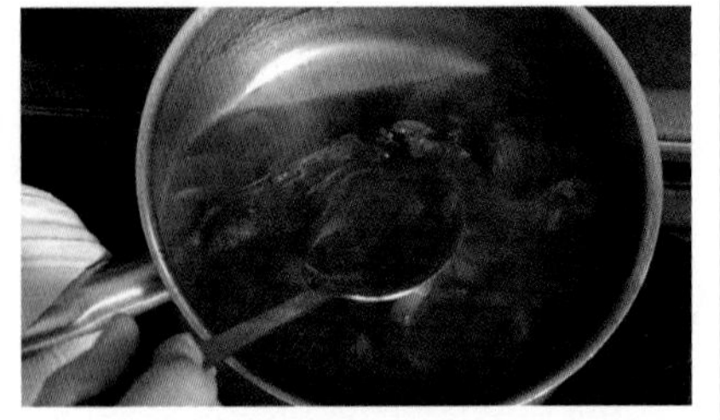

9. Replace the meat; do not cover, but baste frequently and continue cooking for 2–2½ hours in all. Braised beef should be well cooked (about 35 minutes per ½ kg plus 35 minutes). To test if cooked, pierce with a trussing needle, which should penetrate the meat easily and there should be no sign of blood.
10. Remove the joint and correct the colour, seasoning and consistency of the sauce.

11 Braised chicken leg forestière

Energy	Calories	Fat	Saturated fat	Carbohydrates	Sugar	Protein	Fibre	Sodium
1,878 kJ	448 kcal	15.9 g	3.9 g	16.9 g	8.7 g	49.9 g	3.6 g	1.0 g

Ingredient	4 portions	10 portions
Chicken legs	4	10
Salt and pepper		
Olive oil	2 tbsp	5 tbsp
Onions, sliced fairly thickly	2	5
Smoked bacon, thickly sliced rashers cut into lardons	3	8
Clove of garlic, crushed	1	2
Whole button or small chestnut mushrooms (if larger, cut in half)	100 g	250 g
Oyster mushrooms, sliced in half	100 g	250 g
Plain flour	1½ tbsp	4 tbsp
Tomato purée	1 tbsp	2½ tbsp
Red wine	250 ml	625 ml
Brown chicken stock	400 ml	1 litre
Tomatoes, blanched, peeled, concassée	3	7½
Fresh tarragon and parsley, chopped	15 g	35 g

These quantities will produce a moderate portion to be served as part of a three-course meal. Allow two chicken legs per person for a hearty portion.

Cooking

1. Season the chicken with salt and pepper. Heat the olive oil in a lidded sauté pan or shallow casserole and pan-fry the chicken over a medium-high heat, turning, until golden on both sides.
2. Remove from the pan and keep to one side. You will need about 2 tablespoons of fat left in the pan to cook the onions so, if the legs have released a lot of fat, drain off the excess.
3. Add the onions and fry for 2–3 minutes before adding the bacon, garlic and mushrooms to the pan. Continue to stir until they have a little colour and the mushrooms are beginning to soften.
4. Sprinkle over the flour and stir until the flour has lightly browned.
5. Stir in the tomato purée and then gradually add the red wine and chicken stock, stirring until the liquid has fully mixed into the flour and purée paste.
6. Return the chicken to the pan and bring to a simmer. Place a lid on the pan and continue to cook, allowing the sauce to just simmer for about 1 hour, or until the meat is completely tender.
7. To finish, remove the chicken legs, place on to a plate or tray and keep in a warm place, e.g. the side of the stove. Skim the sauce of any further excess fat and adjust the consistency as necessary.
8. Adjust the seasoning before adding the tomatoes.
9. Place the chicken legs back into the sauce and scatter over the chopped herbs before serving.

12 Braised rice (pilaf)

Energy	Calories	Fat	Saturated fat	Carbohydrates	Sugar	Protein	Fibre
774 kJ	184 kcal	10.4 g	4.5 g	22.1 g	0.3 g	1.9 g	0.6 g

* Using white rice and hard margarine. Using brown rice and hard margarine, 1 portion provides: 769 kJ/183 kcal energy; 10.9 g fat; 4.6 g saturated fat; 20.7 g carbohydrates; 0.7 g sugar; 1.9 g protein; 1.0 g fibre

Ingredient	4 portions	10 portions
Oil, butter or margarine	50 g	125 g
Onion, finely chopped	25 g	60 g
Rice, long grain	100 g	250 g
White stock, vegetable or chicken	200 ml	500 ml
Salt		

Mise en place

Finely chop the onion.

Cooking

1 Place half the fat into a thick-bottomed pan.

2 Add the onion and cook gently without colouring until the onion is soft (2–3 minutes).

3 Add the rice and stir to mix. Cook over a gentle heat without colouring for 2–3 minutes.

4 Add exactly twice the amount of stock to rice (ratio 2 to 1).

5 Season lightly, cover with greased paper and bring to the boil.

6 Place in a hot oven (230–250°C) until cooked (approximately 15 minutes).

7 When cooked, remove immediately to a cool container or pan. (If the rice is left in the hot pan, it will continue cooking, which will result in it overcooking and being spoilt.)

8 Carefully mix in the remaining half of the fat using a two-pronged fork.

9 Taste, correct the seasoning and serve.

ACTIVITY

Cook two dishes of pilaf, one with a good, richly flavoured chicken stock and the other with water. Taste and compare them.

VARIATION

- Add sliced mushrooms, at the same time as the onions.
- Finish with tomato concassée to slightly colour and flavour the rice.
- Add freshly grated cheese (10–100 g) with the fat at the end.

13 Braised mushrooms 'east–west'

Energy	Calories	Fat	Saturated fat	Carbohydrates	Sugar	Protein	Fibre	Sodium
630 kJ	151 kca	7.3 g	1.0 g	17.5 g	2.2 g	4.7 g	1.2 g	705.0 g

* Including 1/4 teaspoon of salt

Ingredient	4 portions	10 portions
Olive oil	2 tbsp	5 tbsp
Shallots	4	10
Fresh young ginger	3 cm	7 cm
Dried ceps	50 g	125 g
Black Chinese mushrooms	50 g	125 g
White button mushrooms	400 g	1 kg
Light soy sauce	2 tbsp	5 tbsp
Chives	2 tbsp	5 tbsp
Chicken stock	120 ml	300 ml
Salt and freshly ground black peppercorn to taste		

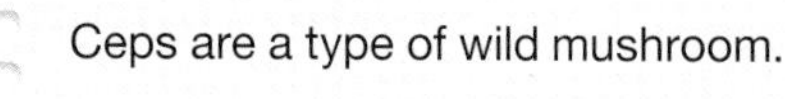

Ceps are a type of wild mushroom.

Mise en place

1. Place the ceps in a bowl, cover them with hot water and leave to soak for 30 minutes.
2. Squeeze the water out and cut them into wide strips. Set aside.
3. Peel and finely chop the ginger and shallots.
4. Clean and slice the button mushrooms.
5. Chop the chives.

Cooking

1. Heat the olive oil in a medium-sized frying pan. Add the shallots, ginger and then all the mushrooms and sauté for 3 minutes.
2. Add in the soy sauce, chives and chicken stock. Cook over a medium heat for a further 10 minutes to completely reduce the liquid.
3. Season with salt and pepper to taste.

206 Baking, roasting and grilling

The purpose of this chapter is to help you develop skills, knowledge and understanding of the processes involved in preparing and cooking food by baking, roasting or grilling to produce a variety of dishes.

Learning outcomes

In this chapter, you will be able to:

1 produce baked products, including:
- **1.1** selecting food items for baking
- **1.2** applying preparation methods for baking
- **1.3** applying techniques to produce baked products
- **1.4** applying finishing methods for baked products

2 produce roasted products, including:
- **2.1** selecting food items for roasting
- **2.2** applying preparation methods for roasting
- **2.3** applying techniques to produce roasted products
- **2.4** applying finishing methods for roasted products

3 produce grilled products, including:
- **3.1** selecting food items for grilling
- **3.2** applying preparation methods for grilling
- **3.3** applying techniques to produce grilled products
- **3.4** applying finishing methods for grilled products

Recipes included in this chapter

Baking	
1	Red onion and sweetcorn frittata
2	Baked cod with a cheese and herb crust
3	Short pastry
4	Sweet pastry
5	Fruit tartlets
6	Fruit pies
7	Banana loaf
8	Apple crumble
9	Fruit buns
10	Baked apple
11	Simple white loaf
12	Bread rolls
13	Gluten-free bread
14	Victoria sandwich
15	Genoise sponge
16	Fresh cream and strawberry gateau
17	Millionaire's shortbread
18	Scones
19	Macaroni pasta bake
20	Arlie potatoes
21	Savoury (boulangère) potatoes
22	Shepherd's pie
23	Steak pie
24	Stuffed peppers (piment farci)
25	Baked rice pudding
Roasting	
26	Roast rump of Glamorgan lamb on lava bread potato cake with Welsh stout and berry sauce
27	Traditional roast beef and gravy
28	Horseradish sauce
29	Yorkshire pudding
30	Roast loin of pork with apple and onion sauce
31	Roast rack of lamb
32	Mint sauce
33	Roast chicken with dressing (poulet rôti à l'anglaise)
34	Roast potatoes
35	Roasted beetroot
36	Roasted vegetables
Grilling	
37	Grilled pollock with allspice and lime
38	Grilled sardines
39	Lamb kebabs
40	Grilled pork chops
41	Grilled beef steak
42	Grilled gammon rashers
43	Grilled chicken (poulet grillé)
44	Grilled vegetable bake

1 Produce baked products

Baking is cooking food with dry heat in an oven. Although the food is cooked in a dry oven, steam can also play a big part in this method of cookery.

PROFESSIONAL TIP

Baked goods can be produced in bulk, all cooked for the same amount of time and all coming out the same colour.

The purpose of baking is to:

- produce tender, tasty food with deep flavours that is digestible and enjoyable to eat
- make food visually appealing, with a good colour and texture
- maintain the nutritional value of the dish
- make food safe to eat.

1.1 Selecting food items for baking

Foods that are often baked include:

- eggs, which could be baked on their own or mixed with other products such as milk to make an egg custard
- fish, such as salmon or cod
- fruit, such as apples, pears or peaches
- mixed ingredients for flour-based products, including bread products, scones, pasties and pastries
- pasta, either pre-blanched or ready-to-bake pastas such as lasagne and cannelloni
- vegetables, such as potatoes, tomatoes and field mushrooms.

Quality checks when selecting food items

- **Appearance** – Checking that food items appear the way they should – for example, when checking vegetables and/or fruits, look for signs of damage or bruising. Check for any signs of decay. The appearance of fish can also provide a clear indication as to its quality. The eyes should be bright and bulbous; scales should be intact (if the fish is scaly) and the gills should be a deep red colour. It is also very important to check the use-by and best-before dates on products and/or their packaging to ensure that they are safe to use.
- **Freshness** – The appearance of food gives a good indication of freshness. Other indications include the feel of foods – for example, fruit may be very soft if it is overripe. A fish will lose firmness of its flesh the longer it is left unused. Our sense of smell also provides a strong indication of the freshness of foods. If foods such as meat or fish start to have strong, rancid or unpleasant smells, this is a clear indication that the food is deteriorating and very likely to be unsafe to use. It will at the very least provide an unpleasant eating experience for the consumer and foods in this condition should not be used.
- **Size and shape** – The size and shape of foods need to be considered when baking foods. For example, a bread roll will bake faster than a loaf.
- **Texture** – As with size and shape, the texture of foods to be baked will have an impact on the cooking time. For example, a tomato, with its delicate structure and very high water content, will take considerably less time to bake than a potato with a much firmer texture.
- **Type** – As with all the examples described above, the type of food selected will have an impact on the methods that can be successfully used when cooking. From the texture of vegetables to the size of a pastry or bread product or the connective structure of different cuts of meat, all of these factors will require consideration when baking, roasting or grilling.

1.2 Applying preparation methods for baking

There are several preparation methods using in baking.

- **Coating** – Certain baked items may be coated with a crumb or crust. This will give the item additional texture as well as protecting it from direct heat – a salt-crusted fish, for example.
- **Cutting** – As with many other processes, many food items that are baked will be cut before being prepared. For example, vegetables to be prepared for a pasta dish have to be cut before cooking. Other products are cut to shape prior to baking. This process is used when baking biscuits or Chelsea buns.
- **Egg washing/glazing** – Products are coated with milk, water- or egg wash either before or after baking. A syrup is usually applied to products after baking, such as currant buns.
- **Greasing** – Using oil or butter on the tray or dish to prevent food from sticking.
- **Lining** – Trays or flan rings need to be lined before adding foods to be baked. Lining can be achieved by brushing lightly with oil or butter, sometimes with an extra fine coating of flour. It can also be achieved by covering with a sheet of greaseproof paper or baking parchment.

- **Marking and scoring** – Some products, such as pie lids, can have their appearance and presentation enhanced by having them marked or scored before baking. This is done to pastry to enhance the appearance of the finished dish. Shortbread is another example.
- **Weighing and measuring** – When baking, it is essential to weigh and measure ingredients in order to produce well-balanced, high-quality products. Mixed items, such as pastry and bread, will result in faults if they are not weighed and measured accurately.
- **Kneading** – When making doughs, it is a requirement that the dough is kneaded to form a smooth dough and also to develop the gluten. This will allow the yeast to ferment and the dough to prove, developing carbon dioxide and flavour.
- **Mixing** – This ensures the correct finished texture of the dish, providing an even balance of ingredients before cooking.
- **Aerating** – This is done to create light textures; products are aerated through whisking (for example, when using eggs and sugar); chemical aeration is provided with the addition of baking powder (for example, when baking scones); fermentation produces gas for aeration (this is used for dough).
- **Portioning** – Certain dough products require portioning either before or after baking. For example, bread rolls will be divided into the required size from a batch of dough before baking and biscuits will be cut into the required shape. Other items may be divided after baking, such as rounds of shortbread or a batch of traditionally baked Chelsea buns.
- **Proving** – Proving is the period of time given to doughs and dough products to allow them to rise. During the proving process, yeast ferments, producing carbon dioxide and stretching the gluten in doughs to expand. This results in the soft, airy texture within breads, rolls and buns.
- **Resting** – This applies to products that are produced from flour. To 'relax' the gluten in certain products that require a short, snappy or crumbly texture, it is necessary to rest the product before processing further and baking. Failure to do this can result in products springing back during processing, and shrinkage when baked. Such products bake better after relaxing (for example, scones and biscuits) and resting helps maintain their shape.
- **Rolling** – Rolling applies to many pastry products, biscuits and some breads. Biscuits and pastries usually require rolling using a rolling pin to get an even, fairly thin base or height, whereas breads and bread rolls are usually rolled by hand.
- **Shaping** – This applies to the various shapes that can be given to doughs and pastry products. Breads can be shaped into knots and plaits, and pastry products into rounds – for tartlets, for example, or crescents for products such as a turnovers. Pastry is often rolled out to line or cover a dish.
- **Cooling** – To prevent baked items going soggy they are placed on cooling racks to stabilise.
- **Finishing** – Finishes include glazing, dusting with sugar, or even splitting and filling with cream.

Quality checks when preparing to bake food items

To ensure the quality of products, there are a number of things that help a chef during preparation.

- **Ingredients cut and prepared to specification** – Regardless of the product, it is important to ensure that ingredients are cut and prepared to the specifications. This will help to achieve the high-quality product that is being aspired to.
- **Minimal waste** – As with all preparation and cooking, minimising waste is an essential part of a chef's role. Not only is it a waste of resources to dispose of usable food, it is unethical and a waste of money. A commercial food-based operation should aim to utilise as much food product as possible to increase sales potential and minimise expenditure.

Lining a flan, pressing the edges

1.3 Applying techniques to produce baked goods

Techniques to produce baked products

- **Humidity control** – Certain foods, such as crusty bread, benefit from being baked with increased humidity. Specialist baking ovens have the facility to inject steam directly into the oven (there will be a control on the oven to do this). To achieve this in a conventional oven, a bowl of water can be placed at the base of the oven to increase the humidity of the air (the moisture in it), which in turn increases the water content of the food, keeping it moist and pleasant to eat.

- **Oven positioning** – The control of temperature and the placement of products in the oven are essential when baking. The size and type of product will determine the temperature that is required to bake it to the desired degree. Oven positioning also needs consideration as higher shelves will be hotter than lower ones in general-purpose ovens. When baking items such as biscuits or breads in conventional ovens, the higher in the oven the items are placed, the quicker they will cook/brown, even though the oven temperature is set by the thermostat. Therefore, it is important to keep a close eye on the development of products during the baking process. If moving products to different areas of the oven to compensate, do this quickly and gently to avoid rapid drops in temperature or damage to light products through heavy contact with surfaces. In combination and convection ovens, the temperature is more evenly regulated in all parts of the oven, so you should be able to place the shelves anywhere without worrying about this issue. Specialist deck ovens are used by many professional bakers in industry. These ovens provide very accurate temperatures and have additional control of base heat (from below) and top heat (from above) as well as steam injection.
- **Temperature control** – Temperature control is essential. Always preheat ovens to the required temperature before putting food items in them, otherwise the product will be spoiled. Make sure the oven reaches the required temperature before each additional batch of goods is placed in it.

Techniques to produce different types of baked products

- **Traditional baking** – This is done in a dry oven. The water that is naturally found in food turns to steam when it is heated. This steam combines with the dry heat of the oven to cook the food. This method is perfect for cakes, pastries and baked jacket potatoes.
- **Baking with modified heat** – Foods such as baked egg custard require the heat in the oven to be modified (reduced). To do this, place the food in a bain-marie (a tray of water). This makes the food cook more slowly and means that it does not overheat. In the case of egg custard, it also means that the egg mixture is less likely to overcook.
- **Timing** – The time required will vary according to the type and quality of foods to be baked. As a guide, loaves of bread will need longer than bread rolls.
- **Other considerations** – Be accurate in your weighing and measuring, and prepare trays and moulds correctly. Keep baking trays level in the oven so that the product bakes evenly. Do not overload trays.

HEALTH AND SAFETY

Use thick, dry oven cloths when removing trays from the oven.

- **Avoid opening oven doors** whenever possible. Draughts may affect the quality of the product, and the oven temperature will drop. Opening the oven door too quickly may also adversely affect the presentation of products such as Yorkshire puddings and soufflés.

HEALTH AND SAFETY

Do not open oven doors too quickly as there is likely to be a lot of steam, which may scald your face.

- **Use oven space effectively**.
- **Avoid jarring products** (particularly fruit cakes, sponges and soufflés) before and during baking as the quality may be affected.

Quality checks during the baking process

- **Appearance and degree of cooking** – The appearance of food items during the baking process provides a visual guide as to how they are developing. Items that are cooking too quickly will appear to be cooked on the surface but will not be in the centre.
- When baking, **particular care must be taken with certain products**. For example, it is important that breads, cakes, sponges and products made from choux pastry are baked at a stable temperature. Therefore, it is important to try to keep oven doors closed during the baking process to prevent the products from being damaged and losing aeration (preventing the required rise).
- **Temperature** – To maximise the quality of finished products, it is essential that the temperature is accurate throughout the cooking process. Starting to bake a product from an ambient temperature with equipment that has not been preheated is likely to result in a product that is dry and unpleasant to eat. Controlling temperature, linked to timing and product positioning, are key aspects in all three of the cookery processes described in this chapter.
- **Texture** – With some foods, it is possible to check quality by testing texture. For example, baked products such as cakes and breads will become 'spongy' and 'bounce back' once pressed.

1.4 Applying finishing methods for baked products

Finishing methods for baked products include those described below.

- **Decorating and garnishing** – Some baked products benefit from further decoration and garnishing. For example, a slice of apple tart could be enhanced with a swirl of piped cream and some seasonal berries.
- **Dredging and dusting** – A light dredging or dusting of icing sugar helps to enhance the appearance of sweet baked products. Similarly, flour can be dredged on to bread products for the same effect.
- **Glazing** – A glaze will help to provide a sheen or shine to baked products. This could be through the application of a fruit based glaze, such as apricot for a fruit flan, or by glazing a bun product with a fondant or sugar syrup.
- **Portioning** – Many baked products are portioned after baking. For example, a baked tart needs to be sliced into portions before serving. It is important to have clean, sharp knives and serving utensils when portioning baked items. This will help to enhance their appearance when presenting them for service. It is also important to portion items accurately to ensure the correct number of portions is achieved and that the portions are of equal size.
- **Saucing** – Baked items may be enhanced by serving with an accompanying sauce. This applies to both sweet and savoury dishes. For example, a fruit crumble is traditionally served with custard, whereas a baked meat pie is often served with a gravy or jus.

Quality checks when finishing baked products

When finishing dishes, it is important to consider the following points.

- **Appearance** – Dishes should have a fresh and appealing appearance. From the sheen on a sauce to the golden-brown appearance of freshly baked pastries, these are all signs of well-produced items.
- **Aroma** – Dishes should retain a fresh, natural and pleasing aroma that will entice the consumer/customer to the dishes being served. For example, freshly baked bread has a natural aroma that helps to whet the appetite of people who enjoy eating such food.
- **Colour** – Colours should be natural and vibrant, in the case of vegetables, for example. Incorrect cooking of foods, both under- and overcooking, often results in undesired colour.
- **Consistency** – When finishing the final dish ensure consistency of appearance and portion size; add any seasoning and garnish if required.
- **Portion control** – As well as portions being consistent in size and appearance, it is important that they are also of the predetermined size. If portions are smaller than advertised to customers or inadequate for the type of dish being served, it is likely that customers will complain. If the portion size is too big, it is likely that wastage will increase as customers may not be able to eat such large portions and the business will lose money as it will not be able to achieve the number of portions planned for the commodities in question.
- **Presentation** – Chefs have the opportunity to present foods in creative and attractive ways to increase the number of customers. Most importantly, presentation should be neat, consistent and precise. Service equipment, including plates, should be spotlessly clean.
- **Seasoning** – Correcting the seasoning of foods makes a huge difference to the overall eating quality. Although salt consumption should be monitored carefully to promote healthy eating, a little salt and pepper can lift foods to a new level and bring natural flavours to life.
- **Taste** – Ultimately, it is the taste of foods that provides the most pleasure to diners. Linked with texture, it is the experience of eating and the enjoyment of the tastes and flavours that make eating such an enjoyable experience when food is prepared and cooked well.
- **Temperature** – Ensure food is served at the correct temperature. The temperature of food adds to the pleasure of eating and customers will quickly complain if hot food is served below its appropriate temperature. Service temperature can also affect flavour, texture, taste and general enjoyment of dishes.
- **Texture** – Texture provides contrast across foods and dishes. From the crunch of a freshly baked biscuit to the velvety texture of a fruit mousse, these are all dining experiences that bring pleasure to customers when consuming foods. It is therefore very important to achieve the desired textures in foods when preparing and cooking.

2 Produce roasted products

Roasting is cooking in dry heat, in an oven or on a spit, with the aid of fat or oil. The initial heat of the oven seals the food. This prevents too many of the natural juices from escaping. Once the food is lightly browned, the oven temperature (or the temperature of the heat source when spit roasting) should be reduced to cook the inside of the food without hardening or charring the surface.

The purpose of roasting is to:

- create a distinctive taste
- create food that is tender, easy to digest and palatable to the customer
- enhance the flavour and colour of the food, adding to the presentation
- make the food safe to eat.

Roasting

2.1 Selecting food items for roasting

The range of foods that can be roasted includes:

- meats such as beef, pork and lamb
- poultry, including chicken and turkey
- vegetables, such as potatoes, peppers and onions.

Quality checks when selecting food items

As for baking, you need to look at the appearance, freshness, texture, type of items, and size and shape. For example, a bread roll will bake faster than a loaf. The size and shape of a potato will also have an impact on the baking or roasting time required.

2.2 Applying preparation methods for roasting

There are two main methods of roasting food.

1. **Roasting on a spit** – Place prepared meat or poultry on a rotating spit, over or in front of fierce radiated heat.
2. **Roasting in an oven** – Place whole joints and large pieces of meat and fish on a trivet (see page 51). This will prevent the base of the product burning or overcooking. A trivet can consist of chopped vegetables (but larger than mirepoix), or can be made up from the bones or skeleton of the product you are roasting.

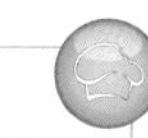

PROFESSIONAL TIP

With spit roasting, you can see exactly how the cooking is progressing and you have easy access to the food.

HEALTH AND SAFETY

- Take care when removing a joint of meat from the oven. It may have released a lot of fat that could cause burns or scalds. Always use thick, dry oven cloths.
- When roasting in an oven there is minimal fire risk because a thermostat is used to control the temperature, so there is no risk of overheating.

Preparation methods for roasting

- **Barding** – Some lean meats and poultry will benefit from extra fat during the roasting process to keep the meats moist and also to assist in the development of flavour. To do this, a layer of fat is placed on the surface of the meat or poultry which will render slowly as the item is roasted.
- **Cutting** – Many foods will have to be prepared before roasting. This could include the trimming of meats or butchering meats into joints suitable for roasting. It could also refer to the preparation of vegetables so that they are ready for roasting.
- **Searing** – This refers to the initial technique used in which the surface of the food (usually meat, poultry or fish) is cooked at high temperature until the surface of the food begins to caramelise. This is normally accomplished by shallow frying but can also be achieved when grilling, roasting and baking at high temperatures. The technique

is commonly used to sear all sides of a particular piece of meat, fish, poultry, etc. before roasting in the oven. To obtain the desired effect, the surface must exceed 150°C, so searing requires the surface of the food to be free of water, which boils at 100°C. This technique remains an essential aspect of cooking meat for several reasons.

  - The browning creates desirable aromas and flavours through caramelisation and the Maillard reaction (a chemical reaction when heating natural sugars and amino acids/proteins present in foods).
  - The appearance of the food is usually improved with a seared surface.
  - The contrast in taste and texture between the surface and the interior makes the food more enjoyable to eat.
  - Typically in grilling, the food will be seared over very high heat and then moved to a lower-temperature area of the grill to finish cooking.
  - In braising, the searing adds flavour and colour, and will enrich the liquid in which the food is being cooked.

- **Seasoning** – Foods such as meats, poultry and fish are usually seasoned with salt and pepper before they are roasted. The seasoning helps to enhance, draw out and develop flavours in foods as they are roasted.
- **Stuffing** – Typically a meat, vegetable, cereal or grain-based mix is placed into the cavity or rolled into the meat or poultry to add an additional dimension to the dish, as well as flavour and texture to the finished dish when it is roasted.
- **Trussing and tying** – Using string or skewers to hold poultry or joints in shape and ensure an even cooking helps to keep joints moist.
- **Preparing a trivet** – A trivet is a rack or base of vegetables that keeps the meat from having direct contact with the tray when roasting.

Quality checks when preparing to roast food items

When roasting foods, it is important that ingredients are cut and prepared to specification. This will add to the overall quality, appearance and presentation of roasted items. For example, when roasting potatoes, it is important that the potatoes are of an even size and shape. This will help to ensure even cooking and crispness to the external area of the potato. It will also provide more even and precise presentation. Accurate and precise knife skills used throughout cutting and trimming will also help to minimise food wastage and achieve gross profit targets. For example, if you have a gross profit target of 70 per cent to achieve, this becomes increasingly difficult as food is wasted through inaccurate and/or poor cutting and trimming. For example, if after trimming and cutting, only 80 per cent of pepper is usable for a roasted pepper accompaniment, after preparing five peppers, the equivalent of a whole extra pepper is wasted. This is where gross profit margins are stretched and become challenging to meet.

2.3 Applying techniques to produce roasted products

Techniques to produce different types of roasted products

- **Basting** – Spooning the fat and cooking juices over the food during cooking helps keep the food moist, and enhances the colour and appearance of the finished dish.
- **Positioning within the oven** – Adjust the shelf position according to the instructions given in the recipe. In general-purpose ovens, the top part of the oven is generally the hottest; in combination and convection ovens, the temperature is evenly distributed using fans and vents to provide a regulated temperature throughout the oven. The cooking time will be affected by the shape, size, type, bone proportion and quality of the food you are cooking. Meat thermometers or probes can be inserted to determine the exact temperature in the centre of the joint (the core temperature).
- **Temperature control** – Always preheat ovens to the required cooking temperature. Follow the oven temperature given in the recipe.
- **Turning** – To get an even caramelisation and distribution of heat through roasted products, it is important to turn them carefully during the roasting process. This applies to all roasted foods, including meats and poultry, as well as other foods such as vegetables and potatoes.

HEALTH AND SAFETY

When basting the product, try to avoid splashing hot fat on yourself, as this could cause burns.

Quality checks during the roasting process, and their importance

As with baking, it is important to consider the following three things during the roasting process:

1. appearance and degree of cooking
2. temperature
3. texture.

2.4 Applying finishing methods for roasted products

Meat carving tips

Joints should be allowed to rest for at least 15 minutes beforehand, as this will allow the joint to 'set' and relax making it easier to carve.

To carve meat properly, a good, well-balanced and properly sharpened carving knife is essential. It should not be serrated, as this encourages a sawing action and gives an unattractive appearance to the meat slices.

- **Bone-in-joints** – Hold the joint at the end of the bone. Carve the meat away from the bone, into approximately $\frac{1}{2}$ to 1 cm-thick slices.

- **Boneless joints** (for example, short saddle of lamb) – Hold the joint in place with a carving fork or tongs. Carve the meat across the grain into slices approximately ½ cm thick.

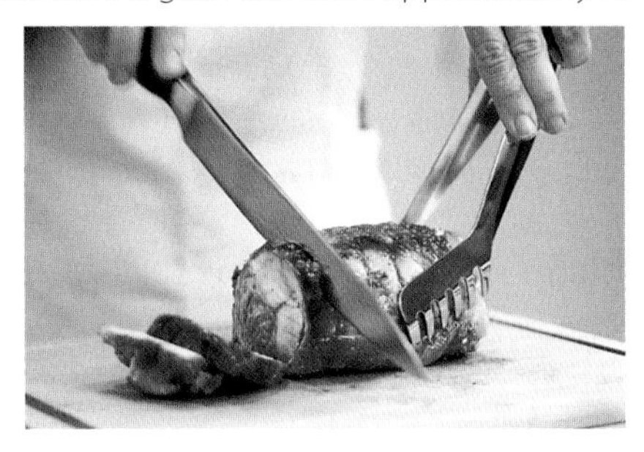

- **Racks and rib roasts** – Hold the meat with the bones facing upward, using a towel or kitchen paper for a firmer grip if necessary. Carve down between the bones into even-sized cutlets, or remove the bones completely by cutting along the bones through the meat; this will enable you to carve the roast into thin slices.

Source: Meat carving and images and text courtesy of Donald Russell: www.donaldrussell.com

Finishing methods for roasted products

- **Garnishing** – Roasted products can be enhanced with herbs or watercress.
- **Portioning** – Many roasted products are portioned after cooking. For example, roasted poultry, such as chicken, will be roasted whole and then carved or portioned for service.
- **Resting** – As meat is roasted the proteins in it heat up and set. The more cooked the meat, the more 'set' the proteins have become. This is why we can test or judge meat's degree of cooking (rare, medium, well done) by touching or prodding: the firmer the meat, the more 'done' it is. When the proteins set they push the meat's juices towards the centre of the meat. Allowing the meat to stand away from the heat before serving allows the juices, which have been driven to the centre of the meat to redistribute throughout the meat and be reabsorbed. As a result the meat will lose less juice when you cut it and be far more tender and juicy to eat.
- **Saucing** – Roast gravy is made by **deglazing** the roasting pan. Sauces that enhance the dish and are considered to aid digestion, including apple with pork, mint with lamb, horseradish with beef and bread sauce with poultry.

Quality checks when finishing roast products

To ensure the quality of finished dishes there are a number of things that the chef can do during the process. As with baking, it is important to consider the following points:

- appearance
- aroma
- colour
- consistency
- portion control
- presentation
- seasoning
- taste
- temperature
- texture.

3 Produce grilled products

This is a fast method of cooking using radiant heat. The heat source transfers heat directly towards the food being grilled.

Grilling creates a distinctive taste and provides interesting variety to the menu; the smell of grilling foods can whet the appetite and some restaurants have grill areas that are open to view so the aroma travels through to diners as they wait. Other purposes of grilling are to:

- create food that is tender, easier to digest and palatable for the customer
- char foods, adding colour and giving food a distinctive appearance, which adds to the presentation
- improve the flavour of the food
- make food safe to eat
- maintain the nutritional value of the food; grilling is often considered to be the best cooking method for reducing fat and retaining nutrients because the food is cooked so quickly.

3.1 Selecting food items for grilling

The range of foods that can be grilled include:

- fish
- meat (beef, pork and lamb)
- poultry (chicken and turkey)
- vegetables
- pre-prepared products.

When grilling meat, the fierce heat seals the surface of the meat, helping to keep the juices in the meat as long as it is not pierced by a fork while cooking. Grilling is suitable only for certain cuts of best-quality meat – inferior meat cooked this way will be tough and unpleasant to eat.

PROFESSIONAL TIP

When grilling you have good control of the cooking process because the food is visible and accessible while it is being grilled.

Quality checks when selecting food items

As for baking and roasting, you need to look at the appearance, freshness, texture and type of items, and their size and shape.

For example, the size and shape of a sirloin steak, as well as its lean composition, make it a suitable product for grilling, whereas a whole sirloin would be unsuitable as it would be too big to grill and therefore more suited to roasting; the texture and composition of a chicken breast, for example, makes it a suitable product for grilling, whereas a steak cut from the thick flank of beef would need considerably more cooking time to break down the connective tissue and collagen within the meat, therefore making it more suited to braising.

3.2 Applying preparation methods for grilling

Preparation methods for grilling

- **Batting out** – Cuts of meat are batted with a meat hammer to give an even thickness and start breaking down the connective tissue to help cooking and increase tenderness.
- **Cutting** – Many foods will have to be prepared before grilling. This could include the preparation of meats into steaks or cutlets, or filleting fish. It could also refer to the preparation of vegetables such as beef tomatoes or field mushrooms so that they are ready for grilling.
- **Marinating** – Items are pre-soaked or coated in a marinade to help flavour, tenderise and in some cases colour food before the cooking process starts.
- **Oiling, greasing and basting** – These techniques prevent items from sticking to the bars of the grill; food items are often oiled or greased lightly prior to cooking, with additional basting during cooking to ensure that items do not dry out.
- **Seasoning** – Foods such as meats, poultry and fish are usually seasoned with salt and pepper before they are grilled. The seasoning helps to enhance, draw out and develop flavours in foods when they are grilled.
- **Traying up** – Items are placed on to trays prior to placing under a salamander; trays are normally lightly greased, allowing space for items to be turned to ensure even cooking.

Quality checks when preparing to grill food items

Cutting to specification ensures that portion sizes are accurate, helping to generate and maintain customer satisfaction. Accurate preparation of food also helps to reduce waste by avoiding poor cutting, often leaving parts of perfectly usable, edible food to go to waste. Ensuring the maximum use of food will reduce food orders as less food will be required, therefore reducing expenditure and making it easier to achieve gross profit targets.

3.3 Applying techniques to produce grilled products

- **Positioning** – The positioning of the shelf or grill above or below the heat will influence the amount of time the item takes to cook and how quickly it will take to sear (brown/colour).
- **Temperature control** – A combination of the temperature and the amount of time food is grilled for should be determined by the texture of the food item itself and, in the case of steaks, the degree of cooking required. It is important to note that rare and medium steaks require less time to grill than those that are to be well done. Other factors to consider include:
  - do not grill foods for too long; cooking the food slowly will dry it out
  - smaller, thinner items should be cooked very quickly
  - sear and colour food on the hot part of the grill, then move to a cooler part to complete cooking
  - basting of food and oiling of bars will help to prevent the food from drying out and sticking to the grill.
- **Turning** – To get an even caramelisation and distribution of heat through grilled products, it is important to turn them carefully during the grilling process. This applies to all grilled foods, including meats, poultry and fish, as well as other foods such as vegetables. It is recommended that grilled foods, particularly fish as it is very delicate, are turned only once during the grilling process.

Grilling

Techniques to produce different types of grilled products

Method

Grilled foods can be cooked over heat (charcoal, barbecues, gas or electric heated grills/griddles), under heat (gas or electric salamanders, over-heated grills) or between heat (electrically heated grill bars or plates).

- **Grilling over heat** – Preheat grill bars and brush with oil prior to use, otherwise food will stick to them. The bars should char the food on both sides to give the distinctive appearance and flavour of grilling. When using solid fuel, allow the flames and smoke to die down before placing food on the bars, otherwise the food will be tainted and spoiled. You can marinate certain foods (such as skewered kebabs and chicken) before cooking. You should brush other foods (such as pork spare ribs) liberally with a barbecue sauce on both sides before and during cooking.
- **Grilling under heat/salamander** – Preheat salamanders and grease the bars. Steaks, chops and items that are likely to slip between the grill bars of an under-heated grill may be cooked under a salamander.
- **Grilling between heat** – This is grilling between electrically heated grill bars or plates, and is used for small cuts of meat.

HEALTH AND SAFETY

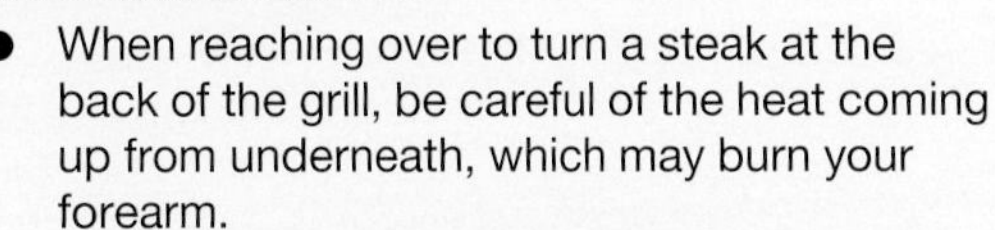

- When reaching over to turn a steak at the back of the grill, be careful of the heat coming up from underneath, which may burn your forearm.
- If meat or fish has been marinated in an oil marinade, ensure that it is well drained before you place it on the grill. Food with too much oil on it may be a fire hazard if it is moved directly from the marinating container to the grill.

Equipment used for baking, roasting and grilling

A number of pieces of equipment that are used for baking, roasting and grilling:

- **ovens** – general purpose, convection and combination
- **grills** – under-fired or traditional grills, salamander, infrared and contact grills
- **small equipment** – tongs, probes, slices, palette knives and skewers.

More information on these types of equipment is provided in Unit 203.

HEALTH AND SAFETY

Always use the correct equipment to turn and lift food on the grill: use tongs to turn and lift cutlets and steaks; use fish slices to turn and lift tomatoes, mushrooms and whole or cut fish.

Quality checks during the grilling process

As with baking and roasting, it is important to consider these three things during the roasting process:

1. appearance and degree of cooking
2. temperature
3. texture.

3.4 Applying finishing methods for grilled products

To finish grilled products, one of the following methods could be used.

- **Garnishing** – Some grilled products benefit from further garnishing. For example, a mixed grill could be garnished with straw potatoes, a grilled tomato and mushroom.
- **Saucing** – Many grilled foods will benefit from and be complemented by an accompanying sauce – for example, a grilled pork cutlet with a red wine sauce or a fillet steak with a peppercorn sauce.

Quality checks when finishing grilled products

To ensure the quality of finished dishes there are a number of things that the chef can do during the process. As with baking and roasting, it is important to consider the following points:

- appearance
- aroma
- colour
- consistency
- portion control
- presentation
- seasoning
- taste
- temperature
- texture.

TEST YOURSELF

1. Briefly describe the process for each of the following methods of cooking:
   a. baking
   b. roasting
   c. grilling.
2. List three ways in which heat is applied to food by grilling.
3. List three types of oven that could be used in a kitchen for baking or roasting foods.
4. List five safety points a chef should consider when baking or roasting foods.
5. What are the traditional accompaniments to the following roast meats:
   a. chicken
   b. leg of lamb
   c. sirloin of beef?
6. List four foods that can be cooked by grilling.
7. List three types of food that could be baked.
8. What are the four main degrees of grilling for a steak?
9. What is trussing?
10. What is the purpose of marinating food before grilling?

Baking recipes

1 Red onion and sweetcorn frittata

Energy	Calories	Fat	Saturated fat	Carbohydrates	Sugar	Protein	Fibre	Sodium
1009 kJ	241 kcal	14.9 g	7.2 g	12.0 g	7.1 g	15.0 g	2.1 g	271.0 g*

* Using semi-skimmed milk

Ingredient	4 portions	10 portions
Oil for frying	5 ml	15 ml
Red onions	½ (or 1 if small)	1
Carrots	50 g	125 g
Ground paprika	½ tsp	¼ tsp
Fresh, ripe tomatoes	2	5
Sweetcorn	20 g	50 g
Potatoes	100 g	250 g
Parsley	1 tsp	2½ tsp
Eggs	3	7–8
Milk	250 ml	625 ml
Black pepper, for seasoning		
Cheddar cheese	100 g	250 g

Mise en place

1. Finely chop the onion and carrot.
2. Peel the tomatoes, then deseed and finely dice them.
3. Peel the potatoes and dice them (cut into 1 cm cubes).
4. Cook the diced potatoes in boiling water. Drain well.
5. Grate the cheese and chop the parsley.

Cooking

1. Shallow fry the onions and carrots in the oil without colouring.
2. Sprinkle with paprika and drain off any excess oil.
3. Add the diced tomatoes, sweetcorn, potatoes and chopped parsley to the pan and combine all the ingredients.
4. Place the mixture into a suitable ovenproof dish.
5. Whisk the eggs and milk together and season with black pepper.
6. Pour the eggs and milk over the vegetables in the ovenproof dish.
7. Sprinkle with Cheddar cheese.
8. Bake in the oven at 180°C for approximately 15 minutes or until the mixture has set.
9. Allow to rest slightly before cutting into portions and serving.

SERVING SUGGESTION
Serve hot, or cold with salad.

2 Baked cod with a cheese and herb crust

Energy	Calories	Fat	Saturated fat	Carbohydrates	Sugar	Protein	Fibre	*
1882 kJ	452 kcal	30.8 g	18.7 g	12.7 g	0.8 g	31.7 g	0.4 g	

* Using mustard powder (1 tsp) for herb mustard

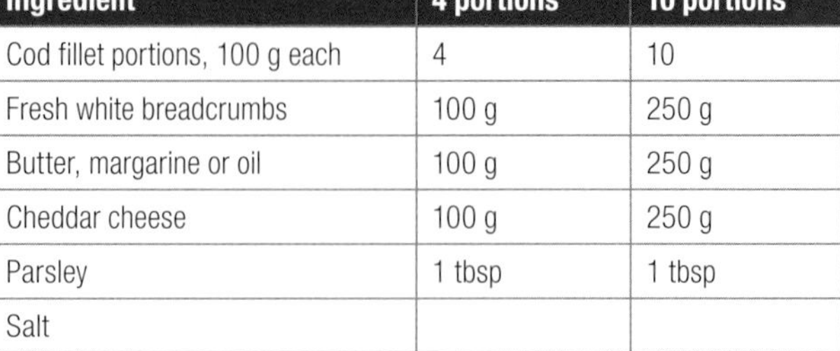

Ingredient	4 portions	10 portions
Cod fillet portions, 100 g each	4	10
Fresh white breadcrumbs	100 g	250 g
Butter, margarine or oil	100 g	250 g
Cheddar cheese	100 g	250 g
Parsley	1 tbsp	1 tbsp
Salt		
Herb mustard	1 heaped tsp	2 heaped tsp

SERVING SUGGESTION

Serve with quarters of lemon (pips removed), or a suitable sauce such as tomato or egg.

Mise en place

1 Prepare, skin, clean, wash and thoroughly dry the fish.

2 Grate the cheese and chop the parsley.

Cooking

1 Place the fillets on a greased tray or ovenproof dish.

2 Combine all the other ingredients thoroughly. Season lightly with salt.

3 Press an even layer of the mixture on to the fish.

4 Bake in an oven at 180°C for approximately 15–20 minutes until cooked and the crust is a light golden brown.

VARIATION

- Add a good squeeze of lemon juice before cooking.
- Add 2 tbsp/5 tbsp milk before cooking.
- Brush with beaten egg before adding the topping.
- Cover with slices of peeled tomato before cooking.
- Add chopped fresh herbs, such as chives, dill, fennel, or a touch of spice, such as garam masala.

ON A BUDGET

Other firm-fleshed fish can be used to produce this dish. As well as white fish, such as haddock or hake, this recipe would also work well with an oily fish such as salmon. Always consider fish that is in plentiful supply and offers good value for money.

ACTIVITY

In groups, prepare, cook, taste and assess four variations of your choice.

3 Short pastry

Energy	Calories	Fat	Saturated fat	Carbohydrates	Sugar	Protein	Fibre	Sodium
7152 kJ	1708 kcal	95.0 g	32.3 g	185.0 g	2.4 g	0.0 g	10.0 g	1,273.00

* Using margarine

Ingredient	5–8 portions	10–16 portions
Flour, soft	200 g	500 g
Salt	Pinch	Large pinch
Lard or vegetable fat	50 g	125 g
Butter or margarine	50 g	125 g
Water	2–3 tbsp	5–8 tbsp

Mise en place

1 Ensure that your hands are well scrubbed, rinsed under cold water and dried.

2 Cut the fat into small pieces.

Preparing the dish

1 Sieve the flour and salt into a bowl or on to a cool surface.

2 Using your fingertips, lightly rub in the fat to the flour until it is a sandy texture.

3 Make a well in the centre of the mixture.

4 Add enough water to make a fairly firm paste. Mix it together, handling it as little and as lightly as possible.

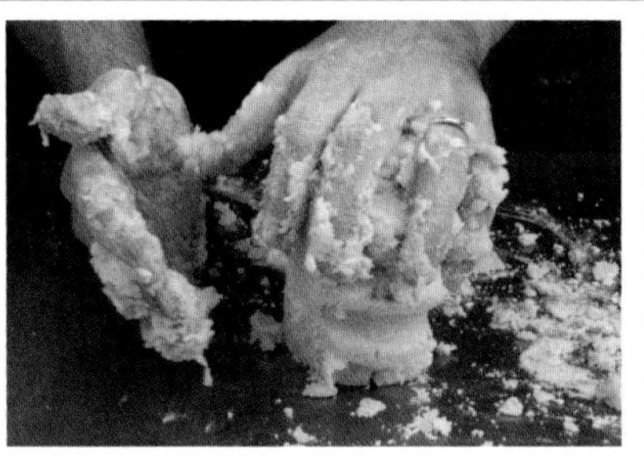

5 Keep working it gently with your hands until it has formed a dough.

6 Allow the pastry to rest, covered with a damp teacloth, in a cool place (refrigerator) before using. This allows the pastry to relax, which means there is less chance of it shrinking when it is rolled out.

4 Sweet pastry

Energy	Calories	Fat	Saturated fat	Carbohydrates	Sugar	Protein	Fibre	Sodium
7515 kJ	1794 kcal	99.0 g	33.4 g	198.0 g	52.0 g	51.0 g	8.0 g	1,352.0 g

* Using margarine

Ingredient	4 portions	10 portions
Butter or margarine	125 g	300 g
Sugar, caster	50 g	125 g
Egg, medium sized	1	2–3
Flour, soft	200 g	500 g
Salt	Pinch	Large pinch

Sweet pastry can be used for flans, tartlets and tarts.

Preparing the dish

1 Cream the fat and sugar together until the fat is completely combined.

2 Beat in the egg. Mix well.

3 Add the flour gradually, then bring the mixture together lightly to form a smooth dough.

4 Allow to rest in the refrigerator covered with clingfilm or a damp cloth.

Troubleshooting when making short or sweet pastry

If your pastry is too soft and crumbly, you may have:

- added too little water
- added too much fat.

If your pastry is blistered, you may have:

- added too little water
- added the water unevenly
- rubbed in the fat unevenly.

If your pastry is soggy, you may have:

- added too much water
- had the oven too cool
- not baked it for long enough.

If your pastry is shrunken, you may have:

- handled and rolled it too much
- stretched it while handling it.

5 Fruit tartlets

Energy	Calories	Fat	Saturated fat	Carbohydrates	Sugar	Protein	Fibre	Sodium
584 kJ	139 kcal	6.1 g	2.2 g	18.6 g	9.7 g	2.6 g	1.4 g	71.0 g

* Using strawberries

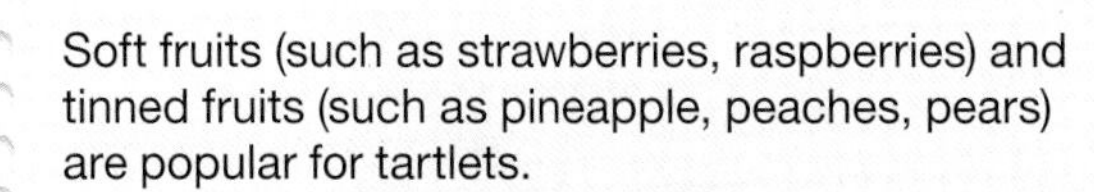

Soft fruits (such as strawberries, raspberries) and tinned fruits (such as pineapple, peaches, pears) are popular for tartlets.

The pastry cases are cooked 'blind', which means that they are cooked before the filling is added.

Ingredient	4 portions	10 portions
Sweet pastry	100 g	250 g
Pastry cream	4 tbsp	10 tbsp
Fruit, fresh or tinned	100 g	250 g
Arrowroot for glaze (optional)		

Mise en place

1. Prepare the sweet pastry as per recipe 4 (see page 156).
2. Prepare the pastry cream (see page 109), or prepare custard.
3. Prepare the fruit if it is fresh. Strawberries should be well washed, completely dried and, depending on size, either kept whole or cut into slices.
4. Preheat the oven to 200°C–220°C.

Cooking

1 Roll out sweet pastry 3 mm thick.

2 Using a fluted (wavy) cutter, cut out rounds.

3 Place the pastry rounds in lightly greased tartlet moulds.

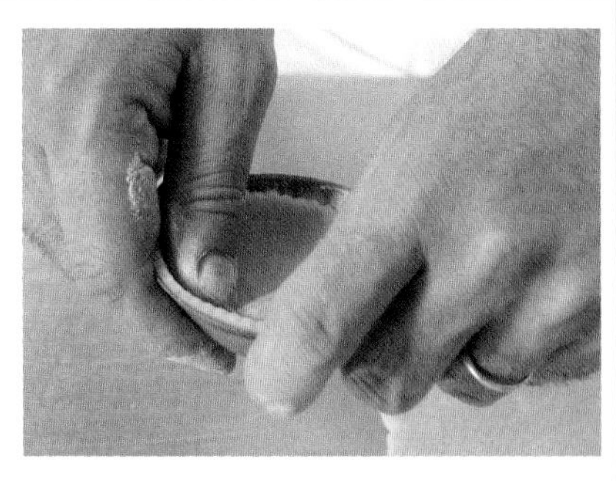

4 Neaten them carefully to shape, using a light coating of flour on the fingers only if necessary.

5 Prick the bottoms gently with a fork in 2–3 places.

6 Cut rounds of greaseproof paper to fit comfortably in each lined tartlet case. Place the paper on top of the pastry and fill the centres with dried peas, beans or pieces of stale bread.

7 Place the tartlets on a baking sheet. Bake at 200°C–220°C for approximately 20 minutes until cooked and nicely browned.

8 Remove from the oven on to a cooling rack.

9 When cooled, remove the papers and beans.

10 Place a thin layer of pastry cream or thick custard in the bottom of each tartlet case.

11 Neatly arrange the fruit on top. Work methodically. In this picture, the chef has spaced out the first blueberries evenly.

12 Now fill in the gaps. The pattern of fruit is neat and regular.

13 Dilute some arrowroot in a basin with a little fruit juice (10 g arrowroot to ¼ litre of the juice). If you used tinned fruit, use the juice from the tin.

14 Boil the remainder of the juice in a small pan and gradually stir in the diluted arrowroot, stirring continuously until it re-boils. Allow the glaze to cool before use.

15 Use this glaze to thinly mask (coat or cover) the fruit in the tartlets.

VARIATION

For soft fruits, a red glaze can be made by diluting a matching jam with a little water or syrup, heating it gently until mixed, then passing it through a fine strainer.

6 Fruit pies

Energy	Calories	Fat	Saturated fat	Carbohydrates	Sugar	Protein	Fibre	Sodium
991 kJ	235 kcal	5.3 g	1.8 g	45.0 g	35.5 g	2.0 g	2.0 g	74.0 g

* Using mixed fresh fruits

Ingredient	4 portions	10 portions
Fruit	400 g	1 kg
Sugar, granulated	100 g	250 g
Water	2 tbsp	5 tbsp
Short pastry using flour weight of	100 g	250 g

Mise en place

1. Prepare and wash the fruit. Remove any stalks, leaves or stones. If using apples, peel, cut into quarters, remove the core and slice.
2. Make the short pastry and keep refrigerated until you need it.
3. Preheat the oven to 220°C.

Cooking

1. Place the fruit in a half-litre pie dish.
2. Add the sugar and water (for an apple pie, also add a clove).
3. Roll out the pastry ½ cm thick to the shape of the pie dish. Use as little dusting flour as possible on the table surface, the pastry and rolling pin. Allow the pastry to relax for a few minutes.
4. Dampen the rim of the pie dish with water or milk and press a thin strip of pastry on to it.
5. Carefully roll the pastry on to the rolling pin and then unroll it over the top of the fruit, being careful not to stretch it.
6. Seal the pastry on to the dish rim firmly and cut off any extra pastry.
7. Brush the pastry with milk and sprinkle with sugar.
8. Place the pie on a baking sheet and bake in a hot oven at 220°C for about 10 minutes.
9. Reduce the heat to 180°C and cook for a further 20–30 minutes (if the pastry colours too quickly, cover it with greaseproof paper or foil).

SERVING SUGGESTION

Serve with custard, cream or ice cream.

Fruit fillings for pies

Bramley apples are ideal. They could be combined with either blackberries, damsons or gooseberries. Rhubarb pie or cherry pie will also work well.

7 Banana loaf

Energy	Calories	Fat	Saturated fat	Carbohydrates	Sugar	Protein	Fibre	Sodium
1057 kJ	251 kcal	11.6 g	3.8 g	32.9 g	19.6 g	4.1 g	2.4 g	261.0 g

* Using margarine

Ingredient	10 portions
Soft brown sugar	125 g
Margarine, butter or vegetable oil	140 g
Eggs, beaten	2
Baking powder	12 g
Wholemeal flour	200 g
Cinnamon	1/8 tsp
Ripe bananas	2
Sultanas	50 g

Mise en place

1. Beat the egg.
2. Peel and mash the banana.

Cooking

1 Cream together the sugar and margarine, butter or vegetable oil.

2 Slowly add the beaten egg and beat well after each addition.

3 Sift the baking powder with the wholemeal flour and cinnamon.

4 Gradually add the flour mix to the sugar, margarine and egg mixture.

5 Carefully incorporate the mashed bananas and the sultanas. Gently mix well.

6 Place the mixture into a bread tin approximately 20 × 12 cm, lined with silicone paper.

7 Bake in the oven at 180°C for approximately 30 minutes.

8 Remove and allow to cool. Cut into portions.

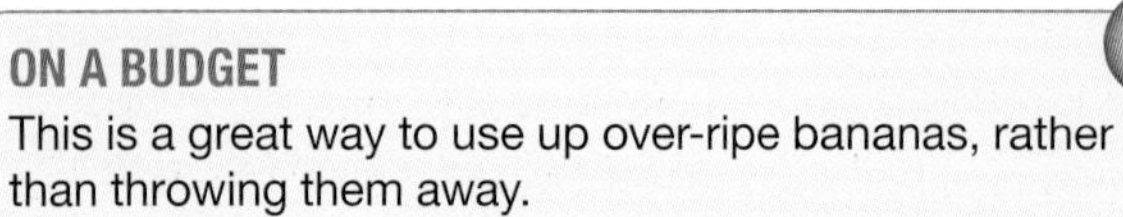

ON A BUDGET

This is a great way to use up over-ripe bananas, rather than throwing them away.

8 Fruit buns

Energy	Calories	Fat	Saturated fat	Carbohydrates	Sugar	Protein	Fibre	Sodium
930 kJ	220 kcal	5.5 g	1.8 g	39.1 g	21.1 g	4.2 g	1.1 g	58.0 g

* Using semi-skimmed milk, margarine and water for bun wash

Ingredient	8 buns	20 buns
Bun dough		
Flour, strong	200 g	500 g
Yeast	5 g	12 g
Butter or margarine	50 g	125 g
Egg, medium sized	1	2–3
Milk and water (50% of each, approx.)	60 ml	150 ml
Caster sugar	25 g	60 g
Dried fruit (e.g. currants, sultanas)	50 g	125 g
Mixed spice		
Bun wash		
Sugar	100 g	250 g
Water or milk	125 ml	300 ml

Mise en place

1 Wash the dried fruit.
2 Beat the egg.

Cooking

1 Sieve the flour into a bowl and warm.

2 Rub the yeast into the flour.

3 Rub in the fat.

4 Make a well in the centre of the flour and pour in the beaten egg.

5 Pour in the mixture of milk and water.

6 Fold together. As you work, add the sugar, dried fruit and mixed spice.

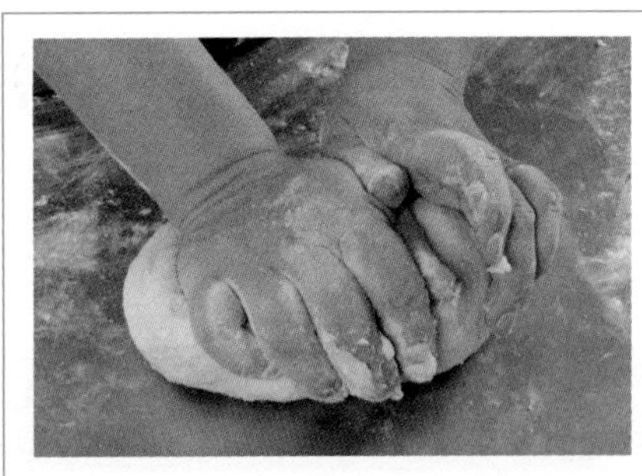

7 Knead well to form a soft, slack dough.

8 Continue kneading until smooth and not sticky.

9 Cover the bowl and allow the dough to prove. It will double in size. (The photo shows the same amount of dough before and after proving. There is no fruit in that dough.)

10 Mould the dough into balls. Place these on a lightly greased baking tray. Cover with a cloth and allow to prove again.

11 Bake in a hot oven (220°C) for 15–20 minutes.

12 Boil together the ingredients for the bun wash until it is a thick syrup.

13 Remove the buns from the oven and brush liberally with bun wash.

14 Remove on to a cooling rack.

VARIATION

To make hot cross buns:

- make fruit buns as above, but use a little more spice
- when moulded, make a cross on top of each bun with the back of a knife
- alternatively, make a slack mixture of flour and water in a greaseproof paper cornet and pipe on neat crosses.

9 Apple crumble

Energy	Calories	Fat	Saturated fat	Carbohydrates	Sugar	Protein	Fibre	Sodium
1967 kJ	464 kcal	10.1 g	3.4 g	90.0 g	63.0 g	4.0 g	4.1 g	100.0 g

* Using margarine

Ingredient	4 portions	10 portions
Crumble filling		
Bramley apples	600 g	1½ kg
Sugar, granulated or brown	100 g	250 g
Cloves	1	2
Topping		
Butter or margarine	50 g	125 g
Plain flour	150 g	400 g
Soft brown sugar	100 g	250 g

Cooking

1 Peel, core and slice the apples.

2 Cook them gently with a few drops of water, sugar and clove in a covered saucepan.

3 Place the cooked apple in a pie dish or in individual moulds. Remove the cloves.

4 Make the topping by lightly rubbing the fat into the flour. Combine this with the sugar.

5 When the fruit is cool, sprinkle on the topping and bake at 190°C for about 30 minutes, until lightly browned.

SERVING SUGGESTION

Serve with custard, cream or vanilla ice cream.

VARIATION

Try some fruit combinations, such as:

- apple and blackberry
- apple and gooseberry
- apple and rhubarb.

Try some topping variations:

- add a little spice, such as cinnamon, nutmeg, mixed spice, ground ginger
- use half flour and half porridge oats.

ON A BUDGET

A fruit crumble is a great way to utilise an abundance of fruit. Any type of apple could be used in this recipe but the amount of additional sugar will vary according to the type of apple.

10 Baked apple

Energy	Calories	Fat	Saturated fat	Carbohydrates	Sugar	Protein	Fibre	Sodium
603 kJ	142 kcal	4.6 g	2.7 g	26.0 g	25.9 g	0.5 g	2.6 g	4.0 g

* Using unsalted butter

Ingredient	4 portions	10 portions
Apples, medium-sized cooking	4	10
Sugar, white or unrefined	50 g	125 g
Cloves	4	10
Butter or margarine	20 g	50 g
Water	60 ml	150 ml

Cooking

1 Core the apples and make an incision 2 mm deep round the centre of each. Wash well. Peel the apples for a modern presentation.

2 Place in a roasting tray or ovenproof dish.

3 Fill the centre with sugar and add a clove to each.

4 Place 5 g butter on each. Add the water.

5 Bake in a moderate oven at 200–220°C for 15–20 minutes.

6 Turn the apples over carefully.

7 Return to the oven until cooked, about 40 minutes in all.

8 Serve with a little cooking liquor and custard, cream or ice cream.

VARIATION

For stuffed baked apple, proceed as for baked apples, but fill the centre with washed sultanas, raisins or chopped dates, or a combination of these.

11 Simple white loaf

Energy	Calories	Fat	Saturated fat	Carbohydrates	Sugar	Protein	Fibre	Sodium
714 kJ	168 kcal	3.4 g	1.9 g	28.3 g	1.6 g	5.4 g	1.2 g	207.0 g

* Using egg for wash, unsalted butter, semi-skimmed milk

Most bread today is leavened (made to rise) by yeast or baking powder (bread made with baking powder is called soda bread). Yeast produces carbon dioxide, which collects in small bubbles throughout the dough and causes the dough to rise.

If using fresh yeast, it is important that it is 'fresh', in good condition and in the correct proportion to the amount of flour used. Mixing and kneading must be thorough to incorporate the yeast. The second kneading should not be too heavy or too much gas will be lost.

Always use strong flour when making bread. Soft flour is unsuitable because it contains less gluten and is likely to collapse during the proving stage.

Bread made without yeast or baking powder is known as 'unleavened' bread. Unleavened bread is flat, such as pitta bread.

Ingredient	10 portions
Yeast, dried or fresh	10 g
Water, warm	125 ml
Caster sugar	2 tsp
Strong flour, plain	375 g
Salt	1 tsp
Melted butter, margarine or vegetable oil	30 g
Milk, warm	125 ml
Egg wash or milk for brushing	30 g

Cooking

1 Combine the yeast, water and sugar in a bowl and whisk until the yeast is dissolved. Cover and stand in a warm place to ferment (bubble) for about 10 minutes or until the mixture is frothy.

2 Sift the flour and salt into a mixing bowl. Add the melted butter, milk and yeast mixture.

3 Mix to form a dough, using the hook attachment on the mixer. Start on low speed for 6 minutes, then turn up to medium for 4 minutes.

4 Place the dough into a lightly floured bowl. Stand it in a warm place covered with a damp cloth and allow to prove (to rise and increase in size) until it has doubled in size.

5 It may take up to 1 hour for the dough to double in size.

6 Turn the dough out on to a floured surface and knock it back (re-knead) to its original size and until it is smooth.

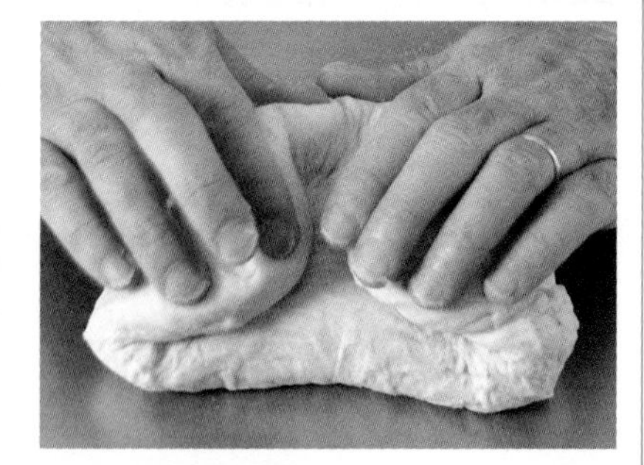

7 Roll the dough into a rectangle 18 × 35 cm. Roll this up like a Swiss roll. Place it in a greased bread tin 14 × 21 cm. Cover and stand it in a warm place for about 20 minutes until it has doubled in size.

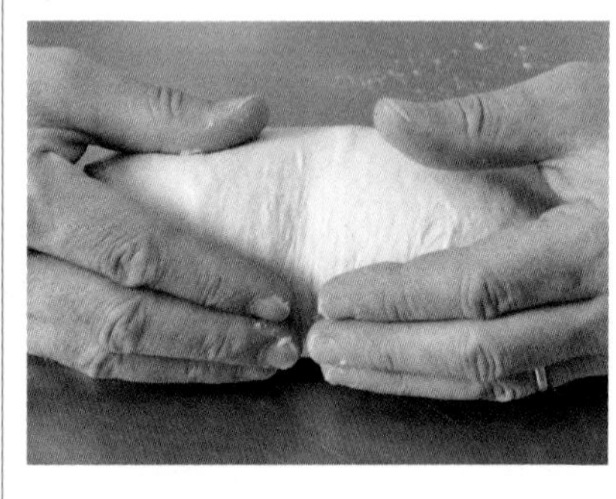

8 Brush the top of the loaf with egg wash or milk to give a rich brown colour. Place it in a preheated hot oven (180°C–200°C) for approximately 30 minutes.

9 Turn out the bread on to a wire rack.

Troubleshooting in bread making

If your bread is heavy, you may have:

- used stale yeast
- destroyed the yeast with hot liquid or hot conditions during the making process
- made or proved the dough in a place that was too cool
- not have used enough liquid
- not have proved the dough for long enough.

If your bread has an uneven texture, you may have:

- not kneaded the dough enough
- over-proved the dough
- placed the bread in an oven that was too cool for the initial cooking, allowing fermentation to proceed for too long.

If your bread is sour, you may have:

- used stale yeast
- used too much yeast
- over-risen or over-proved the dough.

Storage

Uncooked bread and dough products should be kept in the refrigerator until ready for baking. Always keep frozen bread and dough products in the deep freeze until ready for baking.

12 Bread rolls

Energy	Calories	Fat	Saturated fat	Carbohydrates	Sugar	Protein	Fibre	Sodium
633 kJ	150 kcal	3.4 g	0.5 g	26.0 g	1.2 g	5.3 g	1.4 g	0.3 g

Ingredient	8 rolls	20 rolls
Flour, strong	200 g	500 g
Liquid – ½ water, ½ milk	125 ml	300 ml
Yeast	5 g	12 g
Butter or margarine	10 g	25 g
Caster sugar	¼ tsp	½ tsp
Salt	small pinch	large pinch
Egg, beaten for egg wash	1	2

Cooking

1. Sieve the flour into a warm bowl.
2. Warm the liquid to 37°C. Use a thermopen (or similar) to test the temperature.
3. Cream the yeast in a basin with a quarter of the liquid.
4. Make a well in the flour and add the creamed yeast.
5. Sprinkle over a little of the flour, cover with a cloth and leave in a warm place until the yeast ferments (bubbles).
6. Add the remainder of the warmed liquid, the fat, sugar and salt.
7. Knead firmly until smooth and free from wrinkles.
8. Return to the basin, cover with a cloth and leave in a warm place to prove (double in size).
9. Knock back (lightly knead) the dough to remove the air and bring it back to its original size.
10. Mould the dough in a roll and cut into even pieces.
11. Mould the pieces into the shapes you want. Place them on a lightly floured baking sheet and cover with a cloth.
12. Leave in a warm place to double in size.
13. Brush gently with egg wash.
14. Bake in a hot oven at 220°C for approximately 10 minutes.
15. Remove from the oven and place the rolls on a cooling rack.

VARIATION

Gently add 50 g of sultanas and 50 g of chopped walnuts at stage 8.

13 Gluten-free bread

Energy	Calories	Fat	Saturated fat	Carbohydrates	Sugar	Protein	Fibre	Sodium
1730 kJ	412 kcal	16.9 g	5.7 g	52.0 g	3.0 g	10.6 g	6.2 g	529.0 g

* Using unsalted butter, semi-skimmed milk

Ingredient	10 portions
Gluten-free plain flour	450 g
Baking powder	2 tsp
Salt	1½ tsp
Oat bran	180 g
Sunflower seeds	160 g
Butter, margarine or vegetable oil	70 g
Egg	2
Milk	375 ml
Poppy seeds	2 tsp

Some people are allergic to gluten, a protein found in wheat. Coeliac disease is an autoimmune condition where a person has an adverse reaction to gluten. Gluten-free is an alternative to ordinary bread for coeliacs and those allergic to gluten.

Cooking

1 Sift the flour, baking powder and salt into a large bowl. Add the oat bran and stir well. Mix in the sunflower seeds.
2 Rub in the butter or margarine, or mix in the vegetable oil.
3 Beat the eggs and milk. Add this to the mixture.
4 Mix to a dough.
5 Press the dough into a greased loaf tin measuring 14 × 21 cm. Brush with milk. Sprinkle with poppy seeds.
6 Bake in a preheated oven at 160°C–180°C for approximately 1 hour.
7 When baked, allow the bread to stand in the loaf tin for 10 minutes. Turn it out on to a wire rack to cool.

14 Victoria sandwich

Energy	Calories	Fat	Saturated fat	Carbohydrates	Sugar	Protein	Fibre
6866 kJ	1635 kcal	94.3 g	39.3 g	184.7 g	106.6 g	23.3 g	3.6 g

Ingredient	2 × 18 cm cakes
Butter	250 g
Caster sugar	250 g
Soft flour	250 g
Baking powder	10 g
Eggs	5
Vanilla extract	½ tsp
Jam to fill	
Icing sugar for dusting	

This is a classic afternoon tea cake named after Queen Victoria. Although traditionally made in two halves, a slimmer version can be made by using a single sponge and splitting it.

Cooking

1. Cream the butter and sugar until soft and light.
2. Sieve the flour and baking powder twice.
3. Mix together the eggs and vanilla extract.
4. Beat the eggs gradually into the butter and sugar mixture.
5. Fold in the flour.
6. Deposit into buttered and floured cake tins and level.
7. Bake at 180°C for approximately 15–20 minutes.
8. Turn out on to a wire rack to cool.
9. Spread the bottom half with softened jam.
10. Place on the top sponge and dust with icing sugar.

1 Beat the sugar and butter together

2 Place the mixture into buttered cake tins

3 Flatten the top before baking

VARIATION

- In addition to jam the sponge can be filled with either butter icing or Chantilly cream.
- Some versions of the cake are filled with jam only and dusted with a little caster sugar not icing sugar.

15 Genoise sponge

Energy	Calories	Fat	Saturated fat	Carbohydrates	Sugar	Protein	Fibre	Sodium
5805 kJ	1380 kcal	60.0 g	31.5 g	179.0 g	106.0 g	34.6 g	4.0 g	319.0 g

* Per 'single sponge'. Using unsalted butter

Video: making a Genoise
http://bit.ly/2ppqi30

Ingredient	Single sponge	Double sponge
Eggs	4	10
Caster sugar	100 g	250 g
Flour, soft	100 g	250 g
Butter or margarine (melted), or oil	50 g	125 g

Cooking

1. Whisk the eggs and sugar with a balloon whisk in a bowl over a pan of hot water.
2. Continue until the mixture is light and creamy and has doubled in bulk.
3. Remove from the heat and whisk until cold and thick (ribbon stage). Fold in the flour very gently.
4. Take a small amount of the mixture and combine it with the melted butter. Then return this to the rest of the mixture and fold through.
5. Place in a greased, floured genoise mould.
6. Bake in a moderately hot oven, at 200–220°C, for about 30 minutes.

1 Ingredients for Genoise sponge and boiling water ready for use

2 Add the sugar to the eggs

3 Whisk them together over boiling water

4 Carry on whisking as the mixture warms up

5 When the mixture is ready, it will form ribbons and you can draw a figure eight with it

6 Fold in the flour

7 Add part of the flour mixture to the butter

8 Place the mixture into greased cake tins

9 After baking, turn the sponges out to cool on a rack

16 Fresh cream and strawberry gateau

Energy	Calories	Fat	Saturated fat	Carbohydrates	Sugar	Protein	Fibre
1975 kJ	473 kcal	28.4 g	11.1 g	560.0 g	39.7 g	4.5 g	0.9 g

Ingredient	8 portions
Genoise sponge made with vanilla	1
Stock syrup (see page 302)	100 ml
Whipping or double cream	500 ml
Icing sugar	75 g
Raspberry jam	50 ml
Strawberries, sliced	1 punnet

Cooking

1 Carefully slice the sponge cake into three equal discs. Brush each with syrup.

2 Slowly whip the cream with the icing sugar to achieve the correct consistency.

3 Place the first piece of sponge on a cake board. Soak with syrup. Spread with a layer of jam, then a layer of cream. Scatter sliced strawberries on top.

4 Place the next piece of sponge on top. Repeat the layers of syrup, cream and strawberries. Top with additional cream.

5 Place the final piece of sponge on top.

6 Coat the top and sides with cream. Chill.

7 Comb-scrape the sides of the gateau. Pipe 12 cream rosettes on top.

17 Millionaire's shortbread

Energy	Calories	Fat	Saturated fat	Carbohydrates	Sugar	Protein	Fibre	Sodium
1783 kJ	425 kcal	26.4 g	16.5 g	54.0 g	44.0 g	5.0 g	0.9 g	61.0 g

* Using unsalted butter

Ingredient	20 pieces	40 pieces
Shortbread		
Butter	175 g	345 g
Plain flour	265 g	525 g
Caster sugar	85 g	165 g
Filling		
Butter	265 g	525 g
Caster sugar	175 g	345 g
Golden syrup	4 tbsp	8 tbsp
Condensed milk	600 g	1200 g (3 tins)
Topping		
Milk chocolate	300 g	600 g
White chocolate	75 g	150 g

Cooking

1 Place butter, flour and sugar together, and bind together.

2 Press the shortbread mixture into a lined rectangular frame 40 × 20 cm (for 40 pieces) and prick the top with a fork.

3 Bake in the oven (preheated at 180°C) for 20–25 minutes until thoroughly baked and golden brown.

4 To make the filling, place the butter, sugar, golden syrup and condensed milk into a thick-bottomed saucepan and heat gently until the sugar has dissolved.

5 Bring to the boil and simmer for 6–8 minutes, stirring constantly until the mixture becomes a light sand colour.

6 Pour over the baked shortbread base and leave to set.

7 Melt the milk chocolate over a pan of warm water. Spread the melted chocolate over the caramel with a palette knife so it is all evenly distributed. Melt the white chocolate in the same way and pour into a piping bag. Pipe the white chocolate over the milk chocolate.

8 Allow to set.

9 Portion into 2 cm × 10 cm slices using a large cook's knife.

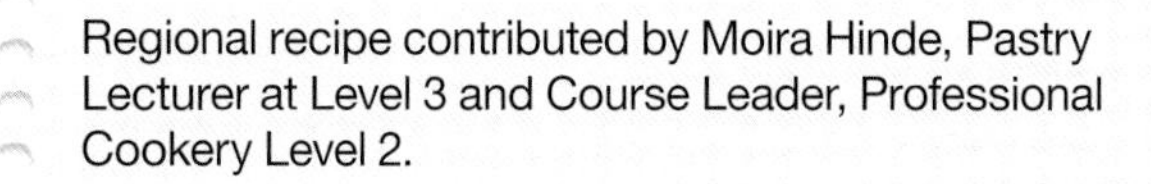

Regional recipe contributed by Moira Hinde, Pastry Lecturer at Level 3 and Course Leader, Professional Cookery Level 2.

18 Scones

Energy	Calories	Fat	Saturated fat	Carbohydrates	Sugar	Protein	Fibre
678 kJ	162 kcal	5.8 g	2.5 g	26.3 g	7.5 g	2.7 g	1.0 g

Ingredient	8 scones	20 scones
Self-raising flour	200 g	500 g
Baking powder	5 g	12 g
Salt	small pinch	large pinch
Butter or margarine	50 g	125 g
Caster sugar	50 g	125 g
Milk or water	65 ml	175 ml
Sultanas	50 g	125 g

Mise en place

Wash the sultanas. Dry them well.

Because of the small amount of fat in the dough, it is essential that you mix gently and handle the dough lightly to produce a light scone.

Cooking

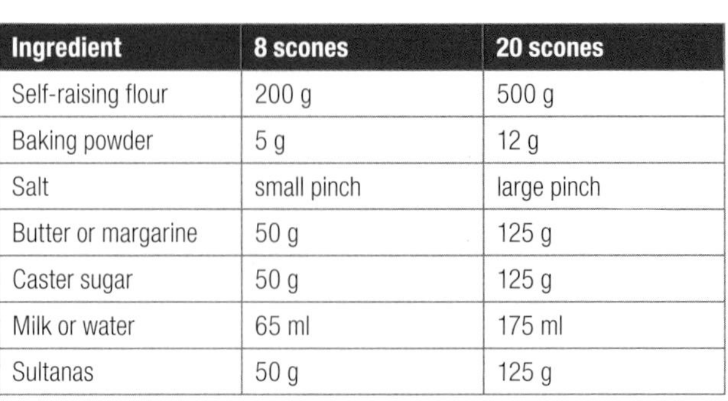

1 Sieve the flour, baking powder and salt into a basin.

2 Gently rub in the fat until the mixture has a sandy texture.

3 Dissolve the sugar in the liquid.

4 Gently and lightly mix in the flour.

5 Divide the dough into two.

6 Lightly sprinkle the work surface with flour and, using as little flour as possible, gently roll out the dough to 1 cm thick.

7 Cut out the rounds using a cutter.

8 Place the rounds on a lightly greased baking sheet.

9 Cut a cross with a sharp knife halfway through the rounds. Brush with milk and bake at 200°C for 15–20 minutes.

VARIATION

Sprinkle with icing sugar to enhance the presentation.
For wholemeal scones, use half self-raising flour and half wholemeal flour.

19 Macaroni pasta bake

Energy	Calories	Fat	Saturated fat	Carbohydrates	Sugar	Protein	Fibre	Sodium
1711 kJ	409 kcal	26.0 g	12.5 g	29.5 g	5.7 g	14.0 g	1.6 g	393.0 g

* Using 1/4 teaspoon salt in recipe for 4 portions. Including 25 g vegetable oil

Ingredient	4 portions	10 portions
Macaroni	100 g	250 g
Oil or butter (optional)	25 g	60 g
Grated cheese	100 g	250 g
Diluted English or continental mustard	¼ tsp	¾ tsp
Thin béchamel sauce	500 ml	1¼ litres
Salt, milled pepper		

Mise en place

1 Prepare the béchamel sauce, as described on page 100.

2 Dilute the mustard powder.

Cooking

1 Plunge the macaroni into a saucepan of lightly salted boiling water.

2 Boil gently, stirring occasionally, for approximately 10–15 minutes (until al dente).

3 Drain well in a colander.

4 Return to a clean, dry pan and add the oil or butter.

5 Mix with half the cheese, the mustard and the béchamel. Season lightly and taste to check.

6 Place in an earthenware dish and sprinkle with the remainder of the cheese.

7 Brown lightly under a grill or in a hot oven.

VARIATION

Add a layer of sliced tomatoes or lightly cooked sliced mushrooms to the top of the finished macaroni before adding the final grated cheese and browning.

20 Arlie potatoes

Energy	Calories	Fat	Saturated fat	Carbohydrates	Sugar	Protein	Fibre	Sodium
1325 kJ	316 kcal	15.1 g	9.6 g	34.4 g	2.5 g	9.7 g	4.3 g	251.0 g

* Using unsalted butter, 1/4 teaspoon salt. Including parmesan cheese

Ingredient	4 portions	10 portions
Potatoes	4	10
Butter, soft	50 g	125 g
Parsley	1 tsp	2½ tsp
Salt and pepper		
Cheese (e.g. Parmesan)	60 g	150 g

Mise en place

1 Bake the potatoes in their jackets.
  a Preheat the oven to 230–250°C.
  b Select good, evenly sized potatoes and scrub well.
  c With the point of a small sharp knife, cut an incision skin-deep around the potatoes.
  d Place the potatoes on a tray in the hot oven for about 1 hour. Turn the potatoes after 30 minutes.
  e Test by holding the potato in a clean teacloth and squeezing gently. If it is cooked, it should feel soft. (The cloth will protect your hand, in case the potato bursts.)

2 Chop the parsley and grate the cheese.

Cooking

1 Cut off the top of each potato, about one-third of the way down.

2 Scoop out the flesh from the potatoes and place it in a bowl. Keep the jackets. Mash or purée the flesh.

3 Add the butter and a little parsley. Season with salt and pepper. Mix.

4 Use a piping bag and star tube to pipe the mixture into the empty jackets.

5 Sprinkle with grated cheese and cook in the oven at 200°C until golden brown.

If you use a microwave to cook the potatoes, be sure to prick the skins first, otherwise they could burst open in the oven.

21 Savoury (boulangère) potatoes

Energy	Calories	Fat	Saturated fat	Carbohydrates	Sugar	Protein	Fibre	Sodium
646 kJ	154 kcal	7.0 g	2.4 g	19.7 g	2.6 g	2.2 g	2.6 g	217.0 g

* Using 37.5 g margarine, 1/4 teaspoon salt

Ingredient	4 portions	10 portions
Potatoes, peeled and washed	400 g	1¼ kg
Onions, peeled and sliced	100 g	250 g
Salt		
Butter, margarine or oil	25–50 g	60–100 g
White stock	½ litre	1¼ litre
Parsley, chopped		

Mise en place

1 Using a mandolin, and taking great care, cut the potatoes into 2 mm slices.

2 Using a large knife, peel, halve and finely slice the onions.

3 Preheat the oven to 230–250°C.

SERVING SUGGESTION

Sprinkle with freshly chopped parsley and serve.

Cooking

1 Put the neatest slices of potato to one side. Mix the remainder with the onions.

2 Season lightly and place in a well-greased shallow earthenware dish or a roasting tin. Make sure the top layer consists of neatly overlapping slices of potato.

3 Brush lightly with oil or dab with butter. Just cover with stock.

4 Cook in a hot oven (230–250°C) for approximately 20 minutes, until lightly coloured.

5 Reduce the heat to 180°C and continue to cook for approximately another ¾–1¼ hours. Press down the potatoes from time to time with a clean, flat-bottomed pan.

6 When cooked, all the stock should have been absorbed.

7 If cooked in an earthenware dish, clean the edges with a damp cloth dipped in salt.

22 Shepherd's pie

Energy	Calories	Fat	Saturated fat	Carbohydrates	Sugar	Protein	Fibre	Sodium
1682 kJ	402 kcal	22.4 g	7.1 g	21.8 g	2.7 g	27.6 g	2.6 g	409.0 g

* Using 30 g egg wash, 1/4 teaspoon salt (in the 4 portion recipe). Using 187.5 ml gravy

The ideal lamb joint for this is shoulder cooked by roasting, but any leftover lamb can be used provided all fat and gristle is removed.

Ingredient	4 portions	10 portions
Onions	100 g	250 g
Oil	35 g	100 g
Cooked lamb or mutton (minced)	400 g	1¼ kg
Salt		
Worcester sauce	2–3 drops	5 drops
Thickened gravy	125–250 ml	300–600 ml
Potato	400 g	1¼ kg
Milk or egg wash		

Mise en place

1. Remove all the fat and gristle from the cooked meat and then mince it.
2. Peel, cook and mash the potatoes.
3. Peel and finely chop the onions.
4. Make the thickened gravy (see page 103) and egg wash.

Cooking

1. Gently cook the onion in the oil in a thick-bottomed pan, without colouring, until soft.
2. Add the cooked meat and season lightly with salt.

3. Add Worcester sauce and sufficient thickened gravy to bind the mixture. This should not be too dry or too sloppy.
4. Bring to the boil, stirring frequently, and simmer for 10–15 minutes.

5. Place into an ovenproof dish.
6. Pipe or neatly arrange the mashed potato on top and brush with milk or egg wash.
7. Colour to a golden brown in a hot oven and under the salamander.

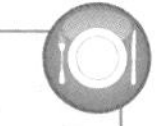

SERVING SUGGESTION

Serve accompanied with a sauceboat of thickened gravy and a suitable vegetable.

The dish can also be served with a light sprinkling of garam masala and grilled pitta bread.

VARIATION

Many variations can be made to this basic dish.

- Cover the meat with canned baked beans before adding the potato.
- Sprinkle with grated cheese before browning.
- Vary the flavour of the meat by adding herbs or spices.
- Vary the potato topping by mixing in grated cheese or chopped spring onion.
- This dish can also be prepared from leftover cooked beef or raw minced beef, which will require extra cooking time until the meat is quite soft. This is known as cottage pie.

HEALTHY EATING TIPS

Alongside the onions, additional (diced) vegetables could be used in this recipe to provide extra nutrients and vitamins. This includes carrots, leeks and celery, but could also include vegetables such as swede, parsnip, celeriac and more aromatic vegetables such as fennel.

ACTIVITY

Prepare, cook, serve and taste your own variation. Assess and discuss.

23 Steak pie

Energy	Calories	Fat	Saturated fat	Carbohydrates	Sugar	Protein	Fibre
1442 kJ	346 kcal	22.2 g	2.9 g	13.6 g	1.8 g	24.3 g	0.4 g

* Using puff pastry (McCance data)

Ingredient	4 portions	10 portions
Oil or fat	50 ml	125 ml
Stewing beef, preferably chuck steak	400 g	1 kg
Onion (optional)	100 g	250 g
Worcester sauce	3–4 drops	8–10 drops
Parsley	1 tsp	3 tsp
Stock or water	125 ml	300 ml
Salt		
Cornflour or arrowroot	10 g	25 g
Short pastry, using flour weight of	200 g	500 g

Mise en place

1. Make your pastry (see recipe 3).
2. Cut the meat into 2 cm strips and then into squares.
3. Chop the onion and parsley.

Cooking

1. Heat the oil in a frying pan, add the meat and quickly brown on all sides.
2. Drain the meat in a colander.
3. Lightly sweat the onion, if using.
4. Place the meat, onion, Worcester sauce, parsley and the liquid in a saucepan. Season lightly with salt.
5. Bring to the boil, skim and allow to simmer gently until the meat is tender.
6. Dilute the cornflour with a little water and stir in to the simmering meat.
7. Re-boil, taste and correct the seasoning.
8. Place the mixture in a pie dish.
9. Carefully roll the pastry on to the rolling pin and then unroll it over the top of the pie, being careful not to stretch it.
10. Seal the pastry on to the dish rim firmly and cut off any extra pastry.
11. Place the pie on a baking sheet and bake at 200°C for approximately 30–45 minutes. If the pastry colours too quickly, cover it with greaseproof paper or foil.

24 Stuffed peppers (*piment farci*)

Energy	Calories	Fat	Saturated fat	Carbohydrates	Sugar	Protein	Fibre
1291 kJ	308 kcal	11.4 g	6.7 g	48.8 g	5.3 g	5.4 g	3.1 g

Ingredient	4 portions	10 portions
Red peppers, medium-sized	4	10
Carrots, sliced	50 g	125 g
Onions, sliced	50 g	125 g
Bouquet garni	1	2
White stock	½ litre	1¼ litres
Salt, pepper		
Pilaf		
Rice (long grain)	200 g	500 g
Salt, pepper		
Onion, chopped	50 g	125 g
Butter	50 g	125 g

Cooking

1. Place the peppers on a tray in the oven or under the salamander for a few minutes, or deep-fry in hot oil at 180°C, until the skin blisters.
2. Remove the skin; carefully cut off the top and empty out all the seeds.
3. Stuff with a well-seasoned pilaf of rice (ingredients as listed above), which may be varied by the addition of mushrooms, tomatoes, ham, and so on.
4. Replace the top of the peppers.
5. Place the peppers on the sliced carrot and onion in a pan suitable for the oven; add the bouquet garni, stock and seasoning. Cover with buttered paper and a lid.
6. Cook in a moderate oven at 180–200°C for 1 hour or until tender.
7. Serve garnished with parsley.

HEALTHY EATING TIPS

- This dish is low in fat if the peppers are placed in the oven or under the salamander, not deep fried, and the butter/oil is kept to a minimum.
- Add little or no salt.
- If extra vegetables are added to the rice, and a vegetable stock used, this dish can be a useful vegetarian starter.

1 Briefly heat the peppers and then peel them

2 Cut off the top and empty out the seeds

3 Fill the pepper and then replace the stem

25 Baked rice pudding

Energy	Calories	Fat	Saturated fat	Carbohydrates	Sugar	Protein	Fibre	Sodium
816 kJ	193 kcal	7.1 g	4.4 g	27.9 g	18.6 g	5.1 g	0.2 g	54.0 g

* Using whole milk, unsalted butter

Ingredient	4 portions	10 portions
Rice, short grain	50 g	125 g
Caster sugar	50 g	125 g
Milk, whole or skimmed	½ litre	1½ litres
Butter	12 g	30 g
Vanilla essence	2–3 drops	6–8 drops
Nutmeg, grated		

Cooking

1. Wash the rice and place it in a pie dish.
2. Add the sugar and milk, and mix well.
3. Add the butter, vanilla essence and the nutmeg.
4. Place the dish on a baking sheet. Clean any milk from the rim of the pie dish.
5. Bake at 180°C–200°C until the milk starts to simmer.
6. Reduce the heat to 150°C and allow the pudding to cook slowly for 1½–2 hours.

Roasting recipes

26 Roast rump of Glamorgan lamb on lava bread potato cake with Welsh stout and berry sauce

Energy	Calories	Fat	Saturated fat	Carbohydrates	Sugar	Protein	Fibre	Sodium
2727 kJ	654 kcal	37.7 g	13.1 g	23.7 g	8.7 g	50.0 g	7.1 g	1,085.0 g

* Using blackberries, streaky bacon, adding 1/4 teaspoon salt

Ingredient	4 portions	10 portions
Pembroke new potatoes	400 g	1 kg
Rump of Glamorgan lamb	4	10
Salt and pepper, for seasoning		
Rapeseed oil	2 tbsp	5 tbsp
Vegetables for mirepoix (carrot, leek, onion, celery)	100 g	250 g
Welsh black beer (Bullmastif brewery) or similar	1 bottle	2 bottles
Redcurrant jelly	1 tsp	2 tsp
Lamb stock	400 ml	1 litre
Tarragon	1 tbsp	2 tbsp
Lardons of bacon	100 g	205 g
Leeks	100 g	250 g
Orange, zest	1	2
Lava bread (pre-prepared product)	200 g	500 g
Fresh blackcurrant or blackberries	1 punnet	2 punnets

Welsh Mountain Sheep are local to Glamorgan and are lean with good flavour. Pembroke new potatoes are a popular variety in Wales. Local beer from a micro-brewery in Cardiff adds a very local dimension to this dish, and using locally reared bacon gives it a very South Wales appeal. Lava bread is now being found in a variety of dishes across Wales, not just as a breakfast ingredient.

Mise en place

1 Prepare and trim the lamb (keep the trimmings to one side). Score the fat if you are going to present the rumps whole for service.
2 Wash the potatoes and vegetables.
3 Cut the vegetables into mirepoix.
4 Chop the tarragon and finely grate the orange zest.
5 Preheat the oven to 185–195°C.

Cooking

1. Cook the potatoes in boiling salted water for about 15 minutes until cooked through. Crush lightly with a fork. Cover and put aside in a warm place.
2. Season the lamb rumps with salt and freshly ground black pepper.
3. Heat the rapeseed oil in an ovenproof frying pan and fry the lamb rumps until lightly browned all over.
4. Transfer the rumps to the oven and roast for 8–10 minutes (for medium rare).
5. Remove from the oven and set aside to rest in a warm place; keep pan for next stage.
6. Place the reserved lamb trimmings and mirepoix of vegetables into the roasting pan and cook over a high heat until all ingredients begin to brown and caramelise.
7. Pour in enough beer to cover the ingredients in the pan and add the redcurrant jelly. Deglaze by scraping up any browned bits from the bottom of the pan with a wooden spoon.
8. Cook until the beer has reduced in volume by half, then add the lamb stock and tarragon. Reduce by half again, checking for flavour. Cook until the consistency of a jus is achieved. Adjust seasoning as necessary.
9. Strain the sauce and keep warm for service.
10. Preheat a heavy bottomed pan and fry the lardons of bacon, leek and orange zest in the pan quickly, using the fat from the lardons as the cooking medium (dry frying). Fry until the lardons are lightly browned and a little crisp.
11. Add the potatoes and lava bread to the pan and mix carefully, crushing down the potatoes a little further. Taste for seasoning and adjust if needed.
12. Place a portion of the potato mixture into a small ring mould in the centre of a plate and de-mould. Put the roast rump of lamb carefully on top (sliced or whole) then pour the jus around the plate. Finish by scattering a garnish of blackberries or blackcurrants around the plate.

VARIATION

- This recipe uses potatoes with the skin on – try making it with peeled potatoes for a smoother texture.
- Add the berries to the sauce after passing it. When the sauce is reheated, this will soften the fruit, changing the texture of the garnish.

27 Traditional roast beef and gravy

Energy	Calories	Fat	Saturated fat	Carbohydrates	Sugar	Protein	Fibre	Sodium
1169 kJ	280 kcal	15.7 g	4.8 g	5.7 g	0.8 g	29.3 g	0.3 g	1,329.0 g

Ingredient
Joint of beef of your own choice and size
Salt
Dripping or oil
Onion, carrot and celery
Brown stock, for the gravy

Mise en place

1. Trim the joint to remove sinew, excess fat and any bones that may make carving difficult. Depending on the joint and the way you prepare it, you may want to tie it with string to keep its shape.
2. Wash, peel and roughly chop the vegetables.
3. Prepare a brown stock (see page 89).
4. Preheat the oven to 250°C.

Suitable roasting joints are:

- first class – sirloin, wing ribs, fore ribs, fillet
- second class – middle ribs, topside.

Cooking

1. Season the joint lightly with salt and place on a trivet (metal or bones) in a roasting tray.
2. Place a little dripping or oil over the meat and cook it in a hot oven at 230–250°C for around 15 minutes, then reduce the heat to 200–220°C, depending on the size of the joint. Roasting time is approximately 15 minutes per ½ kg plus 15 minutes.
3. Baste frequently and, for large joints, gradually reduce the heat by 5–10°C (depending on the size of the joint).
4. Roughly chopped onion, carrot and celery can be added to the roasting tray approximately 30 minutes before the joint is cooked, to give extra flavour to the gravy.
5. Remove the tray from the oven and place the joint on to a dish or plate to check whether it is cooked (see below).
6. Once you are happy that the meat is cooked, cover it with foil and leave to rest in a warm place for at least 15 minutes. This allows the meat to set and become tender for carving.

Testing whether a joint is cooked

If you do not have a temperature probe:

- remove the joint from the oven and place on a dish or plate
- firmly press the meat surface to force out some meat juice
- check the colour of the juice
  - red – indicates that the meat is underdone
  - pink – indicates that the meat is medium done
  - clear – indicates that the meat is cooked through.

If you are using a temperature probe:

- set the required internal temperature according to how the meat is to be cooked and insert the probe horizontally into the centre of the meat
- leave the probe inside the joint during cooking
- it will set off a beeper alerting you when your meat is cooked to perfection.

When using a meat temperature thermometer:

- insert it into the part of the joint that was the thickest before it was placed in the oven

- the internal temperature reached should be as follows
  - rare or underdone meat 50°C
  - medium done (pinkish) 60°C
  - just done (slightly pink) 70°C.

Making the gravy

1. While the meat is resting you can make the gravy by carefully pouring off as much fat as possible, leaving any meat juice or sediment and vegetables in the tray.
2. Place this over a low heat and add sufficient brown stock for the amount of gravy required; allow it to simmer for 5 minutes, scraping off all the sediment and meat juice from the joint with a non-metal spoon.
3. Taste the gravy, correct the seasoning and pass it through a fine strainer. If the gravy is lacking in flavour, a little commercial product can be added.

SERVING SUGGESTION

Carve the meat against the grain, as per the carving guidance given on page 149.

Lay your table with sharp, unserrated steak knives that will cut cleanly through the meat. A blunt knife makes the meat seem less tender, and a serrated knife encourages your guests to 'saw', both of which can ruin even the most beautifully cooked meat.

Serve with Yorkshire pudding (recipe 28), gravy, and a selection of roast and steamed vegetables.

28 Horseradish sauce

Energy	Calories	Fat	Saturated fat	Carbohydrates	Sugar	Protein	Fibre	Sodium
135 kJ	33 kcal	3.0 g	1.9 g	0.7 g	0.6 g	0.7 g	0.3 g	0.0 g

Ingredient	4 portions	10 portions
Horseradish, grated	25 g	65 g
Cream	120 ml	300 ml
Malt vinegar or lemon juice	1 tbsp	2½ tbsp
Salt		

Preparing the dish

1. Thoroughly wash the horseradish, peel and grate finely.
2. Lightly whip the cream.
3. Mix all the ingredients, season lightly with salt and taste.

Horseradish sauce is the traditional sauce offered with roast beef.

29 Yorkshire pudding

Energy	Calories	Fat	Saturated fat	Carbohydrates	Sugar	Protein	Fibre
730 kJ	174 kcal	9.3 g	2.1 g	17.5 g	1.3 g	6.3 g	0.9 g

Ingredient	4 portions	10 portions
Plain flour	85 g	215 g
Eggs	2	5
Milk	85 ml	215 ml
Water	40 ml	100 ml
Salt, pinch		
Beef dripping from the joint or a light oil	20 g	50 g

Cooking

1. Place the flour and eggs in a mixing bowl and mix to a smooth paste.
2. Gradually add the milk and water, beating strongly to incorporate air, which should start to appear in small bubbles on the surface. Add the salt and allow the mixture to rest for 1 hour.
3. Heat the pudding trays in a hot oven at 190°C. Add a little dripping in each tray, preferably from the meat as this will give flavour. Otherwise, use oil.
4. Ladle in the mixture so that each tray is two-thirds full.
5. Place in the oven for 20–30 minutes. When checking, open the oven door only sufficiently to glance at the puddings, then close it slowly without banging.
6. For the last 10 minutes of cooking, take the trays out, turn the puddings over and return them to the oven to dry out and complete cooking. Serve immediately.

Yorkshire pudding is the traditional accompaniment to roast beef.

30 Roast loin of pork with apple and onion sauce

Energy	Calories	Fat	Saturated fat	Carbohydrates	Sugar	Protein	Fibre	Sodium
2273 kJ	545 kcal	38.3 g	14.1 g	9.6 g	9.6 g	39.6 g	2.1 g	261.0 g

* Using 1/4 teaspoon of salt

Ingredient	4 portions	10 portions
Loin of pork on the bone	1 kg	2½ kg
Cooking apples, peeled, cored and quartered	2	5
Onion, peeled and quartered	1	2–3
Cider	60 ml	150 ml
Salt		

Mise en place

1. Use a loin that is on the bone. Saw down the chine bone to make it easier to carve. The chine bone is the bone along the back of the loin that attaches the two loins together.
2. Trim off all sinew and excess fat.
3. If it has not been done by the butcher, score the skin (cut deep with the point of a small sharp knife) in the direction that the loin will be carved. Season lightly with salt.
4. Secure it by tying a string through the chine bone.
5. Peel, core and quarter the apples, and peel and quarter the onion.
6. Preheat the oven to 250°C.

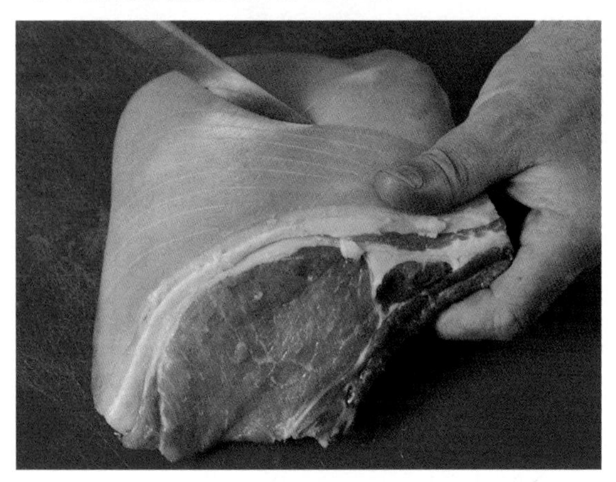

Tying the joint

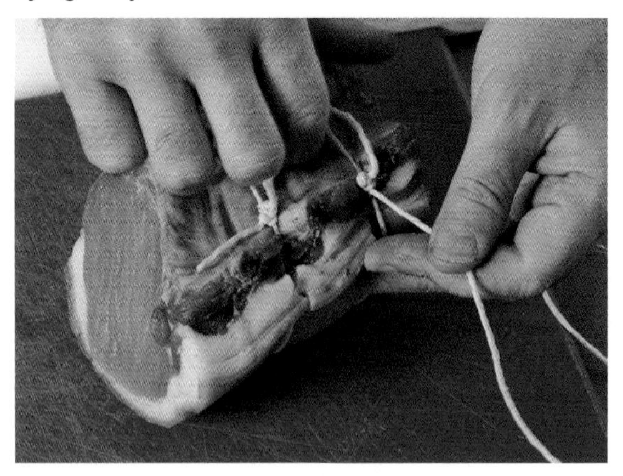

Scoring the skin

Cooking

1 Heat some oil in a frying pan. Place the pork into the oil and seal it on all sides.

2 Remove the pork from the pan. Cook the apples and onions in the same pan.

3 Deglaze the pan with some of the cider.

4 Place the meat, apples and onions in a roasting tin. Add the rest of the cider and roast at 200°C for 25 minutes, then reduce the temperature to 170°C and continue to cook until done, approximately 45 minutes.

5 Remove the joint from the tray and put on a plate or dish.

6 Check that it is cooked by pressing the lean meat – no signs of blood should be in the juice.

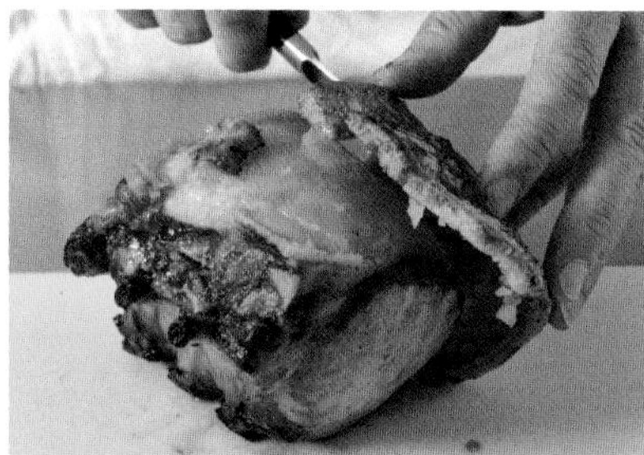

7 Cover the joint loosely with foil and allow it to rest for 10–15 minutes before carving. Remove the crisp skin (crackling) and break it up.

8 Purée the apples and onions in a processor, then reheat. This should be a thickish consistency – if too thick, adjust with cider.

SERVING SUGGESTION

Slice the pork and serve with sauce and roast gravy. A piece of the crisp skin (crackling) should be served with each portion of pork.

31 Roast rack of lamb

Energy	Calories	Fat	Saturated fat	Carbohydrates	Sugar	Protein	Fibre	Sodium
4232 kJ	1025 kcal	89.0 g	38.1 g	0.0 g	0.0 g	56.0 g	0.0 g	787.0 g

* Analysed as 'per rack'

A single rack of lamb (best end) has seven bones, although the one towards the finer end of the rack is quite small and does not cut into a substantial cutlet. Therefore, it is often removed to leave a six-bone rack, This can produce 2 x 3 bone portions or 3 x 2 bone portions, depending of the size of portion required.

A best end is often 'French trimmed' to expose the bone from the cutlet and also to make the rack easier to carve after roasting as a whole.

Ingredient
Rack of lamb (approximately 450 g)
Salt
Vegetable oil
Brown stock for gravy (see page 89)

Mise en place

1 Remove the skin from head to tail (top to bottom) and breast (front) to back, leaving as much fat as possible on the joint.

2 Remove the sinew and the tip of the blade bone.

3 Clean the sinew from between the rib bones and on the bones.

4 Score (lightly cut with the tip of a sharp knife) a line through the fat, 2 cm from the end of the bone.

5 If necessary, trim the overall length of the rib bones to two and a half times the length of the nut of lean meat. (The nut is the main part of the meat.)

6 Score down the middle of the back of each bone.

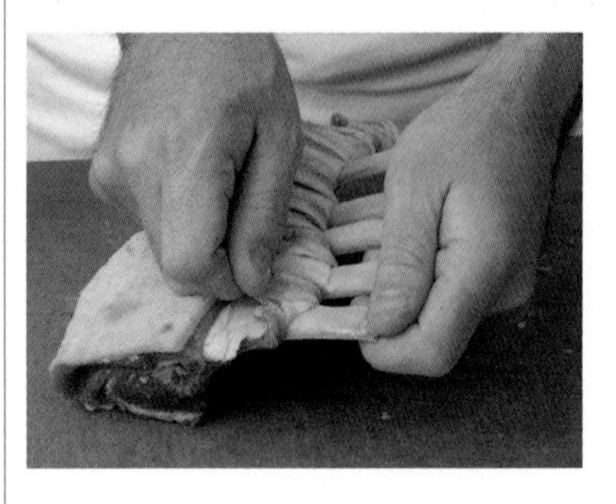

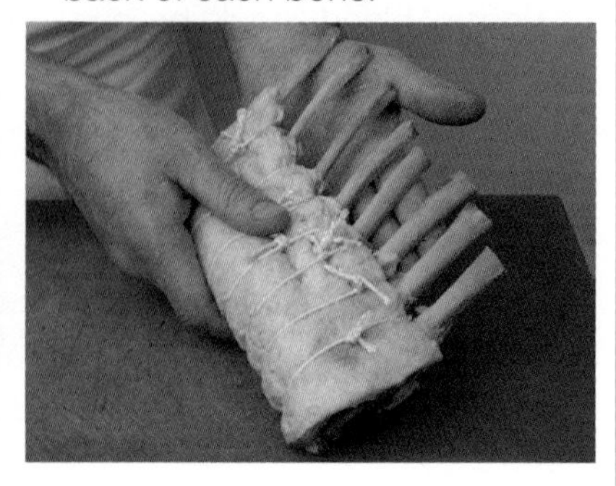

7 Pull the skin, fat and meat away from the end of each bone, so that the bones will be visible after cooking. Clean away any sinew.

8 Cut off the sinew along the other edge.

9 Tie the joint.

Cooking

1. Season the rack lightly with salt and place fat side up on a bed of bones or a metal trivet in a roasting tray.
2. Add a little vegetable oil on top and cook in a hot oven at 175–185°C.
3. Roast for approximately 20–25 minutes. Baste (spoon fat over the joint) two or three times during cooking.
4. To test if cooked, remove the rack, place on a warm plate and press the lean meat to force out a little juice. If the juice does not show any pinkness (sign of blood) it is cooked right through. If the lamb is to be cooked pink, then reduce the cooking time by approximately 5 minutes.

SERVING SUGGESTION

If you are going to make roast gravy with this dish (see recipe 27 for roast beef, which includes instructions for making gravy), add a peeled sliced onion, celery and carrot to the roasting tin with the lamb rack. This will give the gravy more flavour. There are a number of commercial gravy products that can also be used to boost the gravy if it is not tasty enough.

In addition to roast gravy, offer mint sauce (recipe 32) and/or redcurrant jelly.

32 Mint sauce

Energy	Calories	Fat	Saturated fat	Carbohydrates	Sugar	Protein	Fibre	Sodium
26 kJ	6 kcal	0.0 g	0.7 g	0.6 g	0.1 g	0.0 g	0.0 g	0.0 g

Ingredient	
Water	125 ml
Sugar, caster or Demerara	1 tsp
Mint leaves, chopped	2–3 tbsp
Malt vinegar	to taste

Preparing the dish

1. Boil the water and dissolve the sugar in it. Allow to cool.
2. Add the chopped mint leaves and enough malt vinegar to give a slightly sharp but pleasant taste.

33 Roast chicken with dressing (*poulet rôti à l'anglaise*)

Energy	Calories	Fat	Saturated fat	Carbohydrates	Sugar	Protein	Fibre
1363 kJ	327 kca	20.4 g	3.7 g	6.7 g	0.7 g	29.5 g	0.3 g

Based on average edible portion of roasted meat (100 g).

Ingredient	4 portions (per chicken)
Chicken, 1¼–1½ kg	1
Salt and pepper	
Oil or butter	100 g
Onion, chopped	25 g
Chopped parsley, pinch	
Powdered thyme, pinch	
Breadcrumbs (white or wholemeal)	50 g
Liver from the chicken, raw, chopped (optional)	

Cooking

1. Lightly season the chicken inside and out with salt.
2. Place on its side in a roasting tin.
3. Cover with 50 g of the oil or butter.
4. Place in a hot oven for approximately 20–25 minutes, then turn on to the other side.
5. Cook for a further 20–25 minutes. Baste frequently.
6. To test whether the chicken is fully cooked, pierce it with a fork between the drumstick and thigh, and hold it over a plate. The juice issuing from the chicken should not show any sign of blood. If using a temperature probe, insert in the thickest part of the leg; it should read 77°C. Place the cooked chicken breast side down to retain all the cooking juices.
7. To make the dressing, gently cook the onion in the remaining oil or butter without colour.
8. Season, and add the herbs and breadcrumbs.
9. Mix in the liver, if using.
10. Correct the seasoning and bake or steam the dressing separately, for approximately 20 minutes, until thoroughly cooked.
11. Serve with pan juices or a roast gravy – Recipe 13 in Unit 204.

PROFESSIONAL TIP

Arranging the chicken so that it cooks sitting on one leg, then the other, and then the breast, ensures that the whole bird cooks evenly.

HEALTHY EATING TIPS

- Use unsaturated oil to cook the onion.
- Keep added salt to a minimum.
- Serve with plenty of potatoes and vegetables.

34 Roast potatoes

Energy	Calories	Fat	Saturated fat	Carbohydrates	Sugar	Protein	Fibre
956 kJ	228 kcal	7.0 g	1.1 g	39.6 g	0.9 g	4.1 g	1.5 g

Ingredient
Oil or dripping for roasting
Potatoes, washed, peeled and cut (1 kg of old potatoes will yield 4–6 portions)
Salt, pinch

Mise en place

1. Wash, peel and re-wash the potatoes.
2. Cut into evenly sized pieces, 3–4 pieces per portion.
3. Dry the potatoes well.
4. Preheat the oven to 230°C.

Cooking

1. Pour oil into a roasting tray so that the entire base of the tray is lined.
2. Heat the oil or dripping before adding the well-dried potatoes.
3. Shake/turn the potatoes occasionally until lightly browned on all sides.
4. Season lightly with salt and cook for ¾–1 hour in a hot oven (230°C).
5. Turn the potatoes halfway through cooking.
6. Cook to a crisp, golden brown, then drain off the fat and serve.

35 Roasted beetroot

Energy	Calories	Fat	Saturated fat	Carbohydrates	Sugar	Protein	Fibre	Sodium
958 kJ	232 kcal	21.4 g	11.1 g	7.3 g	6.6 g	2.5 g	2.2 g	62.0 g

* Using full fat crème fraiche

Ingredient	4 portions	10 portions
Small young beetroot	4	10
Olive oil	2 tbsp	5 tbsp
Grated horseradish	2 tbsp	5 tbsp
Crème fraîche	150 ml	375 ml
Chives, finely chopped	1 tbsp	2½ tbsp

Mise en place

1 Trim and thoroughly wash the beetroot. Dry well.
2 Preheat the oven to 200°C.

It is not necessary to peel the beetroot. If peeled it will lose colour (bleed).

Cooking

1 Place the beetroot in a roasting tray and sprinkle with olive oil.
2 Roast at 200°C for approximately 1½ hours until cooked.
3 Mix the horseradish into the crème fraîche.

SERVING SUGGESTION

When the beetroot is cooked, place on a serving dish. Cut a criss-cross in the top, halfway through.

Spoon some crème fraîche on to each beetroot and sprinkle with chopped chives.

VARIATION

You can use natural yoghurt or half-whipped cream as alternatives to crème fraîche.

36 Roasted vegetables

Energy	Calories	Fat	Saturated fat	Carbohydrates	Sugar	Protein	Fibre	Sodium
312 kJ	75 kcal	3.8 g	0.6 g	7.6 g	6.7 g	2.6 g	4.3 g	152.0 g

* Using 1/4 teaspoon salt (for 4 portion recipe)

Ingredient	4 portions	10 portions
Red onions, small	1	3
Red peppers	1	3
Yellow peppers	1	3
Courgettes	2	5
Aubergines	1	3
Cloves of garlic, coarsely chopped	1–2	2–4
Olive oil	1 tbsp	2½ tbsp
Balsamic vinegar	1 tbsp	2½ tbsp
Sea salt and freshly milled black pepper		
Fresh rosemary, roughly chopped		
Fresh basil, roughly chopped		

Cooking

1. Peel the onions and cut into eight pieces. Cut the peppers into halves, deseed and cut each into approximately 4–6 even pieces. Cut the courgettes and aubergine into 2 × 1 cm batons.
2. Place all the vegetables (and the garlic) into a suitable roasting dish, sprinkle with the olive oil and balsamic vinegar.
3. Season lightly with sea salt and pepper.
4. Sprinkle with the rosemary and basil.
5. Place in a preheated oven at 180°C for approximately 15 minutes.
6. Serve immediately.

These vegetables may also be chilled and served with a salad as a starter.

HEALTHY EATING TIPS

Lightly brush the vegetables with the olive oil and add the minimum amount of salt.

Grilling recipes

37 Grilled pollock with allspice and lime

Energy	Calories	Fat	Saturated fat	Carbohydrates	Sugar	Protein	Fibre	Sodium
601 kJ	143 kcal	4.2 g	0.4 g	1.2 g	0.7 g	24.9 g	0.6 g	250.0 g

Ingredient	4 portions	10 portions
Scotch bonnet chillies	12 g	30 g
Onions	12 g	30 g
Ginger	8 g	20 g
Fresh thyme	1½ g	3 g
Oregano leaves	1½ g	3 g
Paprika powder	1½ g	3 g
Salt	1½ g	3 g
Turmeric (haldi powder)	1½ g	3 g
Allspice	1 g	10 g
Black pepper, powder	2 g	5 g
Lime juice	12 ml	30 ml
Orange juice	12 ml	30 ml
Pollock fillets, skinless	4	10
Vegetable oil	12 ml	30 ml

Mise en place

1. Chop the chillies and thyme.
2. Dice the onions.
3. Peel and thinly slice the ginger.

Cooking

1. Mix together the chillies, onions, ginger, herbs, spices and juices.
2. Marinade the fish in this mixture for 30 minutes.
3. Brush the fish with oil and grill it. Turn it once. Cook until a core temperature of 75°C is reached.
4. Serve on a suitable plate.

It was developed specially for the athletes' village at the London 2012 Olympic Games. The culinary operations team produced a range of nutritious meals inspired by dishes from around the world. The standard recipe was for 24 portions; it has been scaled down for this book.

38 Grilled sardines

Energy	Calories	Fat	Saturated fat	Carbohydrates	Sugar	Protein	Fibre	Sodium
597 kJ	143 kcal	7.4 g	1.3 g	7.4 g	0.1 g	11.4 g	0.4 g	72.0 g

* Analysed as 3.5 sardines (15 g each) per portion, with 1 teaspoon vegetable oil and 10 g flour per portion

Ingredient
Sardines, 3 or 4 per portion depending on their size
Flour
Light oil

Grilling is cooking under radiant heat. It is a fast method suitable for small whole fish or fillets, whole or cut in portions.

Mise en place

1. Prepare, clean, wash and thoroughly dry the fish.
2. Fillet them if required.

Cooking

1. Pass the fish through flour, shake off surplus and place on an oiled baking sheet.
2. Brush the tops with oil and cook carefully under a hot grill, ensuring they do not burn.
3. After 2–3 minutes, remove the tray and turn the sardines with a palette knife. Return to the grill and cook for 2 minutes, until lightly browned.

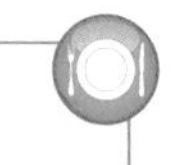

SERVING SUGGESTION

Serve with quarters of lemon (pips removed).

ACTIVITY

Name six other fish that could be grilled whole or in fillets.

39 Lamb kebabs

Energy	Calories	Fat	Saturated fat	Carbohydrates	Sugar	Protein	Fibre
1544 kJ	379 kcal	25.1 g	9.9	7.2 g	5.9 g	29.6 g	20.6 g

Ingredient	4 portions	10 portions
Lamb, lean meat (e.g. from a leg of lamb)	600 g	1½ kg
Red pepper	2	5
Onion	1	3
Bay leaves	4	10
Vegetable oil	2 tbsp	5 tbsp
Thyme, dried	½ tsp	1 tsp

Mise en place

1. Cut the meat into cubes.
2. Deseed the red pepper and cut into cubes.
3. Peel the onion and cut into cubes.

The ideal cuts of lamb are the nut of the lean meat of the loin or rack.

Kebabs, a dish of Turkish origin, are pieces of food impaled on skewers and cooked on or under a grill or barbecue. They are made using tender cuts of various meats with pieces of vegetables or fruits in between.

Cooking

1. Push the squares of meat on to skewers, alternating these with squares of red pepper, onion and a bay leaf.
2. Brush with oil and lightly sprinkle with dried thyme.
3. Cook over or under a grill.

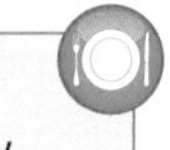

SERVING SUGGESTION

Serve with pilaf rice (page 140) and finely sliced raw onion.

VARIATION

Different flavours can be added by marinating the kebabs. This involves soaking the meat, before cooking, in a combination of oil, vinegar, lemon juice, spices and herbs, for 2 hours at room temperature or 4 hours in the refrigerator.

HEALTHY EATING TIPS

Skinless chicken breast offers a great, high protein and low-fat alternative to red meat. It also absorbs marinades very well to provide a depth of flavour in a kebab.

ACTIVITY

Each member of the group should devise their own kebab from a range of ingredients – meat, vegetables, herbs and spices.

The group then cooks, serves, tastes and assesses each version.

40 Grilled pork chops

Energy	Calories	Fat	Saturated fat	Carbohydrates	Sugar	Protein	Fibre	Sodium
1111 kJ	308 kcal	16.6 g	6.0 g	0.0 g	0.0 g	25.9 g	0.0 g	260.0 g

* Using 150 g pork chop (weighed as lean, fat and bone), 0.5 g salt and 1/2 teaspoon of vegetable oil per portion

Ingredient
Pork chops (1 × 125–175 g chop per portion, depending on requirements, e.g. lunch/dinner or single course/part of a bigger menu)
Salt
Oil
Parsley, sprigs

Mise en place

To preparing a chop from a loin:

- remove the skin, excess fat and sinew from the chops
- cut, saw or chop through the loin in approximately 1 cm slices
- remove any excess bone and trim neatly.

You can buy chops ready prepared, or you can prepare them from a loin as described above.

Cooking

1 Season the chops lightly with salt.

2 Brush with oil or fat and cook on both sides on or under a moderately hot grill or salamander for approximately 10 minutes, until cooked through.

SERVING SUGGESTION

Garnish with a sprig of parsley. Serve with hot apple sauce.

41 Grilled beef steak

Energy	Calories	Fat	Saturated fat	Carbohydrates	Sugar	Protein	Fibre	Sodium
920 kJ	220 kcal	8.7 g	3.1 g	0.0 g	0.0 g	35.1 g	0.0 g	301.0 g

* 6 oz lean sirloin steak used for analysis, 1/2 teaspoon vegetable oil and 0.5 g salt

Ingredient
Steaks – e.g. rib-eye, sirloin, fillet
Salt
Oil

Mise en place

Preheat the grill.

Cooking

1. Season the steaks lightly with salt and brush both sides with oil.
2. Place on hot, preheated greased grill bars.
3. Turn over the steaks halfway through cooking and brush occasionally with oil.
4. Cook to the degree ordered by the customer (see guidance on page 234).

SERVING SUGGESTION

Serve garnished with a small bunch of well-washed and dried watercress, a deep-fried potato and a suitable sauce, such as a compound butter sauce.

VARIATION

Using a barbecue

Instead of grilling the steaks you could barbecue them. Marinate them using a good oil, seasoning and/or herbs before cooking.

To prepare the barbecue:

- if possible, use gas rather than charcoal as it is easier to control the temperature with gas
- secure a layer of tin foil over the barbecue
- wait until the grill bars are hot or the charcoal embers glow (if using charcoal, always wait for the glow before starting to cook; a gas barbecue will take about 30 minutes to preheat)
- remove the tinfoil and brush the grill bars with a firm, long-handled wire brush to remove any unwanted debris.

Grilled steak video, http://bit.ly/XVkyZX

42 Grilled gammon rashers

Energy	Calories	Fat	Saturated fat	Carbohydrates	Sugar	Protein	Fibre	Sodium
1080 kJ	259 kcal	15.1 g	4.5 g	0.0 g	0.0 g	30.6 g	0.0 g	1,540.0 g

* Analysed using 175 g gammon, 1/2 teaspoon vegetable oil

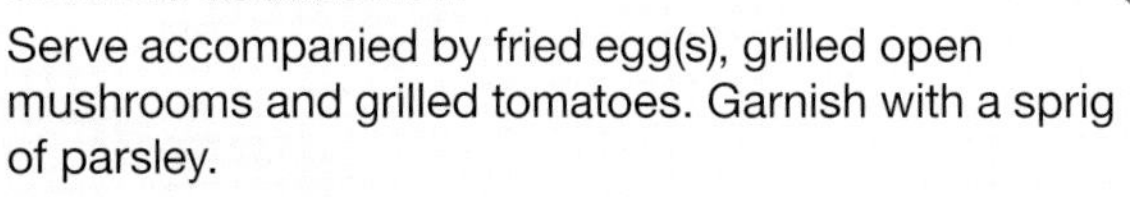

SERVING SUGGESTION

Serve accompanied by fried egg(s), grilled open mushrooms and grilled tomatoes. Garnish with a sprig of parsley.

VARIATION

- Instead of cooking gammon on grill bars, you can cook them on a tray under a salamander. Lightly grease the tray first.
- Gammon rashers can be cooked by gently frying them in a little oil or fat. Use a thick-bottomed frying pan or a sauté pan.
- Rashers of back or streaky bacon can be cooked on lightly greased trays under a preheated grill. Turn them over when they are half cooked. When they are ready they will be lightly browned and slightly crispy. Do not add any fat – they will make their own while they are cooking.
- Bacon rashers can also be fried in a frying pan with just a little fat or oil to prevent them from sticking.

Ingredient
Thick-cut gammon rashers
Oil

Mise en place

Preheat the grill.

Cooking

1. Brush the rashers on both sides with a little fat or oil.
2. Place the rashers on the preheated grill bars and cook for approximately 5 minutes on each side.

43 Grilled chicken (poulet grillé)

Energy	Calories	Fat	Saturated fat	Carbohydrates	Sugar	Protein	Fibre
978 kJ	234 kcal	15.7 g	4.3 g	0.0 g	0.0 g	23.3 g	0.0 g

Ingredient
1 × chicken suprême per person (it is recommended to leave the skin on, particularly during the grilling process)
Salt and mill pepper
Oil or melted butter/margarine, for brushing

Cooking

1. Season the chicken with salt and mill pepper, and prepare for grilling (see page 150).
2. Brush with oil or melted butter/margarine, and place on preheated greased grill bars, or on a barbecue or flat baking tray under a salamander.
3. Brush frequently with melted fat during cooking; allow approximately 15–20 minutes each side.
4. Test if cooked by piercing the drumstick with a skewer or trussing needle; there should be no sign of blood issuing from the leg.
5. Serve garnished with watercress and offer a suitable sauce separately.

VARIATION

Grilled chicken is frequently garnished with streaky bacon, tomatoes and mushrooms.

The chicken may be marinated for 2–3 hours before grilling, in a mixture of oil, lemon juice, spices, herbs, freshly grated ginger, finely chopped garlic, salt and pepper. Chicken or turkey portions can also be grilled and marinated beforehand if desired (breasts or boned-out lightly battened thighs of chicken).

HEALTHY EATING TIPS

- Use a minimum of salt and an unsaturated oil.
- Garnish with grilled tomatoes and mushrooms.
- Serve with Delmonico potatoes and green vegetables.

44 Grilled vegetable bake

Energy	Calories	Fat	Saturated fat	Carbohydrates	Sugar	Protein	Fibre	Sodium
1646 kJ	397 kcal	32.4 g	6.3 g	17.4 g	6.8 g	8.9 g	4.8 g	212.0 g

Ingredient	4 portions	10 portions
Aubergines	250 g	625 g
Courgettes	400 g	1 kg
Red peppers	3	8
Vegetable oil	90 ml	225 ml
Pesto	1 tbsp	2½ tbsp
Garlic cloves	2	5
Breadcrumbs	60 g	150 g
Parsley	1 tbsp	2½ tbsp
Basil	1 tbsp	2½ tbsp
Cheshire cheese	80 g	200 g

Mise en place

1. Peel and crush the garlic, then chop.
2. Cut the aubergine and courgettes into 5 mm slices.
3. Deseed the peppers and cut into 1 cm dice.
4. Chop the parsley and basil.
5. Grate the cheese.
6. Preheat the oven to 150–180°C.

Pesto is a green sauce made from fresh basil leaves, garlic, toasted pine nuts, Parmesan cheese and olive oil. It can be bought ready-made.

Cooking

1. Sprinkle the vegetables with oil, pesto, and the crushed and chopped garlic.
2. Lightly grill the vegetables on a griddle pan.
3. Line a suitable shallow dish with half the breadcrumbs and chopped parsley and basil.
4. Arrange in the dish the courgettes and the aubergines overlapping in rows with the peppers.
5. Add the rest of the breadcrumbs to the grated cheese. Sprinkle this mixture over the vegetables.
6. Bake in a moderate oven (150–180°C) for approximately 20 minutes.

SERVING SUGGESTION

Serve with a suitable salad, such as mixed leaves with rice noodles seasoned with soy sauce garnished with tomato, chopped onion and avocado.

VARIATION

The pesto will provide a fresh garlic and basil twist but can be omitted if these flavours are not desired. Many other cheeses would complement this dish, such as Cheddar or Red Leicester. To reduce the fat content of the dish, the cheese could also be omitted, leaving the breadcrumbs to be browned as the topping. However, the cheese will provide additional flavour, texture and richness to the dish.

207 Deep frying and shallow frying

The purpose of this chapter is to help you develop skills, knowledge and understanding of the processes involved in preparing and cooking food by deep or shallow frying to produce a variety of dishes.

Learning outcomes

In this chapter, you will be able to:

1 produce deep fried products, including:
  - **1.1** selecting food items for deep frying
  - **1.2** applying preparation methods for deep frying
  - **1.3** applying techniques to produce deep fried products
  - **1.4** applying finishing methods for deep fried products

2 produce shallow fried products, including:
  - **2.1** selecting food items for shallow frying
  - **2.2** applying preparation methods for shallow frying
  - **2.3** applying techniques to produce shallow fried products
  - **2.4** applying finishing methods for shallow fried products

Recipes included in this chapter

Deep fried products	
1	Scotch eggs
2	Dorset crab cake with watercress salad
3	Fried fish in batter
4	Fish cakes
5	Fruit fritters
6	Sweet and sour pork
7	Sweet and sour sauce
8	Cheese fritters (*beignets au fromage*)
9	Deep fried chicken
10	Chicken Kiev
11	Chips
12	Mushrooms fried with a polenta crust
Shallow fried products	
13	Scrambled eggs
14	Fried eggs
15	Omelette
16	Shallow fried fish
17	Fried banana
18	Shallow fried lamb cutlets and chops
19	Pan fried steak
20	Egg and crumbed pork escalopes
21	Stir fried pork fillet
22	Canal floddies
23	Pancakes with lemon
24	Sauté of chicken
25	Turkey fajita
26	Stir fried noodles
27	Sauté potatoes
28	Fried mixed vegetables with coconut milk
29	Stir fried rice

1 Produce deep fried products

Deep frying is the process in which generally lean and/or tender pieces of food are totally immersed in hot fat or oil, and cooked quickly. The heat of the oil penetrates the food and cooks it.

Deep fried foods can be cooked quickly and handled easily for service.

Deep frying

> **PROFESSIONAL TIP**
> Holding for service – When fried foods are to be held for service they shouldn't be covered as moisture caused would turn the food soggy.

The purpose of deep frying is to produce food with an appetising golden-brown colour that is crisp and enjoyable to eat. Deep frying:

- tenderises and makes food items more digestible
- ensures food is safe to eat
- enhances the colour, flavour and texture of the finished dish
- enhances the presentation of the dish
- protects items from absorbing the fat.

Deep fried foods are often cooked by applying a coating (usually milk, egg, bread crumbs or batter). Applying a coating means a variety of foods can be cooked in this way and prevents the enclosed food from becoming greasy. The coating also adds a crisp texture and a contrast to the softer texture of the food item itself.

1.1 Selecting food items for deep frying

Fish and chips are probably the most popular kind of deep fried food in the UK. However, many things can be deep fried, including:

- eggs, including eggs from chickens (hens), ducks, quail, etc.
- fish, including – plaice, lemon sole (white flat), cod, sea bass (white round). It is uncommon to see dishes where oily fish such as salmon and mackerel are deep fried. However, flakes of precooked salmon are sometimes used when mixed with puréed potatoes to make salmon fishcakes. These are then coated and deep fried.
- fruit, including fruits such as bananas, pineapple (tropical), apples, pears (hard fruit), peaches, plums (stone fruit)
- meats, including beef, lamb and pork
- mixed ingredients for flour/batter-based products (e.g. dough based or choux paste, sweet and savoury)
- poultry, including chicken and turkey
- vegetables, including mushrooms (fungi), potatoes (tuber), onions (bulb), peppers (fruits)
- ready-made products.

Quality checks when selecting food items for deep frying

- **Appearance** – Check that food items appear the way they should. For example, when checking vegetables and/or fruits, look for signs of damage or bruising. Check for any signs of decay. The appearance of fish can also provide a clear indication as to its quality. The eyes should be bright and bulbous; scales should be intact (if the fish has scales) and the gills should be a deep red colour. It is also very important to check the use-by and best-before dates on products and/or their packaging to ensure that they are safe to use.
- **Freshness** – The appearance of food gives a good indication of freshness. Other indications include the feel of foods. For example, fruit may be very soft if it is overripe. A fish will lose firmness of its flesh the longer it is left unused. Our sense of smell also provides a strong indication of the freshness of foods. If foods such as meat or fish start to have a strong, rancid or unpleasant smell, this is a clear indication that the food is deteriorating and very likely to be unsafe to use. It will, at the very least, provide an unpleasant eating experience for the consumer and foods in this condition should not be used.
- **Size and shape** – The size and shape of foods need to be considered when deep frying foods. For example, due to the high temperatures and rapid cooking of foods that are deep fried, the food items have to be of a suitable size and shape to be cooked through in the time that the surface has coloured to the desired degree. The size and shape of foods to be deep fried have to be considered to work out the time it will take to cook through to the desired texture. Such foods are often sliced thinly or cut into dice – sweet and sour pork, for example, or potatoes cut into batons to make chips.
- **Texture** – As with size and shape, the texture of foods to be deep fried will have an impact on the cooking time. Foods suited to this method of cookery tend to be fairly lean and tender, and can therefore be cooked in fairly short amounts of time. Lean meats, poultry, fish and vegetables are examples of foods with suitable textures to cook using this method. Guidelines for frying ready-made or frozen foods suitable for deep frying need to be followed accurately in order to produce finished products with the desired texture, which are also safe to eat.
- **Type** – As with all the examples described above, the type of food to be deep fried, from its texture to its size, will require different considerations to ascertain a food's suitability when using this method to cook foods. For example, a large food item with a dense texture, such as a thick-cut chip, will require a different approach to deep frying (e.g. time and temperature) compared to a breaded button mushroom.

1.2 Applying preparation methods for deep frying

- **Blanching** – Blanching is the initial cooking of some deep fried foods before the heat of the oil is increased to finish the cooking process. Chips, particularly thick-cut chips, are often cooked in this way. The initial blanching, where the oil is at a lower temperature, ensures that the potato is cooked through and this process helps to soften the texture of the potato. The chips are then drained and can be allowed to cool. To finish, the temperature of the oil is then increased and the chips are placed back into the hot oil where the high temperature will quickly crisp the external surface of the chip and the centre will be cooked through to provide a soft and fluffy texture.

PROFESSIONAL TIP

The texture of chips can vary depending on the water content within the potato. The higher the dry matter/starch in the potato, the dryer and fluffier the cooked chip will be after frying. Varieties such as King Edwards and Maris Piper are widely available potatoes with reasonably high dry matter and therefore good potatoes to select when deep frying.

- **Coating** – This is covering food items prior to frying to help seal them, protecting the food surface from the intense heat of the fat or oil and slowing down the penetration of heat and preventing moisture and nutrients from escaping. Coatings include breadcrumbs, batter and flour. From a quality perspective, it is important to ensure that foods have an even coating.
- **Cutting** – Depending on the type of food to be deep fried, it is often necessary to prepare foods into the appropriate size and shape for the dish required. This could include an onion being sliced into rings before being battered and deep fried.
- **Draining and drying** (pre-cooking) – Items to be deep fried should be free from excess water. Water will cause hot oil to spit quite violently, so it is important that foods are dry before they are placed into hot oil.

Quality checks when preparing to deep fry food items

To ensure the quality of products, there are a number of things that help a chef during preparation.

- **Even coating** – Ingredients coated with a crumb or batter should have an even coating when deep frying. All areas of the surface of the food should be coated to provide an even texture once fried; this also ensures protection of the food item itself from the hot oil.
- **Ingredients cut and prepared to specification** – Regardless of the product, it is important to ensure that ingredients are cut and prepared to specification. This will help to achieve the high-quality product that is being aspired to, as well as even cooking.
- **Minimal waste** – As with all preparation and cooking, minimising waste is an essential part of a chef's role. Not only is it a waste of resources to dispose of usable food, it is unethical and a waste of money. A commercial food-based operation should aim to utilise as much food product as possible to increase sales potential and minimise expenditure.

1.3 Applying techniques to produce deep fried products

Techniques to produce deep fried products

- **Draining and drying** (after cooking) – Once cooked, fried foods should be drained to ensure any oil/fat drains off the food before service. Foods should be lifted carefully from the hot oil, shaken gently (if in a basket) to release excess fat or oil, and placed on to a tray lined with absorbent kitchen paper/roll.
- **Immersion** – Placing the food item in the fat, with or without a basket, depending on the dish; normally, larger items, such as a battered fillet of fish, are cooked without a basket, whereas small items, such as chips, would be fried in a basket.
- **Cooking in batches and reheating** – After removing a batch of food, it is important to allow the fat/oil to heat up again before adding the next batch. The temperature of the fat/oil must be allowed to recover to the required temperature before the next batch is cooked. If not, the food will look pale, unappetising and may be soggy to eat. If reheating foods, ensure that they are reheated sufficiently to a safe core temperature (see Unit 201 for details of safe temperatures) without overcooking/burning the exterior surface of the food item.
- **Temperature control** – Temperature and timing is critical when deep frying. If you are cooking thicker pieces of food, you should lower the temperature to account for the time it will take for heat to penetrate through. This allows the food to cook thoroughly on the inside without burning on the outside. The reverse is also true – the smaller the pieces of food, a hotter frying temperature will be needed and a shorter cooking time.
- **Turning** – To ensure even cooking and colouring, it is important to turn foods during the deep frying process. When deep frying foods, they tend to colour slightly quicker face down in the oil. To achieve a consistent colour and even crispness, foods should be moved around and turned in the oil. This is particularly relevant to lightweight foods that float towards the surface of the oil.

PROFESSIONAL TIP

Do not fry the food too far in advance of serving it – fried foods soon lose their crispness.

Strain oil and fat after use to remove any food particles. If these are left in the fat they will burn when the fat is next heated, spoiling the appearance and flavour of the food.

Always cover oil or fat when not in use to prevent the air from making it rancid.

Techniques to produce different types of deep fried products

Frying mediums: types of oil used

A variety of oils and fats can be used for deep fat frying. Often a mix of vegetable oils is used. There are several varieties of vegetable oil:

- sunflower
- corn
- maize
- rapeseed
- olive.

Some establishments deep fry in goose fat, duck fat or beef dripping. This has become popular because of the flavour it adds to the fried food, in particular chips. However, these fats are higher in saturated fats than, vegetable oils.

HEALTH AND SAFETY

Hot fat can cause serious burns, either through spills or accidents. Deep frying can be a very dangerous method of cooking, especially if people are not correctly trained. Staff should be trained to use deep fryers.

Commercial deep fryers have built-in safety features, such as thermostatic controls and fat-level indicators. These safety features make commercial fryers preferable to pots on stoves.

Points to consider when deep frying

- Never overfill fryers with fat or oil, or with the food to be cooked.
- When deep fat frying, it is essential to maintain the fat at the right temperature. The normal frying temperature is between 175°C and 195°C. A slight heat haze will rise from the fat when it reaches this temperature. When using freestanding fryers without a thermometer, never allow the fat to get so hot that smoke rises from it. This will give the food a bad taste and smell.

HEALTH AND SAFETY

Monitor the temperature – if it is too high, the fat may easily ignite and cause a fire. Never allow fat to heat up so much that it starts to smoke. Smoke means that the hot oil could burst into flames and is very dangerous.

How to deep fry

- Preheat the oil or fat. Thermostatically controlled deep fryers have a light signal to inform the user that the oil has reached the desired temperature.
- Coat the food as required.
- Once it has reached the required temperature, place the food carefully into the oil or fat using baskets, tongs and/or slotted spoons.
- Fry the food until it is cooked and golden brown, using a temperature probe to check the internal (core) temperature of the food.
- Drain the food well before serving. Drain the food carefully, avoiding sharp, rushed movements that may cause food to drop and splash into the hot oil. Have a tray lined with absorbent kitchen paper close by on a well-balanced, safe and secure surface so that the products can be drained and dried safely.

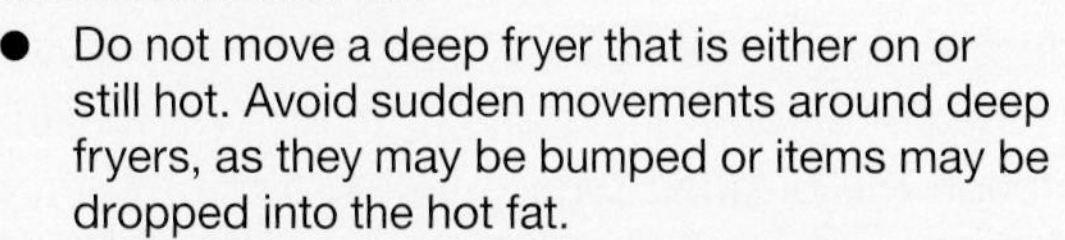

HEALTH AND SAFETY

- Do not move a deep fryer that is either on or still hot. Avoid sudden movements around deep fryers, as they may be bumped or items may be dropped into the hot fat.
- Always keep a close eye on a deep fryer and never leave it unattended.
- Before using a deep fryer, know how to put out a fat fire. Do not try to put out a fat fire with water. Cover the pot or fryer with a lid or fire blanket, and then use the correct fire extinguisher. Fire extinguishing equipment should be kept nearby and staff should be trained in how to use it.
- Stand back when placing food into the fryer to avoid steam and splash burns. Avoid putting your face, arms or hands over the deep fryer.

Quality checks during the deep frying process

- **Appearance and degree of cooking** – Time and temperature are important factors when deep frying foods. The external surface of foods will colour quickly in very hot oil or fat, giving the appearance that the food item is cooked. However, if food is fried too quickly at too high a temperature, the surface may appear to be cooked to the desired degree, but the internal (core) area of the product might not be cooked through. The size, shape and texture of the food also have to be considered. Thicker foods or foods with dense textures, such as thick-cut chips, will take longer to cook through than finer and delicately structured foods, such as goujons of fish. All of these factors need to be considered to achieve the desired appearance and degree of cooking when deep frying foods.

- **Condition of oil/fat** – The condition of oil or fat used when deep frying is vitally important. Oil or fat that has been used to fry many different products will pick up taints and aromas from other foods, particularly foods with strong aromas such as fish. Furthermore, oils and fats lose their freshness and can pick up residue when frying, which can leave burnt particles that can then be transferred on to other foods. Therefore, it is very important that oils and/or fats are in good, clean and fresh condition before they are used to fry food.
- **Sufficient oil/fat** – When deep frying, food items are submerged in the oil or fat. Therefore, the quantity of oil has to be sufficient to allow foods to be completely and safely surrounded with the oil or fat being used. Turning foods helps to ensure a good texture to the external surface of the food and also even cooking.
- **Temperature of oil/fat** – The temperature of oil or fat is a defining aspect when deep frying foods. If the oil or fat is too cool, the food item being fried will absorb the oil, making it greasy and heavy to eat, as well as potentially affecting its texture. For example, when deep frying a breaded mushroom, if the oil is too cool it will penetrate through the breaded surface and into the mushroom itself. By the time the mushroom is cooked, it will have absorbed too much oil, making it very greasy to eat. The crumb itself may also feel greasy and is likely to lack the light, crisp texture of a breaded mushroom deep fried at the correct temperature.
- **Texture** – Deep fried foods tend to have a crisp external texture, due to the high level of heat from the oil or fat that the external area of the food is exposed to. The crisping of the external area provides protection to the interior area of deep fried foods, allowing heat to penetrate through the food item and cooking it through. This produces products with a crisp external texture, and a softer and more delicate internal texture.

1.4 Applying finishing methods for deep fried products

Finishing methods for deep fried products

- **Applying seasonings and flavours** – Some fried products benefit from additional seasonings and flavours. For example, deep fried spring greens can be enhanced by spices, and even the simple chip is enhanced by salt and vinegar.
- **Coating** – Some deep fried products are finished with a coating. For example, sweet and sour pork is coated with the sweet and sour sauce once it is deep fried.
- **Garnishing** – This helps to add to the presentation of deep fried dishes. A simple deep fried piece of fish is often accompanied with a garnish of lemon wedges.
- **Saucing** – Deep fried items may be enhanced by serving with an accompanying sauce. This applies to both sweet and savoury dishes. For example, a deep fried fruit fritter is traditionally served with a hot, sweet sauce.

Quality checks when finishing deep fried products

- **Appearance** – Dishes should have a fresh and appealing appearance. For example, the light, golden brown colour of deep fried breadcrumbed products.
- **Aroma** – Deep fried foods should not generate strong aromas as the flavours developed within foods are encased within the food itself. Deep fried foods produce a light aroma from the frying process but this should not be overly strong. A strong aroma may be due to old oil or oil that has been tainted due to being used to fry strong-smelling foods such as fish.
- **Colour** – Colours should be natural and vibrant, as in the case of vegetables, for example. Incorrect cooking of foods, both under- and overcooking, often results in undesired colour. As frying is performed at high temperatures, the colour of food can change quickly, so it is important to ensure that attention is paid to avoid over-charring or burning the food.
- **Consistency** – When finishing dishes, it is important to ensure the regularity of appearance and portion size. For example, if two customers sit down together and order the same dish, they will be disappointed if one dish is neatly presented with a moderate portion size and the other portion is poorly presented with a much smaller portion size. Consistency demonstrates professionalism and attention to detail, and will go some way to achieving customer satisfaction.
- **Portion control** – As well as portions being consistent in size and appearance, it is important that they are also of the predetermined size. If portions are smaller than advertised to customers, or inadequate for the type of dish being served, it is likely that customers will complain. If the portion size is too big, it is likely that wastage will increase as customers may not be able to eat such large portions. In this case, it is likely that the business will lose money as it will not be able to achieve the number of portions planned for the commodities in question.
- **Presentation** – Chefs have the opportunity to present foods in creative and attractive ways, to impress and potentially increase customer numbers. Most importantly, presentation should be neat, consistent and precise. Service equipment, including plates, should be spotlessly clean.

- **Seasoning** – Correcting the seasoning of foods makes a huge difference to the overall eating quality. Although salt consumption should be carefully monitored to promote healthy eating, a little salt and pepper (if appropriate) can lift foods to a new level and bring natural flavours to life.
- **Taste** – Ultimately, it is the taste of foods that provides that most pleasure to diners. Linked with texture, it is the experience of eating, and the enjoyment of the tastes and flavours, that make eating such an enjoyable experience when food is prepared and cooked well.
- **Temperature** – It is important to ensure that the correct temperature is applied when deep frying foods. If foods are fried at too low a temperature, they are likely to absorb oil and become greasy. Foods that are fried at a temperature that is too high are likely to burn before they are adequately cooked through. Additionally, foods that are cooked at temperatures that are too high will appear to be cooked from the outside, but it is possible that they will not be cooked through and this could be dangerous from a food safety perspective.
- **Texture** – Texture provides contrast across foods and dishes. The crisp external texture of deep fried foods contrasting with a softer internal texture provides a dining experience that brings pleasure to customers. It is therefore very important to achieve the desired textures in foods. For example, think of a freshly fried chip. It should have a light and crisp, lightly golden external surface, contrasting with a delicate, dry and fluffy textured potato beneath.

2 Produce shallow fried products

Shallow frying is cooking food in a small quantity of preheated fat or oil in a shallow pan (a frying pan, sauté pan or wok) or on a flat surface (a griddle plate). As the food is in direct contact with the fat, it cooks rapidly. The high temperature used in shallow frying seals the surface of the food almost instantly and prevents the natural juices from escaping.

Shallow frying video, http://bit.ly/Xt1t1R

Shallow frying

The purpose of shallow frying is to brown food, giving it a different colour and an interesting and attractive flavour. Shallow frying:

- tenderises and makes food items more digestible
- ensures food is safe to eat and maintains its nutritional value
- enhances the colour, flavour and texture of the finished dish
- enhances the presentation of the finished dish.

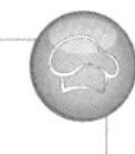

PROFESSIONAL TIP

Browning – Colour changes caused through the cooking process by cooking at the right temperature.

2.1 Selecting food items for shallow frying

Food items that may be shallow fried include:

- eggs, including eggs from chickens (hens), ducks, quail, etc.
- fish, including all types – plaice, lemon sole (white flat), cod, sea bass (white round), salmon, mackerel (oily)
- fruit, including fruits such as bananas, pineapple (tropical), apples, pears (hard fruit), peaches, plums (stone fruit)
- meats, including beef, lamb and pork
- mixed ingredients for flour/batter-based products (sweet and savoury)
- noodles, including flour- and rice-based noodles
- poultry, including chicken and turkey
- rice, including different varieties and types (e.g. long-grain, basmati, white, brown)
- vegetables, including mushrooms (fungi), potatoes (tuber), onions (bulb), peppers (fruits).

PROFESSIONAL TIP

Some of the frying medium (oil or butter) will be absorbed by the food, which will change its nutritional content (in other words, it will make it fattier). Protect items from absorbing the fat in which they are cooked by applying a coating.

Quality checks when selecting food items for shallow frying

As with deep frying, you need to check the quality of the food items before using, including:

- appearance
- freshness
- size and shape – shallow fried foods are often fairly thin, such as a fillet of fish or an escalope of chicken, so it can cook evenly; the size and shape of foods to be shallow fried have to be considered to work out the time it will take to cook through to the desired texture; such foods are often sliced thinly or cut into dice for sweet and sour pork, for example
- texture
- type.

2.2 Applying preparation methods for shallow frying

Preparation methods for shallow frying

- **Batting (out)** – Cuts of meat and poultry are batted out using a meat hammer or bat to give an even thickness and to start breaking down the connective tissue to help even cooking, resulting in a more tender final product.
- **Coating** – Covering food items prior to frying to help seal them. When shallow frying, this is usually done by coating lightly with lightly seasoned flour or by coating in breadcrumbs (pané).
- **Cutting** – Depending on the type of food to be shallow fried, it is often necessary to prepare foods into the appropriate size and shape for the dish required. This could include cutting an escalope of pork to be crumbed (pané) and shallow fried.
- **Marinating** – Items are pre-soaked or coated in a marinade to help flavour, tenderise and in some cases colour food before the cooking process starts. This is often done to impart flavours and spices into meats before shallow frying – strips of chicken in a stir fry provides a good example.
- **Mixing** – This ensures the correct finished texture of the dish, providing an even balance of ingredients before cooking. Again, a stir fry provides a good example, ensuring that there is an even mix and quantity of ingredients.

Quality checks when preparing to shallow fry food items

- **Even coating** – Ingredients coated with a crumb or batter should have an even coating when shallow frying. All areas of the surface of the food should be coated to provide an even texture once fried and this also ensures protection of the food item itself from the hot oil.
- **Ingredients cut and prepared to specification** – Regardless of the product, it is important to ensure that ingredients are cut and prepared to specification. This will help to achieve the high-quality product that is being aspired to, as well as even cooking.
- **Minimal waste** – As with all preparation and cooking, minimising waste is an essential part of a chef's role. Not only is it a waste of resources to dispose of usable food, it is unethical and a waste of money. A commercial food-based operation should aim to utilise as much food product as possible to increase sales potential and minimise expenditure.

2.3 Applying techniques to produce shallow fried products

Techniques to produce shallow fried products

- **Basting** – To help to develop flavour and texture, shallow fried foods are basted during the frying process. This is a process where the fat or oil is spooned back over the food item being fried.
- **Draining and drying** (after cooking) – Once cooked, fried foods should be drained to ensure any oil/fat drains off the food before service. Foods should be lifted carefully from the hot oil and placed on to a tray lined with absorbent kitchen paper/roll.
- **Reheating** – Shallow fried items are best served immediately on their initial frying, unless you are just blanching foods to be finished at a later time. If foods do need to be reheated, it is essential that they are cooked through to a safe internal temperature (75°C). Check the core (internal) temperature of reheated foods using a clean, calibrated temperature probe.
- **Sautéing** – To sauté (meaning to toss or jump) tender cuts of meat and poultry, cook them in a sauté pan or frying pan in the same way as for shallow frying. Once the food is cooked on both sides, remove it from the pan, discard the fat and deglaze the pan with stock or wine. This liquid is then used to make the sauce to go with the food. Food such as potatoes, onions and kidneys can also be sautéed. Cut them into slices or pieces and toss them in hot shallow fat or oil in a frying pan until golden brown and cooked through.

- **Stir frying** – Stir fry vegetables, strips of fish, meat or poultry in a wok or frying pan by fast frying them in a little fat or oil. Due to the high temperatures used when stir frying, it is important that food items are moved or tossed throughout the process.
- **Temperature control** – It is essential to control the temperature when shallow frying foods. This will ensure that they are evenly cooked through, without over-charring or burning. Controlling temperature will also help to achieve the desired colour and texture.
- **Tossing** – This is a general term used to describe how foods are moved around to prevent over-charring, and to ensure foods are cooked evenly and to the right texture.
- **Turning** – To ensure even cooking and colouring, it is important to turn foods during the frying process. When shallow frying delicate items, such as a fillet of fish, it is recommended that the fish is turned only once and that the presentation surface of the fillet – the surface that was previously attached to the skeleton of the fish rather than the skin side – is placed into the pan first. This is to ensure that the presentation of the fish is clean and free from any fried debris that can occur naturally during the frying process.

Techniques to produce different types of shallow fried products

Frying mediums

The same fats and oils are used as in deep frying.

If shallow-fried food needs to be cooked in butter, it is advisable to use clarified butter, which has a higher burning point than unclarified butter, so it will not burn as easily. To clarify butter, melt it and then carefully strain off the fat, leaving behind the clear liquid.

Points to consider when shallow frying

- When shallow frying continuously over a busy period, prepare and cook the food in a systematic way.
- Cleaning the pans after every use, even in batch cooking, will ensure the best presentation.
- Food should be dry to ensure that it fries correctly and that oil/fat does not spit out of the pan towards the chef.
- Food items should be placed in the pan presentation side down first. Turning just once will help enhance presentation of the finished dish

HEALTH AND SAFETY

Add food to the pan carefully, away from you, to avoid being splashed by hot fat. Always keep your sleeves rolled down to prevent splashing fat from burning your forearms.

Temperature and time control are particularly important as all shallow fried foods should have an appetising golden-brown colour on both sides. The temperature should initially be hot; the heat should then be reduced and the food turned when necessary.

PROFESSIONAL TIP

Select the correct type and size of pan. If it is too small the food will not brown evenly and may break up. If it is too large, the areas of the pan not covered by food will burn and spoil the flavour of the food.

HEALTH AND SAFETY

Move pans carefully in case they jar and tip fat on to the stove. Use a thick, clean, dry cloth when handling pans.

Equipment used for deep and shallow frying

In most kitchens there will be a variety of large or small pieces of equipment used for frying, depending upon the style of cooking and dishes served.

Equipment specific to frying includes:

- deep fryer, thermostatically controlled, friture or pressure fryers
- shallow frying pans, sauté pans and bratt pans (for large quantities)
- specialist fryers or pans, woks, omelette, blinis, tava, griddle plate.

Quality checks during the deep and shallow frying process

- **Appearance and degree of cooking** – As many shallow fried dishes are made from lean and tender products, the cooking process is relatively fast. It is therefore essential to pay close attention to their appearance and the changes that take place from a raw state to a cooked one. Another consideration is that some shallow fried meat dishes can be cooked to different degrees. This could be a fillet steak, for example, which a customer could order rare, medium or well done. Refer to the section on 'Temperature of oil/fat' (page 212) to see how the importance of temperature affects shallow fried products.
- **Condition of oil/fat** – The condition of the oil or fat used when shallow frying is vitally important. Oil or fat that has been used to fry many different products will pick up taints and aromas from other foods,

particularly foods with strong aromas such as fish. Furthermore, oils and fats lose their freshness and can pick up residue when frying, which can leave burnt particles that can then be transferred on to other foods. Therefore, it is very important that oils and/or fats are in good, clean and fresh condition before they are used to fry food.

- **Quantity of oil/fat** – When shallow frying foods, items are placed on to a hot surface (e.g. a frying pan or griddle surface) that is lined with oil or fat. In this case, it is only this area of the food that is in direct contact with the oil or fat and why many foods, excluding items such as fried eggs, have to be turned during the cooking process. Turning foods helps to ensure a good texture to the external surface of the food and also even cooking. When shallow frying, only a small amount of oil or fat is used to line the frying surface.
- **Temperature of oil/fat** – The temperature of oil or fat is a defining aspect when shallow frying foods. If the oil or fat is too cool, the food item being fried will absorb the oil, making it greasy and heavy to eat, as well as potentially affecting its texture. When shallow frying foods, such as steaks in particular, the temperature and severity of the heat that is in direct contact will affect the speed of browning and caramelisation on the exterior surface of the meat. Essentially, steaks cooked to varying degrees should have the same external appearance, regardless of whether they are cooked rare, medium or well done. It is the variance in temperature and time that dictates the degree to which the steak is cooked.
- **Texture** – When shallow frying foods, it is sometimes possible to sample the texture. In the case of meats, the degree of cooking can be judged by inserting a temperature probe into the centre of the food. It is also possible to judge by pressing the meat and seeing how much 'give' (softness) there is in terms of texture. The firmer the meat, the more well cooked it is. With multiple cooked items, such as a stir fry, it is also possible to remove a small amount of food with a clean spoon, or equivalent, and taste the food for texture, as well as check to ensure seasonings and other flavourings are as desired. This is part of the skill set a chef requires while monitoring foods when shallow frying.

2.4 Applying finishing methods for shallow fried products

Finishing methods for shallow fried products

- **Applying seasonings and flavours** – Some fried products benefit from additional seasonings and flavours. For example, sauté potatoes are enhanced by salt and vinegar.
- **Filling** – Some shallow fried dishes, such as escalope of pork 'cordon bleu', are filled before they are fried. In this case, a slice of ham and cheese is placed in between two battened-out escalopes of pork before being crumbed and shallow fried.
- **Garnishing** – This helps to add to the presentation of shallow fried dishes. Some simple sauté potatoes are enhanced with a little freshly chopped parsley, for example.
- **Saucing** – Shallow fried items may be enhanced by serving with an accompanying sauce. This applies to both sweet and savoury dishes. For example, a shallow fried fillet of breaded (pané) fish is usually served with tartare sauce.

Accompanying products when deep and shallow frying foods

- Accompaniments and associated products include the traditional items that would be offered with specific dishes.
- Sauces and garnishes are normally indicated in recipes and may include jus-lié with escalopes of meat or lemon wedges with other fried dishes.

Quality checks when finishing shallow fried products

As with deep fried products, you need to look at the quality of products when finishing them, especially the following.

- **Appearance** – Dishes should have an appealing appearance. For example, the caramelised appearance of shallow-fried meats.
- **Aroma** – Particularly when shallow frying dishes, aroma is an important aspect of the dining experience. For

example, when meat is shallow fried, the proteins and sugars naturally present start to caramelise, a process known as the Maillard reaction, which releases the meaty aromas that customers will enjoy.

- **Temperature** – It is important to ensure that the correct temperature is applied when shallow frying foods. If foods are fried at too low a temperature, they are likely to absorb oil and become greasy. Foods that are fried at a temperature that is too high are likely to burn before they are adequately cooked through. Additionally, foods that are cooked at temperatures that are too high will appear to be cooked from the outside, but it is possible that they will not be cooked through and this could be dangerous from a food safety perspective.
- **Texture** – The light, crisp external texture of a freshly shallow fried fillet of fish provides a dining experience that brings pleasure to customers. Other textures to consider when shallow frying include the caramelisation and softening of sliced onions or the bubbling and light crispiness of a fried egg. It is therefore very important to achieve the desired textures in foods when cooking by shallow frying.

Also important are:

- colour
- consistency
- portion control
- presentation
- seasoning
- taste.

For more information about these points, see page 208 in section 1.4.

TEST YOURSELF

1. Briefly describe the process for the following methods of cooking:
   a deep frying
   b shallow frying.
2. List three types of coating that could be applied to fish before frying.
3. List five safety points a chef should consider when cooking by deep frying.
4. What are the traditional accompaniments to the following fried dishes:
   a deep fried cod
   b pan fried fillet of plaice?
5. List five oils that can be used for frying foods.
6. List three types of food that could be deep fried.
7. Briefly describe the term blanching in relation to deep fried potato dishes.
8. Describe how you would griddle sausages.
9. What is the benefit of using clarified butter when shallow frying foods?
10. Describe why it is best practice to turn a fillet of fish only once during the shallow frying process.

KEY TERMS

Basting: Moistening meat periodically, especially while cooking, using a liquid such as melted butter or a sauce

Batting (out): Cuts of meat and poultry are batted out using a meat hammer or bat to give an even thickness and start breaking down the connective tissue to assist even cooking, resulting in a more tender final product

Marinating: Items are pre-soaked or coated in a marinade to help flavour, tenderise and in some cases colour food before the cooking process starts

Sautéing: To sauté (meaning to toss or jump) tender cuts of meat and poultry, cook them in a sauté pan or frying pan in the same way as for shallow frying

Deep fried products

1 Scotch eggs

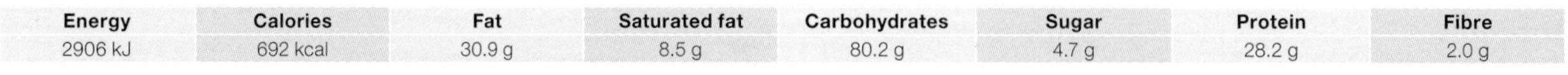

Energy	Calories	Fat	Saturated fat	Carbohydrates	Sugar	Protein	Fibre
2906 kJ	692 kcal	30.9 g	8.5 g	80.2 g	4.7 g	28.2 g	2.0 g

Ingredient	4 portions	10 portions
Eggs	4	10
Pork sausage meat	275 g	700 g
Fresh thyme leaves	1 tsp	2½ tsp
Fresh parsley, chopped	1 tsp	2½ tsp
Spring onion, very finely chopped	1	2½
Salt and freshly ground black pepper, rock salt for finishing		
Plain flour, seasoned	125 g	300 g
Egg, beaten	1	2½
Breadcrumbs	250 g	625 g
Vegetable oil for deep frying		

Mise en place

1. To breadcrumb (pané) the Scotch eggs, have three trays prepared. The first should contain seasoned flour, the second beaten egg and the third breadcrumbs. Try to avoid getting the flour in the egg and the egg in the breadcrumbs when passing from one tray to the next. Shake off any excess between each stage. This process is easier with three people, especially if making large quantities, as one person can be assigned to one of the three tasks, reducing the likelihood of getting excess flour in the egg, and likewise with the egg into the flour.
2. Have a clean tray at the end of the process on which to place the crumbed eggs on completion.

Cooking

1. Place the eggs, still in their shells, in a pan of water.
2. Place over a high heat and bring to the boil, then reduce the heat to simmer for approximately 9 minutes.
3. Drain and refresh the eggs under cold running water, then peel.
4. Mix the sausage meat with the thyme, parsley and spring onion in a bowl, season well with salt and freshly ground black pepper.
5. Divide the sausage meat mixture into four and flatten each out on a clean surface into ovals about 12 cm long and 8 cm at the widest point.
6. Roll the boiled egg in the seasoned flour.
7. Place each egg on to a sausage meat oval, then wrap the sausage meat around the egg, making sure the coating is smooth and completely covers the egg.
8. Dip each meat-coated egg in the flour, then in the beaten egg, covering the entire surface area.
9. Roll the egg in the breadcrumbs to coat completely.
10. Heat the oil in a deep heavy-bottomed pan, to 180°C.
11. Carefully place each Scotch egg into the hot oil and deep fry for 6–8 minutes until golden and crisp and the sausage meat is completely cooked.
12. Carefully remove from the oil with a slotted spoon and drain on kitchen paper.

1 Flatten out an oval of the sausage meat mixture

2 Flour the egg and wrap the meat around it until it is completely covered

3 Dip in flour, then beaten egg

4 Roll the egg in the breadcrumbs

5 The egg should be completely coated in breadcrumbs, ready for frying

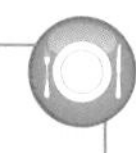

SERVING SUGGESTION

To serve, cut the egg in half and season slightly with rock salt. Scotch eggs can be served hot, warm or cold.

VARIATION

- For a vegetarian version of the traditional pork Scotch egg, follow the same method as above, replacing the sausage meat with 350 g of dry mashed potato.
- A fish version can also be made. Follow the same method as above, using 300 g fish mousse (this works best using salmon) instead of sausage meat.

2 Dorset crab cake with watercress salad

Energy	Calories	Fat	Saturated fat	Carbohydrates	Sugar	Protein	Fibre	Sodium
1155 kJ	272 kcal	4.1 g	0.5 g	39.9 g	2.6 g	17.9 g	2.0 g	536.0 g

* Added 20 g flour for coating, 1/2 tablespoon oil for frying, 1/4 teaspoon salt, 50 g watercress

Ingredient	4 portions	10 portions
Dorset white crab meat	200 g	500 g
Lime, zest and juice	½	1½
Ginger	1 cm	2½ cm
Spring onions	1	3
Dorset Naga chilli, small	½	1½
Coriander leaves	⅛ bunch	½ bunch
Soft white breadcrumbs	200 g	500 g
Eggs	1	3
Flour and beaten eggs, for coating		
Oil, for cooking		
Salt and pepper		
Dorset watercress	1 bunch	2½ bunches

Regional recipe contributed by Christophe Baffos of Bournemouth and Poole College.

Mise en place

1 Wash all the vegetables and herbs.
2 Peel and finely grate the ginger, finely slice the spring onions, chop the coriander and brunoise the chilli.
3 Pick the watercress and set aside, ready to be dressed.

Cooking

1 Pick the crab meat and place in a mixing bowl, add the zest of the lime (reserve the juice for the dressing), ginger, spring onion, chilli, coriander, half the breadcrumbs (reserve half for pané) and beaten eggs. Mix thoroughly. Season to taste.
2 Divide the mix into eight cakes, flour, egg and breadcrumb them (pané à l'anglaise) and shape using a palette knife.
3 Deep fry at 175°C until golden. Probe the cakes and ensure they reach 75°C (core temperature). Drain on absorbent paper.
4 Serve hot on a bed of watercress dressed with a vinaigrette made from Dorset honey, lime juice, English mustard, salt, pepper and grape seed oil.

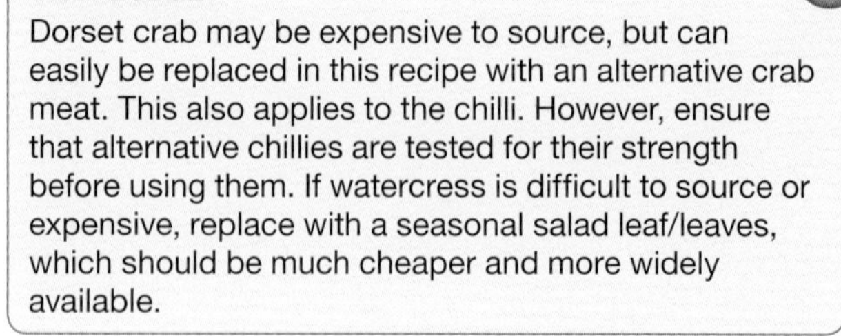

ON A BUDGET

Dorset crab may be expensive to source, but can easily be replaced in this recipe with an alternative crab meat. This also applies to the chilli. However, ensure that alternative chillies are tested for their strength before using them. If watercress is difficult to source or expensive, replace with a seasonal salad leaf/leaves, which should be much cheaper and more widely available.

3 Fried fish in batter

Energy	Calories	Fat	Saturated fat	Carbohydrates	Sugar	Protein	Fibre
736 kJ	415 kcal	14.0 g	1.8 g	41.6 g	3.5 g	33.2 g	2.1 g

Ingredient	4 portions	10 portions
White fish fillets	400 g	1 kg
Light oil in deep fryer		
Lemons, cut into halves or wedges	2	5

Batter		
Flour	200 g	500 g
Extra flour to pass the prepared fish through		
Salt	5 g	12 g
Egg	1	2–3
Water or milk	250 ml	625 ml
Oil	2 tbsp	5 tbsp

Deep frying is suitable for cuts and fillets of white fish, such as cod and haddock. The fish must be coated with something that prevents the cooking fat or oil from penetrating into the fish. This recipe uses batter.

Mise en place

1. Prepare, clean, wash and thoroughly dry the fish.
2. Cut into 100 g portions.

Preparing the batter

1. Sift the flour and salt into a basin.
2. Make a well (a small hollow) in the dried ingredients and pour in the egg and the milk or water.
3. Gradually incorporate (mix in) the flour, using a wooden spoon or whisk.

4. Beat the mixture until it is smooth.
5. Mix in the oil and allow the mixture to rest for ½–1 hour before using.

Cooking

1 Pass the prepared fish through flour (cover it in flour).

2 Shake off any surplus and then pass it through the batter.

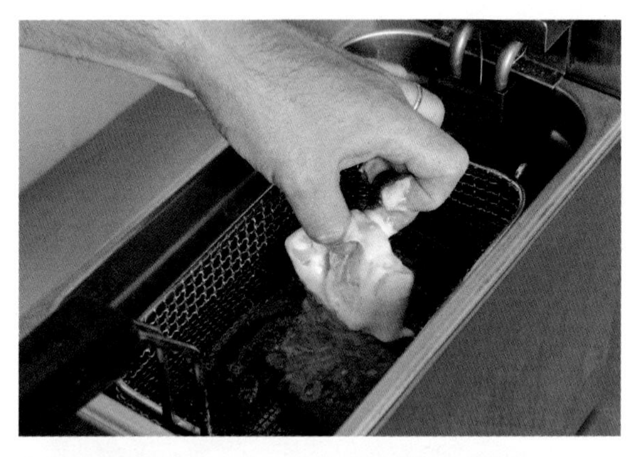

3 Taking great care, gently lower the fish, away from you, into deep fat at 175°C.

4 Allow to cook until the fish turns a golden brown.

5 Remove carefully on to kitchen paper and allow to drain well.

VARIATION

- Add yeast or stiffly beaten egg whites to the batter, along with chopped fresh herbs, grated ginger or garam masala.
- If a yeast batter is used, you must allow time for the yeast to ferment (bubble) and raise (lighten) the batter.
- Instead of batter, the fish could be coated with:
  - milk and flour
  - flour, beaten egg and fresh white breadcrumbs.

SERVING SUGGESTION

Serve with either quarters of lemon (pips removed) or tartare sauce. Make the tartare sauce by chopping 25 g capers, 50 g gherkins and a sprig of parsley, and adding these to 250 ml of mayonnaise (see pages 257–258).

ON A BUDGET

Any white fish fillet can be used in this recipe (e.g. plaice, lemon sole, cod, haddock). Shop around for the best value to select the best fish available.

4 Fish cakes

Energy	Calories	Fat	Saturated fat	Carbohydrates	Sugar	Protein	Fibre	Sodium
988 kJ	235 kcal	9.7 g	1.5 g	19.9 g	1.3 g	16.5 g	1.1 g	288.0 g

* Potatoes mashed with milk and fat. Using baked cod

Ingredient	4 portions	10 portions
White fish and/or salmon, cooked	200 g	500 g
Potato, mashed	200 g	500 g
Flour	25 g	60 g
Eggs, beaten	1	2-3
Fresh white breadcrumbs	50 g	125 g
Salt and pepper, for seasoning		

Mise en place

1 Prepare, clean, wash and thoroughly dry the fish, then poach it.
2 Prepare the mashed potato.
3 Beat the eggs.

Cooking

1 Combine the fish and mashed potatoes. Taste and correct the seasoning.

2 Using a little flour, form the mixture into a long roll on a clean work surface.

3 Divide the mixture into two or four pieces per portion.

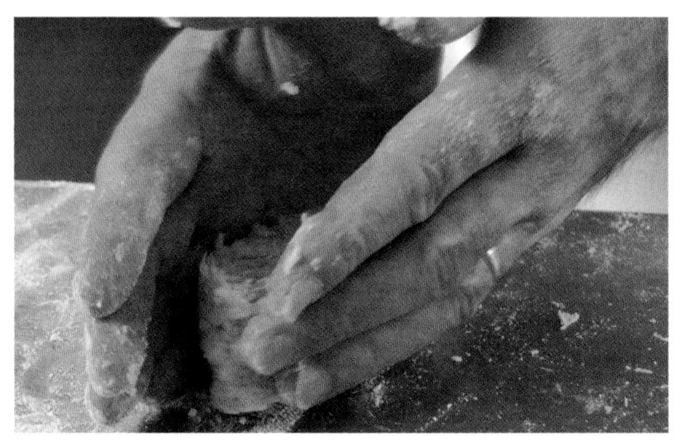

4 Mould each piece into a ball.

5 Pass the balls through flour, beaten egg and breadcrumbs.

6 Using a palette knife, flatten each shape firmly. Neaten the shapes and shake off surplus crumbs.

7 Deep fry in hot fat at 185°C for 2–3 minutes until golden brown.

8 Lift out carefully and transfer to kitchen paper to drain.

SERVING SUGGESTION

Serve the fish cakes with a suitable sauce, such as tomato or tartare.

VARIATION

Bake the fish cakes in a hot oven at 250°C for 10–15 minutes. If oven baked, it is not necessary to pass them through flour, egg and breadcrumbs. They should be shaped and placed on lightly greased baking trays.

Healthy eating tips

Another suggestion to increase the fibre content in the recipe would be to use wholemeal breadcrumbs.

ACTIVITY

1. In groups, prepare, cook, taste, serve and assess four variations of your choice.
2. Prepare one that will cater for someone on a gluten-free diet and list the adjustments you have made to the basic recipe.

5 Fruit fritters

Energy	Calories	Fat	Saturated fat	Carbohydrates	Sugar	Protein	Fibre	Sodium
1522 kJ	360 kcal	13.2 g	2.5 g	51.0 g	14.0 g	9.3 g	3.7 g	72.0 g

* Using 250 g each of apple, banana, pineapple and plum to make up the 1 kg of fruit. Using semi-skimmed milk, extra 24 g sunflower oil (2 tbsp) for assumed penetration during deep fat frying

Left to right: apple, fig and banana fritters

For the batter

Ingredient	10 portions
Flour	500 g
Salt	pinch
Eggs	3
Milk	625 ml
Sunflower oil	75 ml
Caster sugar	25 g

1. Sieve the flour and salt.
2. Separate the eggs, add the egg yolks and half the milk, whisk until smooth.
3. Add the rest of the milk and the oil. Pass through a conical strainer, cover and allow to rest for 30 minutes before using.
4. Just before using, whisk the egg whites with the sugar until soft peaks form, then fold in to the batter.

To make the fritters

The fruit you use should be firm but ripe. Use approximately 1 kg in total.

Ingredient	10 portions
Apples, peeled, cored and cut into thick slices	
Banana, peeled and cut into three pieces on the slant	
Pineapple, peeled, cored cut into slices and halved	
Plums, halved and stoned	
Figs, cut into quarters	
Apricots, halved and stoned	
Kirsch (optional) – other flavours could be used such as dark rum, for example; this would complement the tropical fruits: banana and pineapple. Brandy, cognac or Armagnac would complement the plums and apricots, and a coffee-based liqueur would complement the figs	60 ml
Caster sugar	50 g
Lemon juice	20 ml

Cooking

1. Place the prepared fruit in a bowl and add the kirsch (if using), sugar and lemon juice. Mix carefully (do not use your hands) and leave to marinate for 30 minutes.
2. Set a deep fat fryer at 180°C (make sure the oil is clean).
3. Drain the fruit (do not throw away the liquid).
4. Dip the individual pieces of fruit in batter, transfer to the fryer and cook for 2–3 minutes until a pale golden colour, lift out and drain on absorbent paper.
5. Sprinkle with icing sugar and serve hot on a paper napkin, with a fruit coulis or a sabayon flavoured with the liquid saved from the fruit.

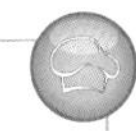

PROFESSIONAL TIP

It is fashionable – for example, on tasting menus – to serve a pre-dessert. This is a small portion of dessert served before the main dessert. Beignets could easily be adapted for this (for example, strawberries in tempura batter served with black pepper ice cream).

PROFESSIONAL TIP

Keep an eye on the temperature of the oil. If it falls below 180°C, wait and allow it to recover before continuing.

VARIATION

Tempura batter

Ingredient	? portions
Egg yolk	1
Ice cold sparkling water	450 ml
Self-raising flour, sieved	125 g
Cornflour, sieved	125 g

Preparing the dish

1. Beat the egg yolk and add the water.
2. Add half the sieved flours, lightly mix, add the rest of the flours and mix lightly with chopsticks or similar. (This batter will be lumpy but it should never be over-mixed. Throw in a few ice cubes to keep the mixture really cold.)
3. Use this batter to prepare the fritters, as described above.

6 Sweet and sour pork

Energy	Calories	Fat	Saturated fat	Carbohydrates	Sugar	Protein	Fibre
3067 kJ	730 kcal	43.9 g	9.2 g	69.7 g	54.7 g	13.4 g	1.6 g

Ingredient	4 portions	10 portions
Loin of pork, boned	250 g	600 g
Sugar	12 g	30 g
Dry sherry	70 ml	180 ml
Soy sauce	70 ml	180 ml
Cornflour	50 g	125 g
Vegetable oil, for frying	70 ml	180 ml
Oil	2 tbsp	5 tbsp
Clove of garlic	1	2½
Fresh root ginger	50 g	125 g
Onion	75 g	180 g
Green pepper	1	2½
Chillies	2	5
Sweet and sour sauce (see page 223)	210 ml	500 ml
Pineapple rings, fresh or canned	1	3
Spring onions – sliced into rings	2	5

Mise en place

1. Chop or finely slice the garlic and ginger.
2. Chop the onions and chillies.
3. Dice the green pepper into 1 cm cubes.

Cooking

1. Cut the boned loin of pork into 2 cm pieces.
2. Marinate the pork for 30 minutes in the sugar, sherry and soy sauce.
3. Pass the pork through cornflour, pressing the cornflour in well.
4. Deep-fry the pork pieces in oil at 190°C until golden brown, then drain. Add the tablespoons of oil to a sauté pan.
5. Add the garlic and ginger, and fry until fragrant.
6. Add the onion, pepper and chillies, sauté for a few minutes.
7. Stir in the sweet and sour sauce, bring to the boil.
8. Add the pineapple cut into small chunks, thicken slightly with diluted cornflour. Simmer for 2 minutes.
9. Deep-fry the pork again until crisp. Drain, mix into the vegetables and sauce or serve separately.
10. Serve garnished with the rings of spring onion.

PROFESSIONAL TIP

It is important to allow the pork enough time to marinate.

7 Sweet and sour sauce

Energy	Calories	Fat	Saturated fat	Carbohydrates	Sugar	Protein	Fibre	Sodium
791 kJ	185 kcal	0.1 g	0.0 g	46.0 g	46.0 g	46.0 g	0.4 g	583.0 g

	4 portions	10 portions
White vinegar	375 ml	1 litre
Brown sugar	150 g	375 g
Tomato ketchup	125 ml	300 ml
Worcester sauce	1 tbsp	2½ tbsp
Seasoning		

Cooking

1 Boil the vinegar and sugar in a suitable pan.

2 Add the tomato ketchup, Worcester sauce and seasoning.

3 Simmer for a few minutes then use as required. This sauce may also be lightly thickened with cornflour or another thickening agent.

8 Cheese fritters (*beignets au fromage*)

Energy	Calories	Fat	Saturated fat	Carbohydrates	Sugar	Protein	Fibre	Sodium
1069 kJ	257 kcal	19.4 g	10.0 g	11.2 g	0.3 g	9.1 g	0.6 g	171.0 g

* Using unsalted butter, white flour and added 0.5 g salt

Ingredient	4 portions	10 portions
Water	125 ml	310 ml
Butter	50 g	125 g
Flour, white or wholemeal	60 g	200 g
Eggs, medium	2	5
Parmesan cheese	50 g	125 g
Salt, cayenne pepper		

Mise en place

Grate the Parmesan cheese.

Cooking

1 Bring the water and butter to the boil in a thick-based pan. Remove from the heat.

2 Add the flour; mix with a kitchen spoon.

3 Return to a gentle heat and mix well until the mixture leaves the sides of the pan. Remove from the heat. Allow to cool slightly.

4 Gradually add the eggs, beating well. Add the cheese and season.

5 Using a spoon, scoop the mixture in pieces the size of a walnut and place into deep hot fat at 185°C.

6 Allow to cook, with the minimum of handling, for about 10 minutes.

7 Drain and serve sprinkled with grated Parmesan.

HEALTHY EATING TIP

- Use sunflower margarine for the fritters.
- No extra salt is needed as the cheese has salt in it.
- Fry in hot sunflower oil and drain on kitchen paper.

9 Deep-fried chicken

Energy	Calories	Fat	Saturated fat	Carbohydrates	Sugar	Protein	Fibre
1754 kJ	421 kcal	28.6 g	6.1 g	14.5 g	0.4 g	27.2 g	0.5 g

Ingredient	4 portions
Skinless chicken pieces of your choice, e.g. boneless cuts, suprêmes	4, approx. 100–125 g per portion
Plain flour	50 g
Dried spices, e.g. paprika, Chinese five spice, chilli	to taste
Light batter	
Plain flour	75 g
Egg, beaten	1
Milk	100 ml
Salt	pinch

Mise en place

1. Prepare the batter. Sieve the flour into a bowl and add the salt. Mix the egg and milk together. Make a well in the centre of the flour and add the egg and milk mix. Mix together gently using a whisk to form a light batter. Cover and leave to relax in a fridge for a few hours before using. Any small lumps in the batter should have dissolved by this point. Strain only if necessary.
2. Mix together the flour and dried spices.
3. Heat the fat to 175°C.

Cooking

1. Coat the chicken pieces in (pass them through) the mixture of flour and spices.
2. Then pass them through the batter, letting any excess batter drain off
3. Place carefully into the preheated oil, occasionally turning carefully. Frying time will vary according to the shape and size of the chicken pieces.
4. Once cooked (core temperature above 72°C), remove from the oils and drain on to a tray lined with absorbent paper.
5. Serve with suitable dips (salsa, yoghurt based) and accompaniments (e.g. potato wedges, salads).

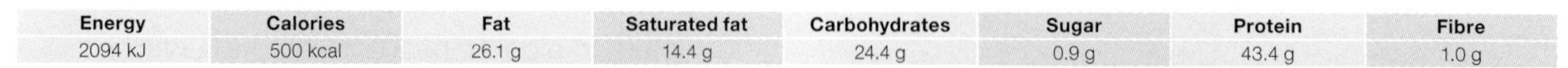

10 Chicken Kiev

Energy	Calories	Fat	Saturated fat	Carbohydrates	Sugar	Protein	Fibre
2094 kJ	500 kcal	26.1 g	14.4 g	24.4 g	0.9 g	43.4 g	1.0 g

Ingredient	4 portions	10 portions
Chicken suprêmes, skin removed, 150 g each	4	10
Butter	100 g	250 g
Flour	25 g	65 g
Salt, to season the flour		
Egg for egg wash	1	2
Fresh, white breadcrumbs	100 g	250 g

Mise en place

1. Lightly season the flour with salt.
2. Beat the eggs to make the egg wash.

Cooking

1 Carefully make an incision (cut) in the top of each suprême with a sharp knife.

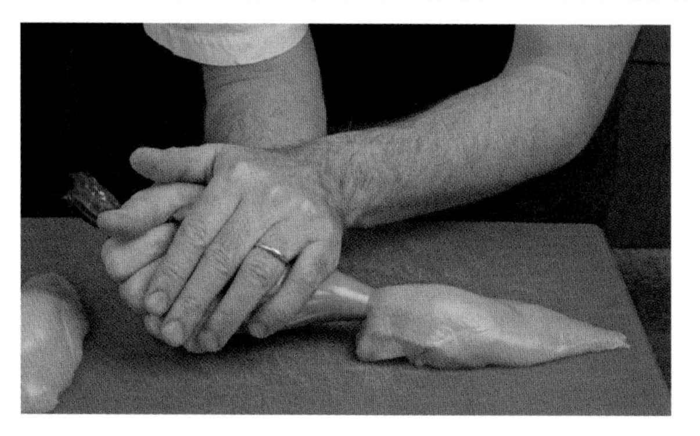

2 Pipe 25 g of softened butter into each incision. Press down the opening to keep the butter inside.

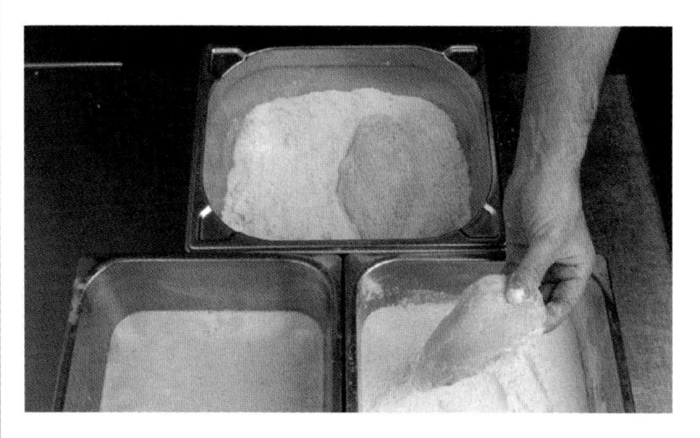

3 Pané the chicken. This means pass it through the seasoned flour, beaten egg (egg wash) and breadcrumbs. Make sure the chicken is well coated. Pass it through the egg wash and crumbs twice if necessary.

5 Deep fry the suprêmes at a temperature of approximately 175°C–180°C.

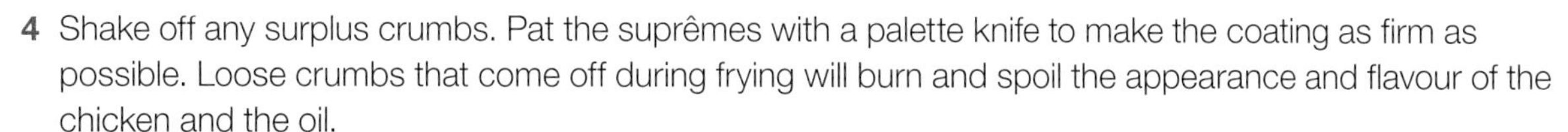

4 Shake off any surplus crumbs. Pat the suprêmes with a palette knife to make the coating as firm as possible. Loose crumbs that come off during frying will burn and spoil the appearance and flavour of the chicken and the oil.

6 Fry until golden brown.

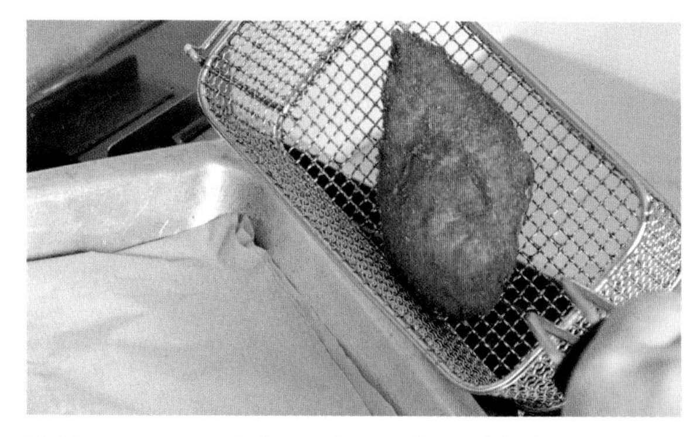

7 Remove carefully and transfer to kitchen paper to drain.

VARIATION

The butter in a Chicken Kiev can be flavoured with garlic and/or herbs.

11 Chips

Energy	Calories	Fat	Saturated fat	Carbohydrates	Sugar	Protein	Fibre
1541 kJ	367 kcal	15.8 g	2.8 g	54.1 g	0.0 g	5.5 g	1.5 g

* Using old potatoes and peanut oil

Ingredient
Potatoes, scrubbed (1 kg will yield 4 to 6 portions)

Mise en place

1. Peel and wash the potatoes.
2. Cut into slices 1 cm thick and 5 cm long.
3. Cut the slices into chips 5 cm × 1 cm × 1 cm.
4. Wash well and dry in a cloth.
5. Preheat the oil in a deep fat fryer to 165°C.

Cooking

1. Place the chips in a frying basket and, slowly and carefully, immerse in moderately hot (165°C) deep fat.
2. When they are almost completely cooked, drain them and place them on kitchen paper on trays until they are needed.
3. When required, raise the temperature in the fryer to 185°C. Put the required amount of chips in a frying basket and immerse them in the deep fat.
4. Cook until crisp and golden brown.
5. Drain well, season lightly with salt and serve.

12 Mushrooms fried with a polenta crust

Energy	Calories	Fat	Saturated fat	Carbohydrates	Sugar	Protein	Fibre	Sodium
1160 kJ	280 kcal	20.0 g	7.9 g	15.2 g	1.7 g	9.4 g	2.2 g	142.0 g

* Using full fat cream cheese

Ingredient	4 portions	10 portions
Cream cheese	150 g	375 g
Chives	1 tsp	2½ tsp
Black pepper to taste		
Closed cup mushrooms	32	80
Sesame seeds	3 tbsp	7½ tbsp
Polenta (maize meal)	75 g	187 g
Eggs	2	5
Vegetable oil for deep frying		

Mise en place

1. Remove the stalks from the mushrooms.
2. Trim the mushrooms, stalk side up, so that two mushrooms can be pressed together.
3. Chop the chives.
4. Beat the eggs.

Cooking

1. Season the cream cheese with chives and black pepper.
2. Sandwich two mushrooms together with the cream cheese filling and make sure they fit snugly together.
3. Add the sesame seeds to some polenta. Pass the mushrooms through beaten egg and the polenta and sesame seed mixture.
4. Chill well.
5. Deep fry the mushrooms in hot oil until golden brown all over.
6. When cooked, drain on absorbent paper.

SERVING SUGGESTION

Serve hot with a tomato sauce.

VARIATION

- You could add a little chopped chilli or paprika to the cream cheese.
- You can shallow fry the mushrooms instead of deep frying them.

Shallow fried products

13 Scrambled eggs

Energy	Calories	Fat	Saturated fat	Carbohydrates	Sugar	Protein	Fibre
1105 kJ	263 kcal	22.9 g	8.7 g	0.5 g	0.5 g	13.9 g	0.0 g

* Using hard margarine instead of butter

Ingredient	4 portions	10 portions
Butter, margarine or oil	50 g	125 g
Eggs (medium or large)	6–8	15–20
Milk (optional)	2 tbsp	5 tbsp
Salt – use sparingly		

Mise en place

1 Break the eggs into a basin, season lightly with salt and mix thoroughly using a whisk.

2 Add milk, if using.

Cooking

1 In a thick-bottomed pan, melt half of the fat.

2 Add the eggs and start to cook over a gentle heat, stirring.

3 Stir continuously with a wooden spoon until the eggs are lightly cooked.

4 Remove from the heat, taste and correct the seasoning.

5 Mix in the remaining fat.

The reason for removing the eggs when they are only lightly cooked is because after the pan is removed from the stove it will still be hot and the eggs will continue to cook. Cooking scrambled eggs is a delicate task and they can easily be overcooked and spoiled.

SERVING SUGGESTION

Serve on slices of hot buttered toast or in individual egg dishes.

ACTIVITY

1 As a group, try the following.
- Cook two scrambled eggs following the recipe.
- Cook two scrambled eggs as quickly as possible.
- Cook two scrambled eggs using butter.
- Cook two scrambled eggs using margarine or oil.

2 Taste, compare and discuss the four versions.

14 Fried eggs

Energy	Calories	Fat	Saturated fat	Carbohydrates	Sugar	Protein	Fibre
536 kJ	128 kcal	31.0 g	9.8 g	0.0 g	0.0 g	7.6 g	0.0 g

* Fried in sunflower oil

Only fresh, top-quality eggs should be used for frying. For the best flavour use butter or sunflower oil.

Mise en place

Break the eggs into bowls. Doing this gives a chef the chance to check them for freshness and quality. Any eggs that do not pass this quick inspection can be discarded.

Ingredient	
Butter, margarine or oil	25 g per egg
Eggs	1 or 2 per portion

ACTIVITY

1 As a group, try the following.
- Fry one egg using butter.
- Fry one egg using oil.
- Fry one egg using margarine.

2 Taste, compare and discuss the three versions.

Cooking

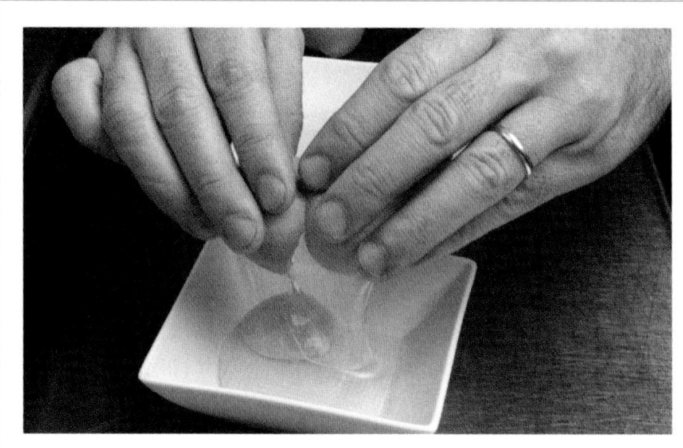

1 Melt the butter, margarine or oil in a small non-stick frying pan.

2 Add the eggs carefully and gently to the pan, without breaking the yolks.

3 Cook slowly over a moderate heat and serve on a warmed plate.

15 Omelette

Energy	Calories	Fat	Saturated fat	Carbohydrates	Sugar	Protein	Fibre
990 kJ	236 kcal	20.2 g	9.1 g	0.0 g	0.0 g	13.6 g	0.0 g

* Using 2 eggs per portion. Using 3 eggs per portion, 1 portion provides: 1330 kJ/317 kcal energy; 26.2 g fat; 11.0 g Saturated fat; 0.0 g Carbohydrates; 0.0 g sugar; 20.3 g protein; 0.0 g fibre

Ingredient	1 portion
Butter, margarine or oil, for frying	
Eggs	2–3
Salt	small pinch

Mise en place

1 Break the eggs into a basin and season lightly with salt.

2 Mix thoroughly with a fork or whisk until whites and yolks are thoroughly combined and no streaks of white can be seen.

Cooking

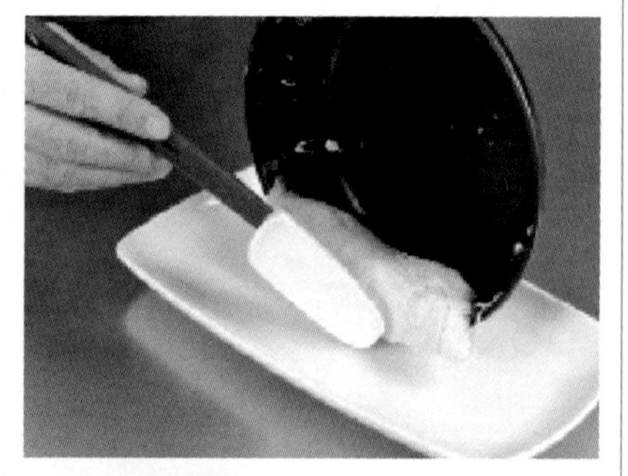

1 Heat a non-stick omelette pan and wipe thoroughly clean with a dry cloth.

2 Add the butter, then turn up the heat to maximum until the butter is foaming but not brown.

3 Add the eggs and cook quickly, stirring continuously with a fork until lightly set. Remove from the heat.

4 Using the fork, carefully fold the mixture in half at a right angle to the handle of the pan.

7 Pointing the pan slightly downwards, sharply tap the pan handle with your other hand to bring the edge of the omelette up to the bottom of the pan.

8 Carefully using the fork, bring up the opposite edge of the omelette as near to the first edge as possible.

9 Take a warm plate in one hand and, holding the pan under the handle, carefully tip the folded omelette on to the plate.

10 Neaten the shape if necessary, using a clean teacloth, and serve immediately.

VARIATION

There are many variations that can be made by adding other ingredients to the mixed eggs before cooking, such as:

- chopped soft herbs – parsley, chives, chervil
- mushrooms – sliced and cooked in butter
- grated cheese can be added to the omelette before it is folded.

ACTIVITY

Practice is the only way to make good omelettes.

Suggest three variations. Prepare all three, then taste, discuss and assess them.

16 Shallow fried fish

Energy	Calories	Fat	Saturated fat	Carbohydrates	Sugar	Protein	Fibre	Sodium
731 kJ	172 kcal	3.9 g	0.4 g	14.7 g	0.1 g	19.3 g	0.8 g	91.0 g

* Using cod

Ingredient	4 portions	10 portions
White fish fillets or small whole fish	400 g	1 kg
Flour to lightly coat (approx.)	80 g	200 g
Vegetable oil	1 tbsp	2½ tbsp

Mise en place

Prepare, clean, wash and thoroughly dry the fish.

Cooking

1 Completely cover the fish with flour and shake off all surplus. (If you are using a non-stick pan, it is not essential to flour the fish.)

2 Heat the frying medium (usually a light oil) in the frying pan.

3 Shallow fry on the presentation side first.

4 Carefully turn and fry the other side.

SERVING SUGGESTION

When cooked and placed on the serving plates or dishes, add:

- a slice of lemon (remove the yellow and white pith and any pips first)
- a sprinkling of lemon juice.

Do not overcrowd the pan because this will cause the temperature of the oil to drop and will affect the way the fish cooks. The fish should not be overcooked but should have an appetising light golden-brown colour.

VARIATION

Once the fish is cooked, carefully heat 10–25 g butter per portion in a frying pan until it turns a nutty brown colour. Pour this over the plated-up fish, sprinkle with chopped parsley and serve.

17 Fried banana

Energy	Calories	Fat	Saturated fat	Carbohydrates	Sugar	Protein	Fibre	Sodium*
1155 kJ	273 kcal	10.4 g	6.6 g	46.0 g	44.0 g	1.3 g	1.4 g	2.3 g

* Including butter (unsalted)

Don't prepare the bananas before they are needed. Once peeled, bananas start to oxidise and will discolour (go brown) very quickly.

Ingredient	4 portions
Bananas, ripe	4
Caster sugar	100 g
Butter (optional), cut in cubes or slices	50 g

Mise en place

1. Get your equipment together: a non-stick pan and a palette knife for turning the bananas.
2. Place the sugar into a tray for dipping.

Cooking

1. Warm the non-stick frying pan on the stove to a medium heat.
2. Peel the bananas and slice them lengthways. These slices can be cut in half if shorter pieces of banana are required.
3. Place the flat side of each banana in the tray of sugar to provide a good, even coating.
4. For a richer flavour, add the butter to the warmed pan and let it melt until it starts to lightly bubble. This stage is optional as the bananas can be dry fried (without oil or butter).
5. Place the bananas, sugar side down, into the pan and fry for 1–1½ minutes until a light caramelisation (browning) is achieved.
6. Using the palette knife, turn carefully and lightly fry on the curved side of the banana for 1 minute. Serve accordingly.

18 Shallow fried lamb cutlets and chops

Energy	Calories	Fat	Saturated fat	Carbohydrates	Sugar	Protein	Fibre	Sodium
736 kJ	176 kcal	9.2 g	4.1 g	0.0 g	0.0 g	23.2 g	0.0 g	259.0 g

* Average chop = 82 g cooked weight, adding 0.5 g salt per portion

Ingredient
Light oil or fat
Lamb cutlets or chops
Salt

Both cutlets and chops are equally suitable to cook in this way.

Mise en place

Gather all equipment required including a thick-bottomed pan, oil, seasoning and tongs to turn the cutlet during the cooking process.

Cooking

1. Place a thick-bottomed frying pan or a sauté pan on a hot stove.
2. Add a little light oil or fat to the pan.
3. Season the meat lightly with salt.
4. When the fat is hot, carefully place the meat in the pan. Put the edge of the meat closest to you in first and lay it away from you. This way, if any hot fat splashes it will splash away from you rather than on to you.
5. Cook on a high heat until lightly browned, then turn over and repeat.
6. Lower the heat by a half and cook for approximately 4–5 minutes in total (depending on the thickness of the meat).

SERVING SUGGESTION

Serve as for lamb cutlets or offer a suitable potato and vegetable, such as sauté potatoes (with or without onions) and leaf spinach with toasted pine nuts.

ACTIVITY

Fry a dish of cutlets or chops and serve with your idea of a suitable garnish or a potato, vegetable and/or salad. Taste, assess and discuss.

19 Pan fried steak

Energy	Calories	Fat	Saturated fat	Carbohydrates	Sugar	Protein	Fibre	Sodium
1374 kJ	329 kcal	18.2 g	10.0 g	0.1 g	0.1 g	41.0 g	0.0 g	271.0 g

* Using unsalted butter and adding 1/4 teaspoon salt per recipe (to make 4 portions). Using 175 g lean sirloin per portion

Ingredient	4 portions	10 portions
Butter or oil	50 g	125 g
Sirloin steaks (approx. 150–200 g each)	4	10
Salt and pepper		

Rare, medium or well done?

Customers may request their steak to be cooked to different degrees. Precise cooking will depend on variants such as the thickness of the steak and the temperature the steak is cooked at. This is where a chef's experience and knowledge is important.

- **Very rare** (or **blue**) – cooked over a fierce heat for only a few seconds each side to give a good brown colour (literally just seared on all sides).
- **Rare** – the cooked meat has a reddish tinge (approximately 2–2½ minutes on each side).
- **Medium** – the cooked meat is slightly pinkish (approximately 3–4 minutes on each side).
- **Well done** – thoroughly cooked with no sign of pinkness (approximately 5–6 minutes on each side).

This method is perfect for small to medium-sized cuts.

Mise en place

Lightly season the steaks on both sides with salt and pepper.

Cooking

1 Heat the butter or oil in a sauté pan.

2 Fry the steaks quickly on the first side, keeping them underdone.

3 Turn the steaks over carefully.

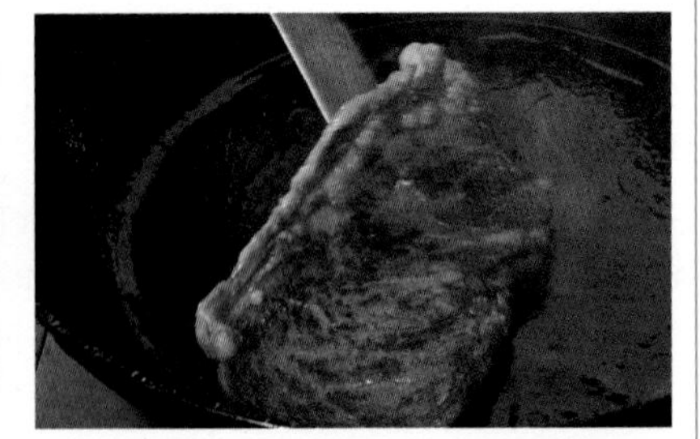

4 Fry the other side, still keeping them underdone.

5 Dress the steaks on a serving dish.

Use finger pressure and the springiness of the meat, together with the amount of blood that comes from it, to check how well it is cooked: the more underdone the steak, the more springy it is and the more blood will appear on the plate.

You can also test with a temperature probe. Insert the probe into the thickest part of the meat. The internal reading should be:

- rare 45–50°C
- medium 55–60°C
- well done 75–77°C.

SERVING SUGGESTION

Serve the steaks with mushrooms and tomatoes.

20 Egg and crumbed pork escalopes

Energy	Calories	Fat	Saturated fat	Carbohydrates	Sugar	Protein	Fibre	Sodium
1350 kJ	323 kcal	19.5 g	2.4 g	13.6 g	0.6 g	23.0 g	0.6 g	171.0 g

* Added 0.5 g salt to the flour to make the seasoned flour. Using lean pork steaks with weight of 87.5 g per portion. Using vegetable oil

Ingredient	4 portions	10 portions
Pork fillet or nut from the loin, 75–100 g	4	10
Flour, seasoned	25 g	60 g
Egg	1	2–3
Fresh white breadcrumbs	50 g	125 g
Oil for frying	60 ml	150 ml

Mise en place

1 Trim and remove any sinew from the meat.

2 Using a little water, bat out with a meat hammer as thinly as possible to ½ cm at least.

3 Beat the eggs to make egg wash.

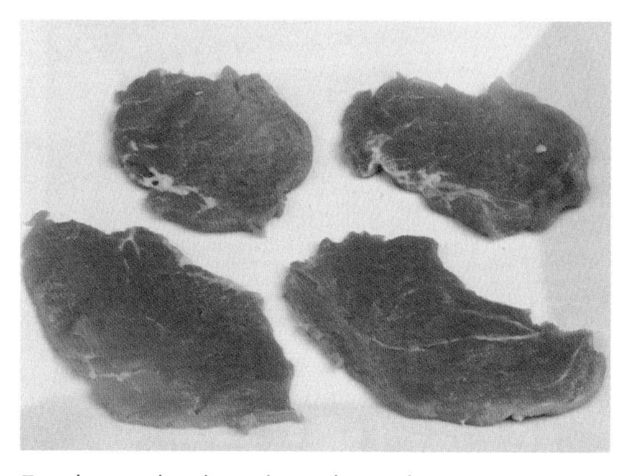

Escalopes that have been batted out

Cooking

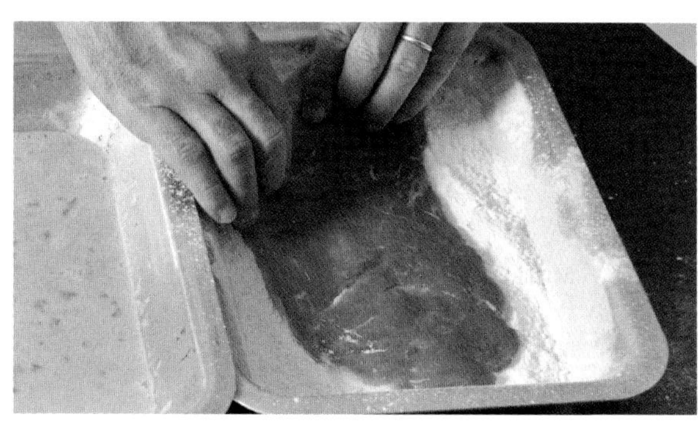

1 Each escalope needs to go through the pané process. First, pass the escalope through seasoned flour.

2 Ensure that both sides are coated in the flour.

3 Pass the escalope through the egg wash.

4 Allow the egg wash to drain off.

5 Pass the escalope through the breadcrumbs.

6 Shake off any surplus crumbs and pat each side firmly with a palette knife.

7 Shallow fry in hot fat or oil on both sides until they are golden brown and crisp.

8 Drain on kitchen paper.

SERVING SUGGESTION

Serve with a suitable sauce. For example:

- thickened gravy (page 103), with some thinly sliced small gherkins added
- an apple purée thinned down with cream or yoghurt.

21 Stir fried pork fillet

Energy	Calories	Fat	Saturated fat	Carbohydrates	Sugar	Protein	Fibre
831 kJ	199 kcal	9.8 g	2.2 g	5.1 g	4.2 g	22.9 g	0.8 g

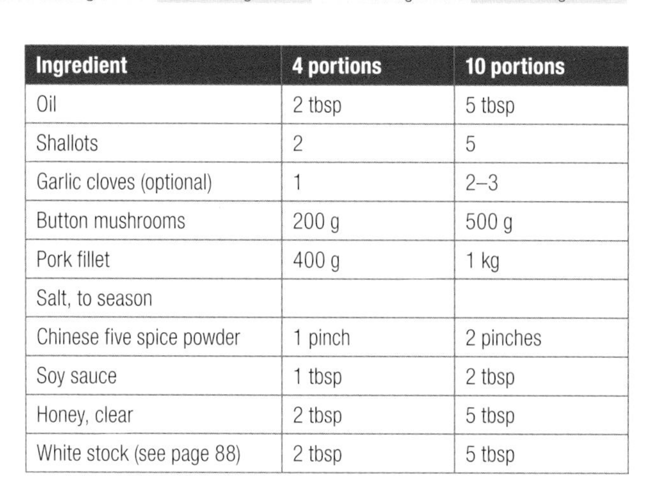

Ingredient	4 portions	10 portions
Oil	2 tbsp	5 tbsp
Shallots	2	5
Garlic cloves (optional)	1	2–3
Button mushrooms	200 g	500 g
Pork fillet	400 g	1 kg
Salt, to season		
Chinese five spice powder	1 pinch	2 pinches
Soy sauce	1 tbsp	2 tbsp
Honey, clear	2 tbsp	5 tbsp
White stock (see page 88)	2 tbsp	5 tbsp

Mise en place

1. Peel and finely chop the shallots.
2. Finely slice the mushrooms.
3. Cut the pork into thin strips or slices.

SERVING SUGGESTION

Serve with noodles, braised rice (page 140) or stir fried vegetables, or a combination of these.

HEALTHY EATING TIP

Steamed vegetables such as pak choi, bok choi, broccoli and other green vegetables would provide a healthy, vitamin-rich and low-calorie accompaniment to this dish.

Cooking

1. Heat the oil in a wok or frying pan.
2. Add the shallots and sweat gently for 1 minute, then add the garlic (if using).
3. Add the mushrooms and cook gently until softened.
4. Increase the heat and add the pork fillet strips or slices.

5. Season lightly with salt, add the spice powder and cook for 3–4 minutes, tossing continuously.
6. Reduce the heat, add the soy sauce, honey, white stock and reduce for 2–3 minutes.
7. Taste, correct seasoning and serve.

22 Canal floddies

Energy	Calories	Fat	Saturated fat	Carbohydrates	Sugar	Protein	Fibre	Sodium
1441 kJ	345 kcal	20.1 g	3.2 g	26.8 g	4.0 g	12.4 g	5.7 g	437.0 g

* Added 1 tbsp mushy peas (30 g) per portion; 120 g for the recipe of 4 portions. Added 1/4 teaspoon salt per recipe of 4 portions

Ingredient	4 portions	10 portions
Floddies		
Potatoes (preferably heritage potatoes from Northumberland)	350 g	875 g
Onion, medium	1	2
Sundried tomatoes	10	25
Self-raising flour	25 g	65 g
Eggs, medium free-range	1	3
Salt and pepper		
Vegetable oil	2 tbsp	5 tbsp
To serve		
Mushy peas		
Eggs, poached	4	10

Regional recipe contributed by Andy Dodds, Catering teacher at Gateshead College.

This is a slightly updated version of a dish from the Tyneside town of Gateshead. Traditionally these were made by the men digging the Manchester Ship Canal and fried on their shovels over a fire.

The traditional recipe uses diced bacon instead of sundried tomatoes. The tomatoes give this dish a sweet and healthy twist.

Mise en place

1. Finely chop the sundried tomatoes.
2. Peel the onions and potatoes.
3. Beat the eggs for the floddy mixture.

Cooking

1. Coarsely grate the potato, squeeze out any liquid and press between kitchen paper.
2. Grate the onion and mix with the potato and sundried tomatoes.
3. Place the self-raising flour in a mixing bowl and add the beaten egg. Mix well.
4. Add the potato mixture to the flour and egg, season and mix well.
5. Divide the mixture into four (one per portion) and shape into rounds.
6. Heat the oil in a frying pan and when hot add the floddies. Reduce heat a little and fry, turning until well browned on both sides and cooked through.
7. Drain on kitchen paper.
8. Place each floddy on a plate and top with a portion of hot mushy peas and a lightly poached egg.

23 Pancakes with lemon

Energy	Calories	Fat	Saturated fat	Carbohydrates	Sugar	Protein	Fibre	Sodium
893 kJ	211 kcal	5.6 g	2.5 g	34.5 g	16.2 g	6.1 g	1.0 g	97.0 g

* Using semi-skimmed milk, unsalted butter, 1 teaspoon sunflower oil for frying

Ingredient	4 portions	10 portions
Flour	100 g	250 g
Salt	small pinch	pinch
Milk	¼ litre	625 ml
Egg	1	2–3
Butter, melted, or a light oil	10 g	25 g
Light oil for frying		
Sugar, caster	50 g	125 g
Lemon	1	2

When making a batch of pancakes, keep them flat. Pile them on to a warm plate, sprinkling a little sugar in between each. Fold them when ready for service. Lightly sprinkle them again with sugar and dress neatly overlapping on service plates.

Mise en place

To make the pancake batter

1. Sieve the flour and salt into a basin.
2. Make a well and add the milk and egg, gradually incorporating the flour from the side of the bowl.
3. Beat vigorously with a wooden spoon or whisk to a smooth batter. This should be thick enough to just coat the back of a spoon.
4. Mix in the melted fat.

Cooking

1. Heat the pancake pan and clean it thoroughly.
2. Add sufficient oil just to thinly coat the pan. Heat this until it begins to smoke.
3. Add just enough mixture to thinly coat the pan.
4. Cook for a few seconds until brown.
5. Turn over and cook the second side for half the time.
6. Turn on to a warm plate, sprinkle with sugar, fold in half then fold again.

SERVING SUGGESTION

Serve two pancakes per portion with a quarter of lemon (remove the pips).

VARIATION

- If a thicker pancake is required, add another 20–60 g flour to the recipe.
- Use orange segments in place of lemon. Sliced, cooked apple with cinnamon would also provide a tasty alternative.
- Spread the pancakes lightly with warmed jam and roll them up.

24 Sauté of chicken

Energy	Calories	Fat	Saturated fat	Carbohydrates	Sugar	Protein	Fibre	Sodium
2159 kJ	520 kcal	37.4 g	9.3 g	3.6 g	0.5 g	42.0 g	0.2 g	530.0 g

* Using vegetable oil, 1/4 teaspoon salt per recipe. Used medium chicken (1.35 kg)

Ingredient	4 portions	10 portions
Butter, margarine or oil	50 g	125 g
Chicken, whole (1¼–1½ kg)	1	2½
Salt, to season		
Thickened gravy/jus-lié	250 ml	625 ml
Fresh parsley, chopped (for garnishing)		

If using a whole chicken, chop up the carcass and save any trimmings to use when you are making the gravy.

If using ready-cut chicken, for four portions use two drumsticks, two thighs and two suprêmes (breasts cut in half).

Mise en place

1. If you are using a whole chicken (or chickens), cut this into pieces.
2. Prepare the thickened gravy (see page 103).
3. Chop the parsley.

Cooking

1. Place the fat or oil in a sauté pan over a hot stove.
2. Season the chicken pieces lightly with salt. Place them in the pan in the following order: drumsticks, thighs, breasts (you put in the tougher pieces first as they take longer to cook).
3. Cook to a golden brown on both sides. Cover with a lid.
4. Reduce the heat and cook gently until the chicken is tender.
5. Remove the chicken pieces and drain off the fat from the sauté pan.
6. Return the pan to a moderate heat. Add the thickened gravy and bring it to the boil.
7. Taste the gravy and correct the seasoning. Pass it through a fine strainer on to the chicken.
8. Lightly sprinkle with chopped parsley and serve.

VARIATION

You can make lots of variations to this basic recipe, such as adding:

- sliced mushrooms
- tomato concassée or tomato purée halfway through the cooking time
- freshly chopped soft herbs, such as chives, chervil, tarragon
- light spices, such as curry powder, five spice powder.

ACTIVITY

In groups, prepare a selection of variations of chicken sauté. Use your own ideas. Taste one another's dishes and discuss.

25 Turkey fajita

Energy	Calories	Fat	Saturated fat	Carbohydrates	Sugar	Protein	Fibre	Sodium
1955 kJ	465 kcal	17.5 g	2.9 g	41.0 g	9.2 g	34.9 g	5.1 g	524.0 g

* Using vegetable oil

Ingredient	4 portions	10 portions
Oil, for frying	50 ml	125 ml
Onions	100 g	250 g
Garlic cloves	2	5
Turkey, diced	450 g	1 kg
Cajun seasoning	½ tsp	1½ tsp
Green peppers	100 g	250 g
Red peppers	100 g	250 g
Plum tomatoes (canned)	500 g	1¼ kg
Black pepper, for seasoning		
Flour tortillas	4	10

Mise en place

1. Cut the turkey into 2 cm dice.
2. Peel and chop the garlic and shred the onion.
3. Wash the peppers and dice finely.
4. Chop the tomatoes.

Cooking

1. Heat the oil in a suitable pan. Add the onions and garlic and cook for 2 minutes.
2. Add the diced turkey, Cajun seasoning and diced peppers, and fry for another 5 minutes.
3. Add the chopped tomatoes and black pepper.
4. Cook until the turkey is tender and thoroughly cooked.
5. Lay the tortillas out flat. Spoon a portion of the mixture in the centre of each and roll up.

SERVING SUGGESTION

Serve on a suitable plate or heated 'sizzler' dish garnished with flat parsley or perhaps fresh coriander for a more fragrant finish.

26 Stir fried noodles

Energy	Calories	Fat	Saturated fat	Carbohydrates	Sugar	Protein	Fibre	Sodium
1668 kJ	394 kcal	8.3 g	0.8 g	65.0 g	14.0 g	13.9 g	8.9 g	1,387.0 g

* Using mange tout

Ingredient	2 portions
Fine or medium egg noodles	150 g
Vegetable oil	1 tbsp
Fresh ginger	2½ cm piece
Garlic cloves	2
Fresh red chilli	1
Carrot	1 large
Yellow pepper	1
Mangetout, sugar snap peas or frozen peas	100 g
Spring onions	2
Beansprouts	85 g
Soy sauce	2 tbsp
White wine vinegar	1 tsp

Mise en place

1. Finely chop the ginger and garlic.
2. Deseed and thinly sliced the red chilli.
3. Cut the carrot into julienne.
4. Deseed and thinly slice the yellow pepper.
5. Finely chop the spring onion.

Cooking

1. Boil/rehydrate the noodles according to instructions.
2. Heat the oil in a wok, then stir fry the ginger, garlic, chilli carrot, pepper and mangetout (sugar snap or frozen peas) over a high heat for 2–3 minutes.
3. Drain the noodles thoroughly, add to the pan with the spring onions and beansprouts, if using, then stir fry for 2 minutes.
4. Mix together the soy sauce and vinegar, stir into the pan, then cook for 1–2 minutes.
5. Divide between bowls and serve immediately.

VARIATION

- A stir fry doesn't really have any set rules in terms of the ingredients that can be used. To add a protein element to this dish, marinated strips of chicken or beef could be used. This would be added at the beginning of the stir frying process (step 2), before the ginger, etc. Prawns would provide a great alternative for a seafood stir fry.
- In terms of other ingredients and flavours, regular or red onions could be used, as could other types of pepper, for a variation in colour. Sliced leeks or florets of broccoli could be added, alongside other green leaves such as cabbage. For additional flavours and textures, herbs such as coriander or Thai basil could be added at the end of the process to provide fragrance and aroma. The addition of nuts such as cashew or peanuts could provide an extra texture, and a squeeze of fresh lime or lemon would add a fresh citrus twist. The variations are limitless, and a stir fry provides a great, healthy and versatile way in which spare or surplus ingredients can be utilised.

27 Sauté potatoes

Energy	Calories	Fat	Saturated fat	Carbohydrates	Sugar	Protein	Fibre
1249 kJ	297 kcal	11.4 g	1.3 g	46.8 g	0.4 g		4.9 g*

* Using old potatoes and sunflower oil

Ingredient
Potatoes (1 kg of old potatoes will yield 4 to 6 portions)
Oil, for sautéing
Salt, pinch

Mise en place

Scrub the potatoes well (do not peel).

Cooking

1. Plain boil or steam the potatoes for approximately 15 minutes.
2. Cool them slightly and then peel them.
3. Cut them into 3 mm slices.
4. Toss the slices in hot shallow oil in a frying pan until nicely browned.
5. Season *lightly* with salt.

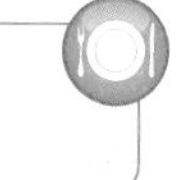

SERVING SUGGESTION

Serve sprinkled with freshly chopped parsley.

28 Fried mixed vegetables with coconut milk

Energy	Calories	Fat	Saturated fat	Carbohydrates	Sugar	Protein	Fibre	Sodium
554 kJ	133 kcal	12.0 g	5.4 g	4.2 g	3.1 g	1.9 g	2.4 g	255.0 g

Ingredient	4 portions	10 portions
Vegetable oil	2 tbsp	5 tbsp
Mustard seeds	½ tsp	1 tsp
Curry leaves	6	15
Shallots	3	8
Garlic cloves	2	5
Chilli powder diluted with 1 tsp water	½ tsp	1 tsp
Turmeric powder diluted with 1 tsp water	¼ tsp	¾ tsp
Tomatoes	50 g	125 g
Coconut milk	125 ml	310 ml
French beans	100 g	250 g
Cauliflower	75 g	185 g
Carrots	50 g	125 g
Salt	½ tsp	1 tsp

Mise en place

1. Cut the French beans into 4 cm lengths.
2. Cut the cauliflower into florets.
3. Deseed and coarsely chop the tomatoes.
4. Julienne the carrots.
5. Slice the shallots lengthwise.
6. Chop the garlic.

Cooking

1. Heat the oil in a wok and fry the mustard seeds and curry leaves for 1–2 minutes. Keep stirring until the seeds pop.
2. Add the shallots and garlic and fry until soft and fragrant.
3. Stir in the chilli and turmeric paste and add the tomatoes. Fry until heated through.
4. Add the coconut milk and bring to a boil. Stir in all the vegetables.
5. Cook for 4–5 minutes until the vegetables are cooked but still crisp. Season lightly with salt and simmer for another 1–2 minutes. Serve immediately.

29 Stir fried rice

Energy	Calories	Fat	Saturated fat	Carbohydrates	Sugar	Protein	Fibre	Sodium
1480 kJ	351 kcal	12.2 g	1.8 g	43.0 g	3.9 g	16.4 g	3.4 g	182.0 g

* Using boiled chicken breast; used 1.5 teaspoons soy sauce. Included beansprouts

Stir fried rice dishes consist of a combination of cold pre-cooked rice and ingredients such as cooked meat or poultry, fish, vegetables or egg.

Ingredient	4 portions
Eggs	2
Sesame oil	2 tsp
Vegetable oil	2 tbsp
Long-grain rice, cooked and left to go cold	200 g
Petits pois (young peas)	100 g
Spring onions, finely chopped	4
Cooked meat or poultry, sliced	100 g
Pepper, finely sliced	1
Beansprouts (optional)	100 g
Soy sauce	1-2 tsp
Ground white pepper to taste	

Cooking

1. Prepare and cook the meat or poultry in fine shreds; dice and lightly cook any vegetables. Add bean sprouts just before the egg.
2. Place a wok or thick-bottomed pan over fierce heat, add some oil and heat until smoking.
3. Add cold rice and stir fry for about 1 minute.
4. Add the other ingredients and continue to stir fry over fierce heat for 4–5 minutes.
5. Add the beaten egg and continue cooking for a further 1–2 minutes.
6. Correct the seasoning and serve immediately.

HEALTHY EATING TIP

- Use an unsaturated oil (sunflower or olive) to lightly oil the pan.
- Soy sauce adds sodium, so no added salt is needed.

208 Producing cold food products

The purpose of this chapter is to introduce you to the production of cold food products. Learners will work with a wide variety of food types including dairy products, fruit and vegetables, meat, poultry and fish. Learners will prepare foods to be served cold, such as sliced meats, pastry items and dressed salads.

Learning outcomes

In this unit, you will be able to:

1 produce cold food products, including:
  - 1.1 selecting food items for cold food products
  - 1.2 applying techniques to produce cold food products
  - 1.3 applying finishing methods for cold food products

Recipes included in this chapter

Cold food	
1	Toasted sandwiches
2	Club sandwiches
3	Bookmaker sandwich
4	Open sandwiches
5	Soused herring or mackerel
6	Vinaigrette
7	Mayonnaise
8	Egg mayonnaise
9	Balsamic vinegar and olive oil dressing
10	Tomato vinaigrette
11	Andalusian sauce
12	Green or herb sauce
13	Tartare sauce
14	Remoulade sauce
15	Mint sauce
16	Thousand Island dressing
17	Shellfish cocktail sauce
Flavoured oils	
18	Herb oil
19	Basil oil
20	Lemon oil
21	Mint oil
22	Vanilla oil
23	Walnut oil
Pickles, chutneys and relishes	
24	Tomato chutney
25	Beetroot relish
26	Pickled red cabbage
27	Date and tamarind relish
28	Pesto
29	Mixed pickle
30	Tapenade
31	Smoked salmon
32	Oysters
33	Dressed crab
34	Cold salmon
35	Fish salad (*salade de poisson*)
36	Sea bass ceviche
37	Crab, lobster, shrimp or prawn cocktail (*cocktail de crabe, homard, crevettes, crevettes roses*)
38	Potted shrimps
39	*Fruits de mer*
Cold meat dishes and pies	
40	Chicken salad
41	Raised pork pie
42	Veal and ham pie
Pâtés and terrines	
43	Liver pâté (*pâté de foie*)
44	Terrine of bacon, spinach and mushrooms
Salads	
45	Potato salad
46	Vegetable salad
47	Beetroot salad
48	Tomato salad
49	Coleslaw
50	Rice salad
51	Green salad
52	Warm Asian bean salad with satay dressing

53	Asian rice salad
54	Pesto pasta salad
55	Green bean salad
56	Greek salad
57	Garden salad
58	Couscous and halloumi salad
59	Italian salad
60	Melon, feta cheese and mint salad
61	Cucumber quinoa salad
62	Avocado and bacon salad

Cold desserts	
63	Fresh fruit salad
64	Crème caramel
65	Fruit mousse
66	Bavarois
67	Vanilla panna cotta served on a fruit compote
68	Fruit fool
69	Trifle
70	Fruit tart, tartlets or barquettes
71	Apple flan

1 Produce cold food products

Cold foods are popular and versatile dishes. Well-planned organisation is essential to ensure adequate preparation of cold foods so that they are assembled with a good workflow and are ready on time. Cold food can be prepared in advance, allowing a large number of people to be served in a short space of time.

Before, during and after being assembled, the foods must be kept in a cool place or refrigerator to minimise the risk of food contamination and growth of bacteria. High standards of personal, food and equipment hygiene must be maintained with all cold work.

Meal occasions when cold food may be presented

- **Breakfast** – Continental breakfast includes croissants, brioche, fresh bread and preserves. It may also include yoghurt, plated fresh fruit, cheeses and cold meats (e.g. ham, salami).
- **Snacks** – These are foods that are available throughout the day. Examples of typical snack foods are nut selections, dried fruit selections, energy biscuits and fresh fruit.
- **Lunch** – A cold buffet lunch will often include a variety of sandwiches, baguettes, paninis, cold meats, smoked fish, terrines and salads. A variety of cold sweets, sometimes gateaux, and often a cheese board will also be available. For table service the range of cold starters includes terrines, salads, fish and shellfish cocktails.
- **Afternoon tea** is a British tradition. A variety of sandwiches, scones, served with clotted cream, jams, tea, and pastries (for example fruit tartlets, éclairs and fondant fancies) are served.
- **High tea** often includes items in afternoon tea, but may also feature some more substantial items, such as open sandwiches, cold chicken drumsticks and wraps.
- **Dinner** menus may offer cold items as a starter. Some establishments, especially resort hotels and cruise ships, may offer a cold buffet in the evening but this will often include some hot items.
- **Supper** menus are usually offered late in the evening. Supper may be offered in some hotels after the normal dinner service, when guests may be offered a selection of cold meats and salads, cold desserts and fresh fruit. Depending on the weather, a hot soup may also be on offer in addition to the cold food. Cold soups such as Gazpacho may be served at lunch or dinner, especially in the summer.
- **Special occasions** – In hotels and restaurants chefs are often required to plan a special buffet. This may include a theme – for example, an opening night for a new film or an awards evening. Here the chef can demonstrate his or her full creativity.

1.1 Select food items for cold food products

Cold main courses include a variety of food types.

- **Fruit** – for example, melon, grapefruit, avocado and orange.
- **Vegetables** – for example, potatoes, onions (peeled and finely chopped, sometimes blanched), mushrooms (cooked or left raw), cauliflower (cut into florets; cooked or left raw), carrots (peeled and cut into fine strips or grated), celery (shredded into crescents or diced), cabbage (diced), beetroot (peeled, chopped, sliced or grated), courgettes (peeled, cut into fine slices and served raw in salads), spinach (shredded and used raw in salads).
- **Meats** – A variety of meat can be served cold – for example, ham, beef, pork, salami, chicken, turkey, and pâtés, terrines and pies.

PROFESSIONAL TIP

When serving cold meat it is advisable to cook the meat, allow it to cool and serve immediately; this helps the eating quality. Leaving cold meats in the refrigerator for long periods affects the eating quality and taste.

- **Fish** – There is a range of types of fish available that can be served cold, including smoked (for example, salmon, mackerel or trout), tinned (for example, sardines and tuna), pickled (for example, herring), precooked and fresh (for example, prawns and salmon), or frozen (for example, crab or prawns – defrost thoroughly before use).

PROFESSIONAL TIP

Serving suggestions for fish:

- fresh salmon can be neatly dressed and garnished with lettuce leaves, cucumber slices and quarters of tomato, accompanied by mayonnaise
- canned fish can be served simply with lettuce leaves
- accompany prawns with mayonnaise and brown bread and butter, or with shells removed and served with shredded lettuce, thin slices of cucumber and/or tomato, and mayonnaise or vinaigrette.

- **Salad items** – These include lettuce (for example, frisée, oakleaf, rosso, raddicio, little gem, lollo), cucumber (peeled or unpeeled and cut into thin slices), tomatoes (skins on or peeled, and cut into slices or segments), cress, radishes and peppers (green, orange, red or yellow, cut into fine strips).

PROFESSIONAL TIP

To peel a tomato, plunge it into boiling water for ten seconds, then remove and cool under cold running water before peeling.

- **Dairy products** – for example, cheese (often served on a cheese board with biscuits or fresh bread and sticks of celery) and eggs (hard-boiled, pickled or Scotch eggs and a variety of quiches can, with self-service salad, provide an appetising and healthy meal).
- **Bread** – A good selection of breads or/and rolls (such as white, brown, wholemeal, wholegrain and speciality) are often served with cold meals.

Quality points when selecting food items

- **Freshness** – All ingredients must be fresh and of the best quality.
- **Appearance** – The appearance of the ingredients must look fresh. Fruit and vegetables must not have any blemishes, bruising or mould.
- **Type/size and shape** – Make sure the ingredients are of the right type, size and shape. For example, specify that you require cherry tomatoes or plum tomatoes, or small new potatoes as opposed to large King Edwards.
- **Texture** refers to the ripeness and the quality of the ingredients once they have been cooked. Different varieties of the same ingredient may yield a different texture.

1.2 Apply techniques to produce cold food products

The following points are very important when preparing ingredients. A chef must be able to master these skills as they will greatly enhance the quality of the dishes.

- **Peeling** – Some vegetables need to be peeled; this must be done carefully so as not to remove too much of the flesh. For example, when peeling a courgette it is important to carefully remove the skin enough to expose the green surface; if peeled too deep the courgette will be white.
- **Cutting and chopping** – Careful cutting and chopping enhances the presentation, texture, mouth-feel and flavour of the dish. Finely chopped herbs in a dish will greatly enhance the flavour; if they are roughly chopped they will not contribute so well.
- **Carving and portioning meats** – Doing this correctly is an important skill and makes sure the correct portion control is achieved to avoid wastage. Good carving enhances the presentation of a dish; in some cases, skilled carving is done in a restaurant in front of customers.
- **Slicing** – Sliced foods include smoked salmon, tomatoes and cucumber. Cucumber sliced too thickly can be very difficult to eat; thinly sliced cucumber looks better and is easier to eat.
- **Shredding** – Many vegetables are shredded, including white cabbage when used to make coleslaw and red cabbage for pickling or to use raw in a salad. Lettuces are also shredded finely for shellfish cocktails. Finely shredded vegetables provide good texture and are easy to eat. Roughly cut shredded vegetables are difficult to eat and do not blend well with other ingredients.
- **Portioning** – Each customer's portion should be the same size and have the same proportions. Correct portioning also helps with planning and costing.
- **Accompaniments and dressings** – Accompaniments and dressings enhance cold food preparation. They add flavour, moisture and a contrasting texture, and improve overall eating quality.
  - A good vinaigrette will improve many salad items. A number of different herbs may be added to the vinaigrette; different spices are used to make the cold dishes more interesting.

  - Mayonnaise is used as an accompaniment or as a dressing.
  - Crème fraîche may be used in place of yoghurt.
  - In some salads soured cream is used.
- **Garnishing and presentation** – This makes dishes more attractive and appealing. Cold dishes are garnished in a number of ways: using a range of mixed leaves, artistically cut lemon, lime, tomato, radish, spring onion. Garnishing should include a balance of colour, flavour and texture.
- **Seasoning** – Cold food can be seasoned by using fresh herbs and spices. Avoid using salt for health reasons.
- **Coating** – Ingredients can be coated with dressings such as mayonnaise and vinaigrette.
- **Combining** – Ingredients may be combined to disperse them evenly in a mix.
- **Cooking** – Different cooking methods may be used with different ingredients to produce a particular dish. Methods used may include:
  - boiling and steaming – for example, when preparing vegetables for salads
  - poaching – for example, poached salmon
  - baking – for example, quiche and terrines
  - roasting – for example, cold roast meats
  - grilling and frying – for example, grilled vegetables and meats for salads and hors d'oeuvre
  - stewing and braising – for example, vegetables for salads and hors d'oeuvres.
- **Cooling** – Cold dishes will need to be quickly cooled down to the correct temperature.
- **Drying** – Removing all excess moisture – for example, in preserving meat or fish.
- **Folding** – Carefully folding the ingredients together using a revolving action.
- **Grating** – Vegetables and fruit can be cut using a grater.
- **Measuring** – It is important to accurately work out the right qualities for each recipe.
- **Mixing** – Ingredients should be combined so that they are evenly dispersed.
- **Storing** – Ingredients and finished dishes must be stored at the correct temperature.
- **Temperature control** – The temperature should be recorded to ensure that ingredients and finished dishes are stored correctly. For goods that are being refrigerated the temperature should be between 3 and 5°C. If food is left out on an unrefrigerated cold buffet table, it must be discarded after two hours.
- **Weighing** – Accurate weighing of ingredients according to the recipe specification is important for correct portion control and to prevent wastage.
- **Whisking** – Ingredients can be whisked to form emulsions, foams and liquid dispersions.

Garnishing of cold dishes: an example

PROFESSIONAL TIP

Use a variety of fresh herbs to enhance the flavour of traditional salads and cold dishes – for example, basil, tarragon, coriander, rosemary, chives, parsley.

Types of cold food products

Hors d'oeuvres

In establishments where lunch and dinner is offered, menus will often include cold hors d'oeuvres, which are served as an appetiser before a main meal. Hors d'oeuvres open the meal and should create a good impression.

A wide variety of foods, different combinations of foods and recipes can be served as hors d'oeuvres and salads. Hors d'oeuvres can be divided into two categories:

1. single cold food items (for example, smoked salmon, pâté or melon)
2. a selection of well-seasoned cold dishes.

Hors d'oeuvres may be served for luncheon, dinner or supper. The wide choice of dishes, their colour appeal and versatility make many items and combinations of items suitable for snacks and salads at any time of day.

Salads

Salads may be made from a wide variety of foods – raw or cooked. They may be served as an accompaniment to hot and cold foods or as dishes in their own right. They can be served for lunch, tea, high tea, dinner, supper and snack meals. Salads can be divided in two types:

1. simple, using one ingredient (for example, tomato, cucumber, green salad, potato salad)
2. mixed or composite, using more than one ingredient (for example, coleslaw, Russian, mixed, Waldorf).

A rice or pasta salad can be a simple salad if it is simply seasoned; it becomes a composite salad when mixed with other ingredients such as diced peppers, sweetcorn, peas, tomatoes or diced cucumber.

Accompaniments (dressings and sauces)

Accompaniments to salads include dressings and cold sauces. There are two basic sauces used with cold food, both of which have many variations. These are:

1 vinaigrette (recipe 6)
2 mayonnaise (recipe 7).

Commercial mayonnaises and vinaigrettes are available in many brands. If you decide to use one of these, always taste it to check that you like it before using it.

Some salads may form part of a composite hors d'oeuvre

> **PROFESSIONAL TIP**
> Always finish salads at the last minute, especially when using vinaigrette, so that they remain crisp and fresh.

Sandwiches

Sandwiches are a quick, timesaving snack and are available from many food outlets. The traditional sandwich is made by spreading butter, or a butter substitute, on two slices of bread, placing a filling on one slice and covering it with the other. The crust may or may not be removed, and the sandwich then cut into two or four pieces.

Sandwiches

Types of bread

There is a wide variety of breads available (for example, white, brown, wholemeal, granary, seeded), and many bakers will bake bread according to your specification (for instance, tomato, basil, rosemary, walnut and olive) and will slice it ready for use.

Fillings

An almost endless variety of sandwich fillings can be used – for example, single food items, such as ham, cheese or roast beef; alternatively, a mix of food items can be used, such as ham and tomato, egg and cress, and chicken and lettuce.

Types of sandwiches

There are many different types of sandwiches available. For example:

- toasted sandwich
- club sandwich
- bookmaker sandwich
- double or triple decker
- open sandwiches.

You will find instructions for making these types of sandwich in the 'Recipes' section below; in hotels, dainty, finger-sized sandwiches sprinkled with cress are offered for afternoon tea.

Cold canapés

Canapés are served at a variety of functions, before a formal dinner or at a buffet reception, and may be offered as an accompaniment to drinks.

Canapés are small items no larger than a 50-pence piece and can be eaten with one bite.

Bases for canapés can be made from a variety of breads (including rye and French breads), pastry (short and puff) and brioche, or with no base at all, such as a cherry tomato scooped out and filled with meat or cream cheese.

A selection of canapés prepared for a function

Examples of canapés include:

- rye bread topped with a slice of lobster, asparagus tip garnished with fresh herbs
- rye bread with slices of smoked duck garnished with mango
- small cooked new potatoes, scooped out and filled with sour cream and chives
- small choux pastry éclairs filled with liver pâté
- brioche croutes with apricot chutney and Gorgonzola
- small choux buns filled with prawns in cocktail sauce.

Preparing cold canapés involves a range of skills to make them easy to eat, flavoursome and appetising. Garnishes need to be cut neatly and canapés can be cut in a range of creative shapes, including round, rectangular, triangular, square or boat shapes.

Canapés are presented in a range of styles on specially designed plates (round, square or rectangular; white or black); they can also be presented on slates or mirrors.

Cold meats and poultry

Cold meats should be sliced as near to serving time as possible and arranged neatly on a serving dish.

Whole joints, particularly ribs of beef, are very often placed on buffet tables. They should either be boned or any bones that hinder carving should be removed before being cooked. Before placing on the buffet, brush with oil.

If chicken is to be displayed whole on a buffet it may be brushed with oil, dressed on a suitable dish garnished with watercress.

To keep roast meats such as chicken, suckling pig or duck moist, roast them two to three hours before they are required and do not refrigerate unless they are not to be served within this time period.

Serving of cold game

Large birds such as pheasant may be sliced or cut into portions. Small birds can be served whole or in halves. The birds are served with watercress and game chips. Smaller birds could be served on a fried bread crouton spread with a little pâté.

Serving of cold turkey or goose

Cold turkey or goose for display may be brushed with oil, otherwise it is normally served sliced with dark meat under the white and garnished with watercress. Serve with stuffing and cranberry sauce. For goose, serve a suitable stuffing and apple sauce.

For more examples of cold food products, see the 'Recipes' section below.

Quality points when preparing cold food

- **Cut and prepare to specification** – Recipes should be prepared according to the specification, and the size and cut of the meat, fish or vegetables followed for ease of service, and for overall eating texture and quality.
- **Minimal waste** – Follow the recipe specification exactly to prevent excessive waste.
- **Temperature** – Cold products must not be allowed to increase in temperature. They should be kept at between 3 and 5°C
- **Consistency and texture** – Always use the freshest of ingredients at the right temperature. This is crucial for consistency and texture. For example, warm, limp lettuce will ruin the texture and consistency of a salad.
- **Freshness** – Foods should be bought frequently, stored correctly and checked carefully to ensure that they are in good condition (with no blemishes) and within the use-by date.
- **Smell** – The smell should always be fresh and appetising.
- **Preparation** – Dishes should always be prepared according to recipes and specifications, cut into even-sized portions and trimmed if necessary, with minimum waste.
- **Portions** – Portion sizes will vary according to the type of establishment and the types of customer you are serving. For example, office workers generally require smaller portions than workers who are involved in manual work.
- **Appearance** – Dishes should be neatly dressed and simply garnished.

1.3 Finishing methods for cold food products

- **Decorating and garnishing** – Garnishing is a form of decorating dishes. Garnishes must be delicate and well balanced.
- **Saucing** – Sauces must complement the dish. Any coating must flow gently over the items being sauced.
- **Portioning** – Portions must be the accurate size for the price and market you are operating in, to prevent overproduction and waste.

Quality points for finished products

- **Appearance** – Dishes must look fresh, well presented and colour balanced.
- **Aroma** – Any aromas must be pleasant, with no unpleasant smells.
- **Colour** – All dishes must be colourful and should look natural.
- **Consistency** – Recipes must give the same product every time they are made.
- **Flavours** – These must be well balanced, with no single flavour being overpowering.
- **Portion control** must be accurate for the type of restaurant in order to prevent wastage.
- **Presentation** – Finished dishes must look appetising, fresh and colour balanced.
- **Seasoning** – Cold food generally requires more seasoning. Seasoning is not just salt and pepper, but can also include the use of fresh herbs and spices.
- **Taste** – Finished dishes are judged on taste, therefore the taste should be well balanced and well seasoned.
- **Temperature** – The finished temperature for service should be at 3–5°C.
- **Texture** – Finished dishes must be crisp, moist, succulent and/or crunchy depending on the type of dish. Sauces must not be too thick, and should be well emulsified, smooth and easy to coat items with.

Food safety and quality for cold food presentation

- At all times maintain the highest standard of food safety when preparing and serving cold food. Separate the raw and cooked items to avoid cross-contamination.
- All equipment and utensils must be kept clean and in good condition to prevent contamination of food.
- Food for cold presentation must be of the best quality and, if cooked, must be prepared and cooked adequately following the recipe and temperature requirements precisely. Do not reheat any cooked food once it has been on display, as this is a dangerous practice. Allow to cool and then serve.
- All food items must be stored in a clean, tidy refrigerator, labelled, covered and dated. Remove the covering at the last minute before service. Ideally serve straight from the refrigerator to avoid any possible contamination. Counters, utensils and serving dishes must be scrupulously clean.
- Remember it is a legal requirement under the Food Safety Act that ambient food is served within four hours. Food not served within this time may be unsafe, and therefore should be thrown away and must not be offered to customers or staff.

PROFESSIONAL TIP

Remember, the quality of the food is assessed by the customer in terms of colour, texture, flavour and portion size.

Presentation of cold food

It is important that cold food is presented well so that it is attractive and appealing to customers. 'Cold presentation' means the preparation and presentation of raw and/or cooked foods into a wide variety of cold items.

Preparing and presenting cold dishes covers areas including salads, bread products, pies, pâtés, cured meats and fish. Cold food is popular in every kind of food service operation for at least three good reasons.

1. **Visual appeal:** when food is displayed attractively, arranged carefully and garnished neatly, customers can have their appetites stimulated by seeing exactly what is being offered.
2. **Efficiency:** cold food can be prepared in advance, allowing a large number of people to be served in a short space of time. Self-service is also economic in terms of staffing.
3. **Adaptability:** if cold food is being served from a buffet, the range of foods can be simple or complex and wide ranging, depending on the type of operation.

Cold foods can either be pre-plated or served from large dishes and bowls. In both cases presentation is important: the food should appear fresh, neatly arranged and not over-garnished.

Quality points

Cold food must look clean and fresh. Its presentation should be appealing to the eye. Seasoning and flavour can be adjusted with accompaniments that enhance the eating experience – for example, lemon and Tabasco sauce may be offered with oysters.

For quality points for specific ingredients, refer to the sections below.

Equipment

Bowls, tongs, whisks, spoons, and so on, as well as food processors, mixing machines and blenders, are used with cold preparations. The correct use of specialist equipment and tools enables the cold preparation chef to ensure consistency in dishes – for example, when grating or slicing vegetables for salads and so on.

HEALTH AND SAFETY

Where possible, use plastic gloves when handling food.

Preparation for cold work

Well-planned organisation is essential to ensure adequate pre-preparation (mise en place) so that foods are assembled with a good workflow and are ready on time. Before, during and after assembling, and before final garnishing, foods must be kept in a cool place, cold room or refrigerator so as to minimise the risk of food contamination. Garnishing and final decoration should take place as close to the serving time as possible.

Develop simple artistic skills that require the minimum of time for preparation and assembly. Provide an attractive presentation of food at all times.

> **HEALTH AND SAFETY**
>
> Whenever possible, the food on display to the public should be kept under refrigeration and the temperature should be checked to ensure that it is being maintained at a safe level.
>
> Where customers are viewing closely, the food should ideally be displayed behind a sneeze screen.

Time and temperature

Because of the requirements of food safety, cold foods are often served straight from the refrigerator. This is an error because, at refrigerator temperature, food flavours are not at their best. Individual portions should be removed from refrigeration and allowed to stand at room temperature for 5–10 minutes before serving.

Styles of service

There is a full range of service styles available, which helps to make the food attractive and presentable.

New ways of individual presentation show the creative and innovative skills of the chef

- **Plate service** – Usually food served in restaurants is plated in the kitchen and served on the plate to the customer.
- **Silver service** – Food is sent in to the restaurant on silver or stainless steel flats, vegetable dishes or other types of service equipment, served from these containers by the waiter or waitress using a spoon and fork, and placed on to the customer's plate. Very few restaurants today use silver service.
- **Function banquets** – At a formal lunch or dinner the cold food is plated. Where the function is a buffet the food is displayed on a service table.
- **Finger buffet** – Items are generally passed around by food servers on plates. It is important that the food served in a finger buffet is prepared so that items are easily eaten with the fingers.
- **Fork buffet** – Food offered should be easily eaten with a fork. The food needs to be prepared for ease of service. It has become fashionable to offer bowl food in a buffet; this is food that can easily be eaten from a china bowl, either with a fork or spoon.
- **Takeaway** – Food is individually priced in takeaway containers and does not need to be eaten in the establishment serving it. This is very popular for people who wish to have a working lunch.

Equipment used to present cold food

The type of equipment a chef uses will depend on the style of service. Food may be served on plates or platters, or in bowls or service dishes. It is usually served straight from the display cabinet. If it is to be displayed for a long time, then a chilled display cabinet is required. For example, in a salad bar in a restaurant all the salads would be held in a chilled display cabinet.

Plain white plates for serving cold food

Silver and stainless steel salvers are used to present cold food on a cold buffet table. Many establishments today serve food on a range of plain white plates of varying shapes and sizes.

For takeaway service, a variety of attractive containers is now available on the market; all food must be clearly labelled and dated, and, if possible, nutritional content included.

TEST YOURSELF

1. Name three meal occasions where cold food items can be served.
2. What are the differences between an open, a closed and a club sandwich?
3. Name two simple salads.
4. Name two compound salads.
5. Give four examples of cold hors d'oeuvres that could appear on a menu.
6. When presenting cold dishes, apart from presentation and garnish what else needs to be considered?
7. What is the appropriate presentation for cold food in a:
   - a finger buffet
   - b canapé reception?
8. Name the types of service equipment that can be used to present food.
9. What is the maximum time a cold buffet can be left for presentation at room temperature?

Cold foods

1 Toasted sandwiches

Preparing the dish

Toasted sandwiches can be made in two ways.

1. Add the filling between the two slices of hot, freshly buttered toast.
2. Use an item of equipment called a sandwich toaster. First, put the filling between two slices of bread and then toast the whole sandwich in the sandwich toaster. Some toasters will seal the sandwich, remove the crusts and cut the sandwich in half.

2 Club sandwiches

Preparing the dish

VARIATION

- Use three or four slices of bread, toasted or untoasted, to make other double-decker and triple-decker sandwiches.

1 Butter three slices of hot toast.

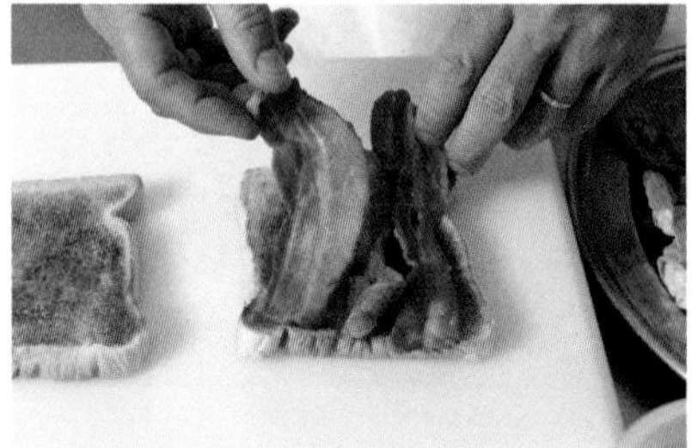

2 On the first slice, place slices of grilled, crispy streaky bacon.

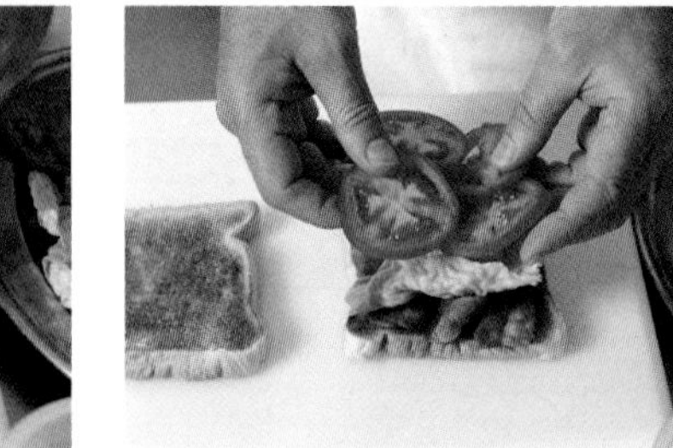

3 Place slices of tomato and lettuce on the bacon.

4 Put the second slice of toast on top of this and spread mayonnaise on it. Layer sliced cooked chicken breast over the top.

5 Add slices of hard-boiled egg.

6 Finally, put the third slice of toast on top. Then press down carefully on the sandwich, make it as compact as possible and secure it with cocktail sticks.

7 Cut it in halves or quarters. Serve with potato crisps.

3 Bookmaker sandwich

Preparing the dish

1 Place an underdone thin sirloin steak between two slices of toast made from a bloomer loaf.

Serving suggestion

The sandwich is usually garnished with salad leaves, tomato cress and served with potato or vegetable crisp.

This kind of steak is known as a minute steak because it needs only a minute over a fierce heat to cook.

4 Open sandwiches

Preparing the dish

To prepare open sandwiches, butter a slice of any type of bread and top this with a variety of foods, such as:

- smoked salmon, lettuce, potted shrimps, slice of lemon
- cold roast beef, sliced tomato, gherkin fan
- shredded lettuce, slices of hard-boiled egg, cucumber slices and mayonnaise
- pickled herring, slices of hard-boiled egg, sprinkled with chopped gherkins, capers and parsley.

5 Soused herring or mackerel

Energy	Calories	Fat	Saturated fat	Carbohydrates	Sugar	Protein	Fibre
2419 kJ	576 kcal	44.5 g	9.4 g	3.0 g	3.0 g	41.0 g	1.1 g

* For 4 portions

Ingredient	4 portions	10 portions
Herrings or mackerel	2	5
Button onions	25 g	60 g
Carrots, peeled and fluted	25 g	60 g
Salt and pepper		
Bay leaf	½	1½
Peppercorns	6	12
Thyme	1 sprig	2 sprigs
Vinegar	60 ml	150 ml

Mise en place

1. Clean, scale and fillet the fish.
2. Peel and wash the onion and carrots, and cut into neat, thin rings.

Preparation

1. Wash the fish fillets well, and season with salt and pepper.
2. Roll up with the skin outside.
3. Place in an earthenware dish.
4. Blanch the onion and carrots for 2–3 minutes.
5. Add to the fish with the remainder of the ingredients.
6. Cover with greaseproof paper or aluminium foil and cook in a moderate oven for 15–20 minutes.
7. Allow to cool.
8. Place in a dish with the onion and carrot.

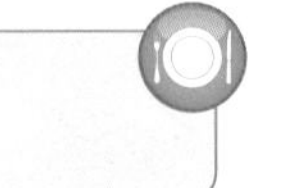

SERVING SUGGESTION

Garnish with picked parsley, dill or chives.

This dish is also known as pickled herring.

6 Vinaigrette (emulsifying technique)

Energy	Calories	Fat	Saturated fat	Carbohydrates	Sugar	Protein	Fibre	Sodium
423 kJ	103 kcal	11.3 g	1.6 g	0.1 g	0.1 g	0.1 g	0.0 g	421.0 g

* Analysed based on 5 portions. Used 1.5 tbsp vinegar and 4.5 tbsp olive oil

Ingredient	4–6 portions
Vinegar	1–2 tbsp
French mustard	1 tsp
Salt	1 tsp
Olive oil	3–6 tbsp

Preparing the vinaigrette

1 Combine vinegar with the mustard and salt.

2 Slowly whisk in the oil.

VARIATION

You could use:

- English in place of French mustard
- chopped fresh herbs, chives, parsley, tarragon, and so on
- different oils, such as sesame oil
- different vinegars, or lemon juice instead of vinegar.

Vinaigrette video, http://bit.ly/XYuqis

7 Mayonnaise (emulsifying technique)

Energy	Calories	Fat	Saturated fat	Carbohydrates	Sugar	Protein	Fibre	Sodium
1153 kJ	280 kcal	27.6 g	4.7 g	0.1 g	0.1 g	0.1 g	0.0 g	144.0 g

* Using vinegar and corn oil

Ingredient	8 portions
Egg yolks, pasteurised (recommended)	3
Vinegar or lemon juice	2 tsp
Small pinch of salt, strongly recommended	
English or continental mustard	½ tsp
A mild-flavoured oil such as corn oil or the lightest olive oil	250 ml
Water, boiling	1 tsp

Because of the risk of salmonella food poisoning, it is strongly recommended that pasteurised egg yolks are used.

Preparing the dish

1 Place yolks, vinegar, salt and mustard in the bowl of a food mixer.

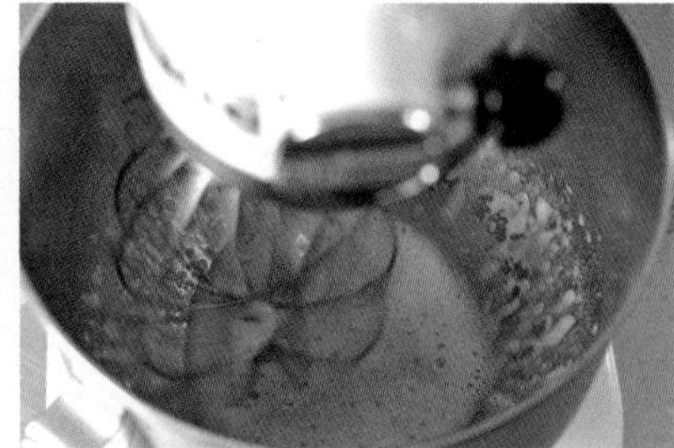

2 Whisk until thoroughly mixed.

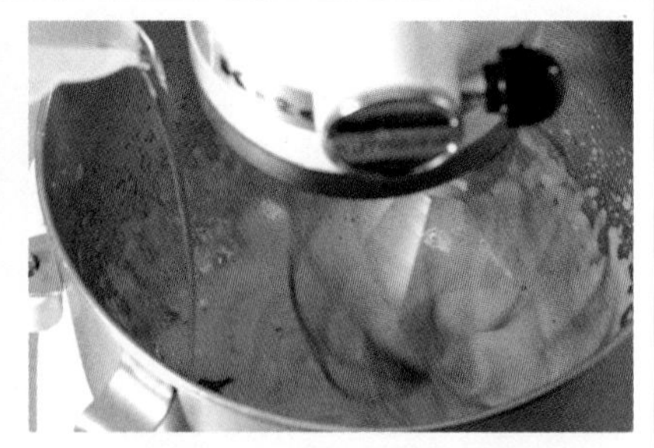

3 Continue to whisk vigorously and start to add the oil – this needs to be done slowly.

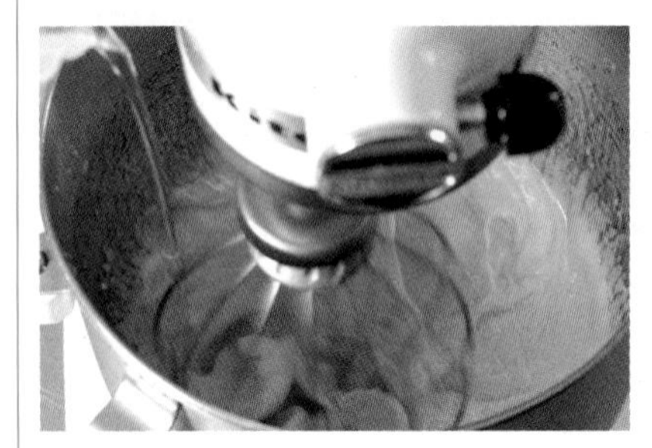

4 Keep whisking until all the oil has been added.

5 Whisk in the boiling water.

6 Taste and correct seasoning if necessary.

VARIATION

Add:

- fresh chopped herbs
- garlic juice – peel a clove of garlic and press it using a garlic press
- thick tomato juice.

If the mayonnaise becomes too thick while you are making it, whisk in a little water or vinegar.

Mayonnaise may separate, turn or curdle for several reasons:

- you have added the oil too quickly
- the oil is too cold
- you have not whisked enough
- the egg yolks were stale and weak.

To reconstitute (bring it back together), either:

- take a basin, pour 1 teaspoon of boiling water and, gradually but vigorously, whisk in the curdled sauce a little at a time, or
- in a clean basin, whisk a fresh egg yolk with ½ teaspoon of cold water then gradually whisk in the curdled sauce.

8 Egg mayonnaise (emulsifying technique)

Energy	Calories	Fat	Saturated fat	Carbohydrates	Sugar	Protein	Fibre	Sodium
1721 kJ	417 kcal	42.0 g	4.2 g	1.6 g	1.5 g	7.8 g	0.0 g	141.0 g

* Added 60 g salad for garnishing (per recipe of 4 portions). Standard mayonnaise

Ingredient	4 portions	10 portions
Hard-boiled eggs	4	10
Salad leaves and micro herbs to garnish		
Mayonnaise	200 ml	450 ml

Preparing the dish

1. Cut the hard-boiled eggs in half lengthwise, arrange the salad garnish on individual plates, then place the hard-boiled eggs on top.
2. Mask with mayonnaise and decorate as required with a little paprika, etc.

Modern egg mayonnaise needs to look attractive. You can use a variety of salad leaves and decorate with micro herbs.

9 Balsamic vinegar and olive oil dressing

Energy	Calories	Fat	Saturated fat	Carbohydrates	Sugar	Protein	Fibre	Sodium
8998 kJ	2187 kcal	250.0 g	33.7 g	13.4 g	12.3 g	0.4 g	0.0 g	606.0 g

* Per 300 ml recipe. Added 1/4 teaspoon salt for seasoning

Ingredient	Makes 300 ml
Water	62 ml
Olive oil	250 ml
Balsamic vinegar	62 ml
Sherry vinegar	2 tbsp
Caster sugar	½ tsp
Seasoning	

Preparing the dish

1. Whisk all ingredients together and correct the seasoning.

PROFESSIONAL TIP

The amount of balsamic vinegar needed will depend on its quality, age, etc. Add more or less as required.

This dressing works well because it is not an emulsion. The oil and vinegar provide a stark contrast and can be stirred just before serving.

10 Tomato vinaigrette (emulsifying technique)

Energy	Calories	Fat	Saturated fat	Carbohydrates	Sugar	Protein	Fibre	Sodium
383 kJ	93 kcal	9.4 g	1.4 g	1.9 g	1.9 g	0.5 g	0.4	245.0 g

Ingredient	4 portions	10 portions
Tomatoes	200 g	500 g
Caster sugar	½ tsp	1¼ tbsp
White wine vinegar	1 tbsp	2½ tsp
Extra virgin olive oil	3 tbsp	8 tbsp
Seasoning		

Preparing the dish

1. Blanch and deseed the tomatoes; purée in a food processor.
2. Add the sugar, vinegar, olive oil and seasoning; whisk well to emulsify.
3. The vinaigrette should be smooth.

11 Andalusian sauce (emulsifying technique)

Energy	Calories	Fat	Saturated fat	Carbohydrates	Sugar	Protein	Fibre	Sodium
6299 kJ	1428 kcal	160.0 g	24.9 g	14.3 g	13.8 g	13.3 g	0.7 g	1,286.0 g

Ingredient	Makes 250 ml
Mayonnaise	250 ml
Tomato juice or ketchup	2 tbsp
Red pepper, cut into julienne	1 tbsp

Preparing the dish

1. Using a blender, combine the mayonnaise with the tomato juice or ketchup and the red pepper.

SERVING SUGGESTION

May be served with cold salads.

PROFESSIONAL TIP

For Andalusian sauce, Thousand Island dressing, green sauce and other similar recipes, use a blender to achieve the desired texture and flavour.

12 Green or herb sauce (emulsifying technique)

Energy	Calories	Fat	Saturated fat	Carbohydrates	Sugar	Protein	Fibre	Sodium
1082 kJ	263 kcal	28.0 g	4.3 g	0.9 g	0.6 g	0.8 g	0.2 g	0.2 g

Ingredient	4 portions	10 portions
Spinach, tarragon, chervil, chives, watercress	50 g	125 g
Mayonnaise	250 g	625 g

Preparing the dish

1. Pick, wash, blanch and refresh the green leaves.
2. Squeeze dry.
3. Pass through a very fine sieve.
4. Mix with the mayonnaise.

SERVING SUGGESTION
May be served with cold salmon or trout.

13 Tartare sauce (emulsifying technique)

Energy	Calories	Fat	Saturated fat	Carbohydrates	Sugar	Protein	Fibre	Sodium
911 kJ	221 kcal	24.0 g	3.6 g	0.8 g	0.6 g	0.6 g	0.1 g	0.2 g

Ingredient	8 portions
Mayonnaise	250 ml
Capers, chopped	25 g
Gherkins, chopped	50 g
Sprig of parsley, chopped	

Preparing the dish

1. Combine all the ingredients.

SERVING SUGGESTION
This sauce is usually served with deep fried fish. It may also be served with grilled fish.

PROFESSIONAL TIP
Finely chop the gherkins and capers, and use a blender to give the desired texture and consistency.

HEALTHY EATING TIP
- Proportionally reduce the fat by adding some low-fat yoghurt instead of some of the mayonnaise. Use olive oil to make the mayonnaise.

14 Remoulade sauce (emulsifying technique)

Energy	Calories	Fat	Saturated fat	Carbohydrates	Sugar	Protein	Fibre	Sodium
907 kJ	220 kcal	24.0 g	3.6 g	0.8 g	0.6 g	0.7 g	0.1 g	0.3 g

Preparing the dish

1 Prepare as for tartare sauce (recipe 13), adding 1 teaspoon of anchovy essence and mixing thoroughly. Makes 8 portions.

SERVING SUGGESTION

This sauce may be served with fried fish. It can also be mixed with a fine julienne of celeriac to make an accompaniment to cold meats, terrines, etc.

15 Mint sauce

Energy	Calories	Fat	Saturated fat	Carbohydrates	Sugar	Protein	Fibre	Sodium
26 kJ	6 kcal	0.0 g	0.7 g	0.6 g	0.1 g	0.0 g	0.0 g	0.0 g

Ingredient	8 portions
Mint	2–3 tbsp
Caster sugar	1 tsp
Vinegar	125 ml

Preparing the dish

1 Chop the washed, picked mint and mix with the sugar.

2 Place in a china basin and add the vinegar.

3 If the vinegar is too sharp, dilute it with a little water.

SERVING SUGGESTION

Serve with roast lamb.

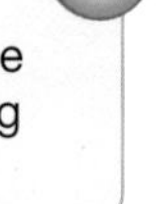

PROFESSIONAL TIP

A less acid sauce can be produced by dissolving the sugar in 125 ml boiling water and, when cold, adding the chopped mint and 1–2 tbsp vinegar to taste.

16 Thousand Island dressing (emulsifying technique)

Energy	Calories	Fat	Saturated fat	Carbohydrates	Sugar	Protein	Fibre	Sodium
928 kJ	225 kcal	24.0 g	3.6 g	2.6 g	2.3 g	0.5 g	0.1 g	0.3 g

Ingredient	
Mayonnaise	250 ml
Tomato ketchup	30 ml
White wine vinegar	1 tbsp
Caster sugar	1 tsp
Onion, finely chopped	15 g
Clove of garlic, finely chopped	1
Tabasco sauce	2 drops
Worcester sauce	½ tsp
Gherkins, finely chopped	2

Preparing the dish

1 Mix all the ingredients together.

SERVING SUGGESTION

Use as a dressing for fish cocktails and salads.

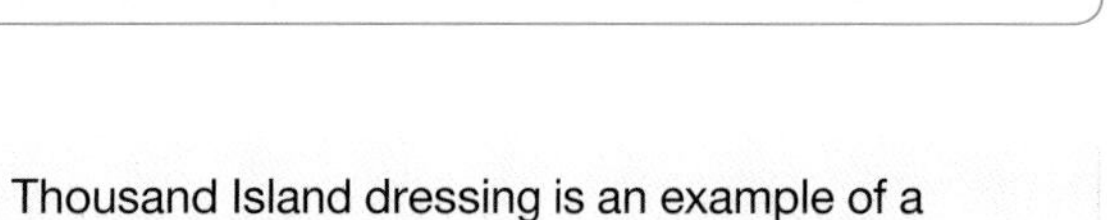

Thousand Island dressing is an example of a dressing that has become a standard condiment.

HEALTHY EATING TIP

- Make the mayonnaise using olive oil.

17 Shellfish cocktail sauce (emulsifying technique)

Energy	Calories	Fat	Saturated fat	Carbohydrates	Sugar	Protein	Fibre
889 kJ	216 kcal	22.7 g	14.2 g	1.9 g	1.9 g	1.2 g	0.1 g

Method 1

Ingredient	4 portions	10 portions
Egg yolk, pasteurised	1	2½
Vinegar	1 tsp	2½ tsp
Salt, pepper, mustard		
Olive oil or sunflower oil	5 tbsp	12½ tbsp
Tomato juice or ketchup to taste		
Worcester sauce (optional)	2–3 drops	5–8 drops

Preparing the dish

1 Make the mayonnaise with the egg yolk, vinegar, seasonings and oil.

2 Combine with the tomato juice or ketchup to taste and Worcester sauce (if using).

Method 2

Ingredient	4 portions	10 portions
Lightly whipped cream or unsweetened non-dairy cream	5 tbsp	12½ tbsp
Tomato juice or ketchup	3 tbsp	8 tbsp
Salt, pepper		
Lemon juice	a few drops	a few drops

Preparing the dish

1 Mix all the ingredients together.

Fresh or tinned tomato juice, or diluted tomato ketchup, may be used for both of these methods, but the use of tinned tomato purée gives an unpleasant flavour.

HEALTHY EATING TIP

- Keep added salt to a minimum.
- Extend the high-fat mayonnaise with low-fat yoghurt to proportionally reduce the fat content.

Flavoured oils

18 Herb oil

Energy	Calories	Fat	Saturated fat	Carbohydrates	Sugar	Protein	Fibre	Sodium
8482 kJ	2063 kcal	226.0 g	32.5 g	3.0 g	2.2 g	0.0 g	5.4 g	149.0 g

Ingredient	Makes 250 ml
Picked flat leaf parsley	25 g
Chives	10 g
Picked basil leaves	10 g
Picked spinach	100 g
Corn oil or olive oil	250 ml

Cooking

1. Blanch all the herbs and spinach for 1½ minutes.
2. Drain well, place with the oil in a liquidiser and blitz for 2½ minutes. Pass and decant when rested.

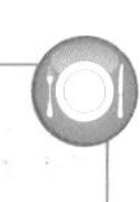

SERVING SUGGESTION

Serve with roast lamb.

19 Basil oil

Energy	Calories	Fat	Saturated fat	Carbohydrates	Sugar	Protein	Fibre	Sodium*
7434 kJ	1808 kcal	200.0 g	13.2 g	1.3 g	0.0 g	0.0 g	0.0 g	804.0 g

* Using vegetable oil

Ingredient	Makes 200 ml
Fresh basil	25 g
Olive oil	200 ml
Salt, to taste	
Mill pepper	

Cooking

1. Blanch and refresh the basil; purée with the oil and add salt and pepper
2. Allow to settle overnight and decant.
3. Store in bottles with a sprig of blanched basil.

VARIATION

- Basil extract can be used in place of fresh basil; 50 g of grated Parmesan or Gorgonzola cheese may also be added to the basil oil.

20 Lemon oil

Energy	Calories	Fat	Saturated fat	Carbohydrates	Sugar	Protein	Fibre	Sodium
9340 kJ	2272 kcal	250.0 g	28.6 g	1.2 g	0.0 g	0.0 g	2.5 g	1.7 g

Ingredient	Makes 250 ml
Lemons, rind (with no pith – the whitish layer between skin and fruit)	3
Lemon grass stick, cut lengthways and chopped into 2 cm strips	1
Grapeseed oil	250 ml
Olive oil	2 tbsp

Preparing the dish

1. Place all the ingredients into a food processor and pulse the mix until the lemon peel and grass are approximately 3 mm thick.
2. Allow to stand for two days. Decant and store in the fridge until ready for use (or freeze for longer if you wish).

21 Mint oil

Energy	Calories	Fat	Saturated fat	Carbohydrates	Sugar	Protein	Fibre	Sodium
5171 kJ	1257 kcal	136.0 g	8.9 g	5.3 g	0.0 g	0.0 g	0.0 g	15.0 g

Ingredient	Makes 150 ml
Mint	100 g
Olive oil	150 ml
Salt	½ teaspoon

Cooking

1. Blanch the mint for 30 seconds.
2. Refresh and squeeze the water out.
3. Place in a blender and slowly add the oil. Add the salt.
4. Allow to settle overnight and decant into bottles.

SERVING SUGGESTION
Uses include lamb dishes, salads and fish dishes.

22 Vanilla oil

Energy	Calories	Fat	Saturated fat	Carbohydrates	Sugar	Protein	Fibre	Sodium
7149 kJ	1737 kcal	180.0 g	11.9 g	1.1 g	1.1 g	1.1 g	0.0 g	2.0 g

Ingredient	Makes 200 ml
Vegetable oil or olive oil	200 ml
Vanilla pods, whole	5
Vanilla pods, used	2
Vanilla extract	50 ml

Cooking

1. Warm the oil to around 60°C; add the vanilla in its various forms and infuse, scraping all the seeds into the oil.
2. Store in a plastic bottle.

SERVING SUGGESTION
Uses include lamb dishes, salads and fish dishes.

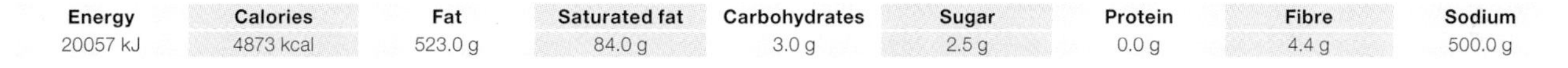

23 Walnut oil

Energy	Calories	Fat	Saturated fat	Carbohydrates	Sugar	Protein	Fibre	Sodium
20057 kJ	4873 kcal	523.0 g	84.0 g	3.0 g	2.5 g	0.0 g	4.4 g	500.0 g

Ingredient	Makes 500 ml
Olive or walnut oil	500 ml
Walnuts, finely crushed	75 g
Parmesan cheese	75 g
Salt, to taste	50 ml
Mill pepper	

Preparing the dish

1. Mix all the ingredients together and bottle until required.

Pickles, chutneys and relishes

24 Tomato chutney

Energy	Calories	Fat	Saturated fat	Carbohydrates	Sugar	Protein	Fibre	Sodium
7232 kJ	1702 kcal	4.0 g	0.2 g	379.0 g	376.0 g	299.0 g	23.3 g	4,157.0 g

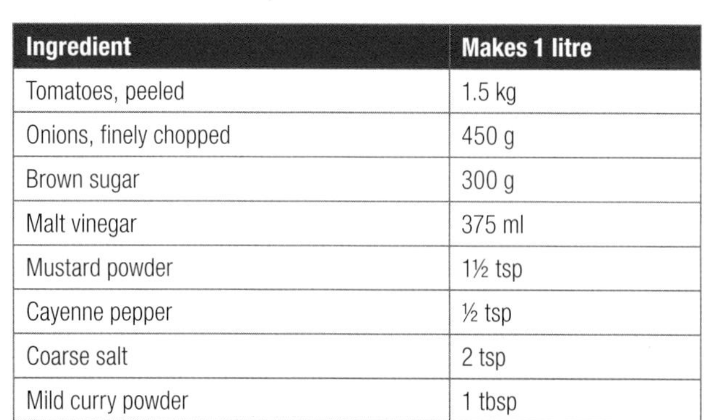

Ingredient	Makes 1 litre
Tomatoes, peeled	1.5 kg
Onions, finely chopped	450 g
Brown sugar	300 g
Malt vinegar	375 ml
Mustard powder	1½ tsp
Cayenne pepper	½ tsp
Coarse salt	2 tsp
Mild curry powder	1 tbsp

Cooking

1. Peel and coarsely chop the tomatoes, then combine with the remaining ingredients in a large heavy-duty saucepan.
2. Stir over heat without boiling until the sugar dissolves. Simmer uncovered, stirring occasionally until the mixture thickens (about 1½ hours).
3. Place in hot, sterilised jars. Seal while hot.

SERVING SUGGESTION
Serve with cheese, cold meats or terrines.

25 Beetroot relish

Energy	Calories	Fat	Saturated fat	Carbohydrates	Sugar	Protein	Fibre	Sodium
7290 kJ	1713 kcal	2.3 g	0.2 g	376.0 g	355.0 g	28.9 g	42.0 g	8,582.0 g

Ingredient	Makes 1.75 litres
Beetroots, peeled and coarsely chopped	1 kg
Onions, finely chopped	800 g
Caster sugar	225 g
Coarse salt	1 tbsp
Ground allspice	1 tsp
Malt vinegar	500 ml
Plain flour	1 tbsp

Cooking

1. Mix the chopped beetroot and onion together, add the sugar, salt, allspice and 375 ml of the vinegar to a large saucepan. Bring to the boil and simmer for 30 minutes.
2. Mix the flour with the remaining vinegar and whisk together well. (Make sure it is smooth and does not contain any lumps.) Add to the beetroot mixture. Stir until it is all well blended and thickens.
3. Place in hot sterilised jars. Seal while still hot.

26 Pickled red cabbage

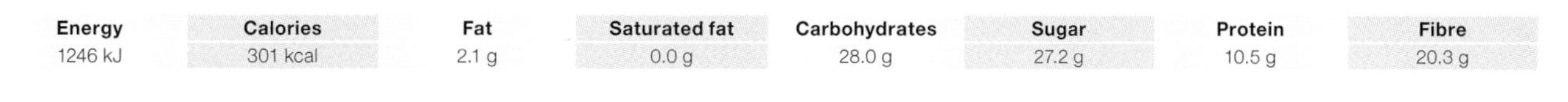

Energy	Calories	Fat	Saturated fat	Carbohydrates	Sugar	Protein	Fibre
1246 kJ	301 kcal	2.1 g	0.0 g	28.0 g	27.2 g	10.5 g	20.3 g

Ingredient	
Red cabbage	2 kg
Spiced vinegar	1.5 litres

Preparing the dish

1. Remove and discard the outer leaves of the cabbage and shred the rest finely.
2. Place in layers in a deep bowl, sprinkling each layer with dry salt, and leave for 24 hours.
3. Rinse and drain, cover with spiced vinegar (see Mixed pickle, recipe 28) and leave for a further 24 hours, mixing occasionally. Pack and cover.

27 Date and tamarind relish

Energy	Calories	Fat	Saturated fat	Carbohydrates	Sugar	Protein	Fibre	Sodium
6937 kJ	1632 kcal	11.7 g	1.9 g	384.0 g	340.0 g	20.2 g	25.1 g	71.0 g

Ingredient	Makes 625 ml
Dried tamarind	75 g
Boiling water	500 ml
Olive oil	2 tsp
Black mustard seeds	2 tsp
Cumin seeds	2 tsp
Fresh dates, stoned and chopped	500 g
Malt vinegar	60 ml

Cooking

1. Place the dried tamarind into a suitable bowl and pour over the boiling water; allow to stand for 30 minutes.
2. Strain the liquid, pressing to extract all moisture, then discard the tamarind.
3. Heat the oil in a suitable saucepan. Cook the mustard seeds until they pop, then add the cumin seeds, dates, tamarind liquid and vinegar, and bring to the boil. Simmer for 5 minutes until almost dry.
4. Purée in a processor until smooth.
5. Place the hot relish into hot sterilised jars. Seal while hot.

28 Pesto

Energy	Calories	Fat	Saturated fat	Carbohydrates	Sugar	Protein	Fibre	Sodium
4218 kJ	1020 kcal	95.0 g	24.9 g	7.1 g	1.2 g	0.0 g	0.7 g	1,339.0 g

Ingredient	Makes 250 ml
Fresh basil leaves	100 ml
Pine nuts, lightly toasted	1 tbsp
Garlic, picked and crumbled	2 cloves
Parmesan cheese, grated	40 g
Pecorino cheese, grated	40 g
Olive oil	5 tbsp
Salt and pepper	

Preparing the dish

1. Place all ingredients into a food processor and mix to a rough-textured sauce.
2. Transfer to a bowl and leave for at least 1 hour to enable the flavours to develop.

VARIATION

- Use flat-leaf parsley in place of basil and walnuts in place of pine nuts.

Pesto is traditionally served with large flat pasta called trenetta.

Pesto is also used as a cordon in various fish and meat plated dishes, e.g. grilled fish, medallions of veal.

29 Mixed pickle

Energy	Calories	Fat	Saturated fat	Carbohydrates	Sugar	Protein	Fibre	Sodium
2126 kJ	512 kcal	6.0 g	0.9 g	41.0 g	39.7 g	5.9 g	22.1 g	6,006.0 g

Ingredient	
For the spiced vinegar	
Blade mace	5 g
Allspice	5 g
Cloves	5 g
Stick cinnamon	5 g
Peppercorns	6
Vinegar	1 litre
Ginger (optional)	
For hot pickle	
Root ginger	5 g
Vegetables	
Cauliflower	1 small
Cucumber	1 small
Green tomatoes	4
Onion	1
Marrow (or courgette)	1 small (2)

Cooking

1. To make the spiced vinegar, tie the spices in muslin, place them in a covered pan with the vinegar and heat slowly to boiling point.
2. Remove from the heat and stand for 2 hours, then remove the bag.
3. Prepare the vegetables, with the exception of the marrow, and soak them in brine for 24 hours.
4. Peel the marrow, remove the seeds and cut into small squares, sprinkle and salt, and let it stand for 12 hours.
5. Drain the vegetables, pack them into jars, and cover with cold spiced vinegar.
6. Cover the jars and allow the pickle to mature for at least a month before use.

30 Tapenade

Energy	Calories	Fat	Saturated fat	Carbohydrates	Sugar	Protein	Fibre
773 kJ	188 kcal	19.8 g	2.9 g	0.3 g	0.1 g	2.0 g	2.7 g

Ingredient	4 portions
Black olives, puréed or finely chopped	250 g
Capers	45 g
Anchovies, finely chopped	6 fillets
Parsley, chopped (optional)	½ tsp
Chives, chopped (optional)	½ tsp
Tarragon, chopped (optional)	½ tsp
Lemon, juice of (optional)	½
Brandy (optional)	1 tbsp
Garlic (optional)	
Olive oil	4 tbsp
Roast cumin and chopped red chilli, to garnish	

Preparing the dish

1 Mix all the ingredients together, adding the olive oil to make a paste.

2 For a smoother texture, place garlic, lemon juice, capers and anchovies into a food processor and process until a smooth texture. Add the olives and parsley, and sufficient oil to form a smooth paste.

3 Season, if required.

4 Garnish with a sprinkle of roast cumin and chopped red chilli.

5 Serve chilled.

Tapenade is a Provençale dish consisting of puréed or finely chopped black olives, capers, anchovies and olive oil. It may also contain garlic, herbs, tuna, lemon juice or brandy. Its name comes from the Provençale word for capers: *tapeno*. It is popular in the South of France, where it is generally eaten as an hors d'oeuvre, spread on toast.

ACTIVITY

1 Suggest three further variations.

2 Deliberately curdle some mayonnaise and reconstitute it.

31 Smoked salmon

Energy	Calories	Fat	Saturated fat	Carbohydrates	Sugar	Protein	Fibre
149 kJ	36 kcal	1.1 g	0.3 g	0.0 g	0.0 g	6.4 g	0.0 g

Mise en place

1. Allow 35–50 g per portion.
2. A side of smoked salmon must be carefully trimmed to remove the dry outside surface before service. Remove all bones (a pair of pliers is useful for this).

Preparing the dish

1. Carve the salmon on the slant, as thinly as possible.

2. Dress neatly, overlapping, on a plate or dish, decorated with sprigs of parsley Accompaniments include brown bread and butter, and lemon.

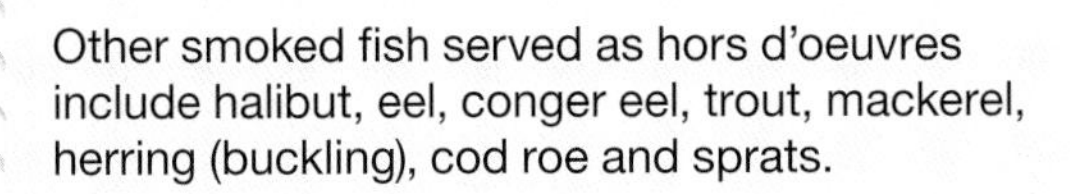

Other smoked fish served as hors d'oeuvres include halibut, eel, conger eel, trout, mackerel, herring (buckling), cod roe and sprats.

HEALTHY EATING TIP

- Oily fish (such as salmon, trout, mackerel, rollmops and sprats) are high in omega-3 fatty acids, which are beneficial for health.

32 Oysters

Energy	Calories	Fat	Saturated fat	Carbohydrates	Sugar	Protein	Fibre
192 kJ	45 kcal	0.9 g	0.2 g	2.7 g	1.0 g	6.8 g	0.4 g

Ingredient	4 portions
Rock or native oysters	24
Lemon	1
To accompany	
Brown bread and butter	
Tabasco or chilli sauce	

Mise en place

1. Select only those oysters that are tightly shut and have a fresh smell (category A is best, which means the waters they have grown in are clean).

Preparing the dish

1. To open an oyster, only the point of the oyster knife is used. Hold the oyster with a thick oven cloth to protect your hand.
2. With the oyster in the palm of your hand, push the point of the knife about 1 cm deep into the 'hinge' between the 'lid' and the body of the oyster.
3. Once the lid has been penetrated, push down. The lid should pop open. Lift up the top shell, cutting the muscle attached to it.
4. Remove any splintered shell from the flesh and solid shell.
5. Return each oyster to its shell and serve on a bed of crushed ice with chilli sauce, brown bread and lemon.

Make sure the oysters have been grown in or fished from clean waters, and take note of the famous rule only to use them when there is an 'r' in the month, although rock oysters are available throughout the year. This applies to the Northern Hemisphere.

33 Dressed crab

Energy	Calories	Fat	Saturated fat	Carbohydrates	Sugar	Protein	Fibre	Sodium
1,974 kJ	474 kcal	28.6 g	4.4 g	0.8 g	0.7 g	53.1 g	0.7 g	1.2 g

Ingredient	1 portion
Whole crab, cooked by boiling	1 (200–300 g)
Salt, pepper	
Worcester sauce	
Mayonnaise	
Fresh white breadcrumbs	
Decoration as required, e.g. parsley and hard-boiled egg	

Preparing the dish

1. Remove large claws and sever at the joints.
2. Remove the flexible pincer from the claw.
3. Crack or saw carefully and remove all flesh.
4. Remove flesh from two remaining joints with the handle of spoon.
5. Carefully remove the soft undershell.
6. Discard the gills (dead man's fingers) and the sac behind the eyes.
7. Scrape out all the inside of the shell and pass through a sieve.
8. Season with salt, pepper, Worcester sauce and a little mayonnaise; thicken lightly with fresh white breadcrumbs.
9. Trim the shell by tapping carefully along the natural line.
10. Scrub the shell thoroughly and leave to dry.
11. Dress the brown meat down the centre of the shell.
12. Shred the white meat, taking care to remove any small pieces of shell.
13. Dress neatly on either side of the brown meat.
14. Decorate as desired, using any of the following: chopped parsley, hard-boiled white and yolk of egg, anchovies, capers, olives.
15. Serve the crab on a flat dish garnished with lettuce leaves, quarters of tomato and the crab's legs.
16. Serve a vinaigrette or mayonnaise sauce separately.

34 Cold salmon

Energy	Calories	Fat	Saturated fat	Carbohydrates	Sugar	Protein	Fibre	Sodium
2,141 kJ	517 kcal	40.3 g	6.5 g	5.1 g	4.5 g	33.0 g	1.8 g	1.2 g

Ingredient	2–3 portions	8–10 portions
Cooking liquid (court bouillon)		
Water	1 litre	2.5 litres
Salt	10 g	25 g
Carrots, sliced	50 g	125 g
Bay leaf	2–3	5–8
Parsley stalks		
Vinegar	60 ml	150 ml
Peppercorns	6	15
Onions, sliced	50 g	125 g
Sprig of thyme	1	2
Salmon for service in darnes or portions		
Salmon, cleaned	500 g	1¼ kg
Court bouillon (see above)	400 ml	1 litre
Cucumber	¼	½
Large lettuce	½	1
Tomatoes	80 g	200 g
Mayonnaise (recipe 7) or green sauce (recipe 12)	100 ml	250 ml

Salmon may be obtained in varying weights from 3.5–15 kg: 0.5 kg of uncleaned salmon yields 2–3 portions.

Size is an important consideration, depending on whether the salmon is to be cooked whole or cut into darnes. A salmon of any size may be cooked whole. When required for darnes, a medium-sized salmon is more suitable.

For the cooking liquid (court bouillon)

1. Simmer all the ingredients for 30–40 minutes.
2. Pass through a strainer; use as required.

Cooking for service in darnes or portions

1. Cook the salmon in the court bouillon, either whole, cut into darnes or into suprêmes.
2. Allow to cool thoroughly in the cooking liquid to keep it moist. Divide a whole salmon into eight even portions; for darnes, remove the centre bone and cut each darne in half, if required.
3. Except when whole, remove the centre bone, the skin and brown surface, and dress neatly on a flat dish.
4. Peel and slice the cucumber and neatly arrange a few slices on each portion.
5. Garnish with quarters of lettuce and quarters of tomato.
6. Serve the sauce or mayonnaise in a sauceboat separately.

Cooking and presenting salmon whole

1. Scrape off all scales, from tail to head, using the back of a knife.
2. Remove all gills and clean out the head.
3. Remove the intestines and clear the blood from the backbone.
4. Trim off all fins. Wash well.
5. Place in a salmon kettle and cover with cold court bouillon.
6. Bring slowly to the boil, skim, then simmer very gently.
7. Allow the following approximate simmering times:
   - 3.5 kg – 15 minutes
   - 7 kg – 20 minutes
   - 10.5 kg – 25 minutes
   - 14 kg – 30 minutes.

8 Allow the cooked salmon to cool then remove it from the liquid. Carefully remove the skin and the dark layer under the skin (which is cooked blood). The now bared salmon flesh should be perfectly smooth.
9 Make sure the salmon is well drained; place it on to the serving dish or board.
10 The salmon is now ready for decorating and garnishing. Keep this to a minimum to avoid over-covering the fish and the dish. Neatly overlapping thin slices of cucumber (the skin may be left on or removed), quartered tomatoes (which can be peeled and neatly cut), small pieces of hearts of lettuce can, if artistically set out, give a quick, neat-looking and appetising appearance. Remember, though, that time is money – there is no justification for spending a lot of time cutting fiddly little pieces of many different items to form patterns that often look untidy.

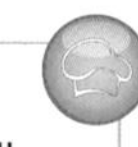

PROFESSIONAL TIP
Always allow the salmon to remain in the court bouillon until cold.

35 Fish salad (*salade de poisson*)

Energy	Calories	Fat	Saturated fat	Carbohydrates	Sugar	Protein	Fibre
978 kJ	233 kcal	13.5 g	3.0 g	1.5 g	1.4 g	26.4 g	1.3 g

* For 4 portions.

Ingredient	4 portions	10 portions
Cooked fish, free from skin and bone	200 g	500 g
Hard-boiled egg	1	2–3
Cucumber (optional)	50 g	125 g
Lettuce	½	1
Parsley or fennel, chopped		
Salt, pepper		
Vinaigrette	1 tbsp	2–3 tbsp

Preparing the dish

1 Flake the fish.
2 Cut the egg and cucumber into 0.5 cm dice and finely shred the lettuce
2 Mix the ingredients together and add the parsley or fennel.
3 Correct the seasoning and mix in the vinaigrette.

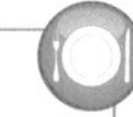

SERVING SUGGESTION
The dish may be decorated with lettuce, anchovies and capers.

Be careful not to overcook the fish.

HEALTHY EATING TIP
- Use salt sparingly.

36 Sea bass ceviche

Energy	Calories	Fat	Saturated fat	Carbohydrates	Sugar	Protein	Fibre	Sodium
540 kJ	128 kcal	3.8 g	0.6 g	3.8 g	3.5 g	19.8 g	0.5 g	0.3 g

Ingredient	4 portions	10 portions
Sea bass fillet, skinless, free of bone	400 g	1 kg
Large lime, juice only	1	2½
Yuzu juice	2 tbsp	5 tbsp
Coriander leaves, finely chopped	1 tbsp	2½ tbsp
Shallots, finely chopped	2	5
Ginger, shredded	1 tsp	2½ tsp
Red chilli, deseeded, finely chopped	1	2½
Sugar	1 tsp	2½ tsp
Light pomace oil or vegetable oil	1 tsp	2½ tsp
To serve		
Sea salt		
Crunchy raw salad of carrot, fennel and celeriac		

Preparing the dish

1. In a shallow, non-metallic tray, combine all the ingredients except the fish.
2. Slice the fish at a 45-degree angle, 5 mm thick.
3. Place the fish into the curing liquid. Refrigerate for 20 minutes until the edges of the fish turn white (do not leave too long as the fish will cure through and resemble rollmops).
4. To finish, lay the fish neatly on a plate with a little of the curing garnish and juice.
5. Season with a little sea salt and serve with a crunchy salad.

Yuzu is a citrus fruit grown in east Asia – the juice is available in bottles.

37 Crab, lobster, shrimp or prawn cocktail (*cocktail de crabe, homard, crevettes, crevettes roses*)

Energy	Calories	Fat	Saturated fat	Carbohydrates	Sugar	Protein	Fibre
966 kJ	230 kcal	21.0 g	3.2 g	0.6 g	0.6g	9.6 g	0.3 g

Ingredient	4 portions	10 portions
Lettuce	½	1¼
Prepared shellfish	100–150 g	250–350 g
Shellfish cocktail sauce (see recipe 17)	125 ml	300 ml

Preparing the dish

1. Wash, drain well and finely shred the lettuce, avoiding long strands. Place about 2 cm deep in cocktail glasses or dishes.
2. Add the prepared shellfish: crab (shredded white meat only); lobster (cut into 2 cm dice); shrimps (peeled and washed); prawns (peeled, washed and, if large, cut into two or three pieces).
3. Coat with the sauce.
4. Decorate with an appropriate piece of the content, such as a prawn with the shell on the tail removed placed on the edge of the glass of a prawn cocktail.

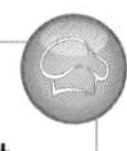

PROFESSIONAL TIP

Portion control is important so that this dish does not cost too much to produce. The cocktail needs to be presented well.

38 Potted shrimps

Energy	Calories	Fat	Saturated fat	Carbohydrates	Sugar	Protein	Fibre	Sodium
3,887 kJ	942 kcal	92.9 g	58.1 g	1.1 g	0.7 g	25.7 g	0.1 g	0.9 g

Ingredient	4 portions	10 portions
Butter	100 g	250 g
Chives, chopped	2 tbsp	5 tbsp
Cayenne pepper, to taste		
Peeled brown shrimps	600 g	1.5 kg
Clarified butter	6 tbsp	15 tbsp

This is a real seaside dish, full of flavour and eaten with plenty of brown bread and butter. Lobster or langoustine can be used, although timings will need to be adapted accordingly. The traditional seasoning for potted shrimps is ground mace.

Cooking

1 Put the butter, chives and cayenne pepper in a medium-sized pan and leave to melt over a gentle heat.

2 Add the peeled shrimps and stir over the heat for a couple of minutes until they have heated through, but don't let the mixture boil.

3 Divide the shrimps and butter between four small ramekins. Level the tops and then leave them to set in the refrigerator.

4 Spoon over a thin layer of clarified butter and leave to set once more. Serve with plenty of brown toast or crusty brown bread.

PROFESSIONAL TIP

Do not let the mixture boil (step 2) – if it does, the shrimps will become tough.

PROFESSIONAL TIP

Remove from the fridge and allow to warm slightly before serving, to bring out the flavour.

39 Fruits de mer

Energy	Calories	Fat	Saturated fat	Carbohydrates	Sugar	Protein	Fibre	Sodium
3,440 kJ	828 kcal	56.5 g	8.7 g	6.8 g	3.7 g	65.6 g	0.9 g	2.3 g

Ingredient	4 portions	10 portions
Lobster, cooked	1	2½
Crab, cooked	1	2½
Large prawns, cooked	12	30
Winkles, raw	100 g	250 g
Fresh clams	200 g	500 g
Fresh cockles	200 g	500 g
Mussels, live	200 g	500 g
Langoustines, live	6	10
White wine	75 ml	200 ml
Parsley stalks	4	10
Shallots, roughly chopped	2	5
Salt		
Oysters	12	30
For the sauces		
Mayonnaise (recipe 7)	250 ml	625 ml
Garlic cloves, finely chopped	2	5
Tomato ketchup	2 tsp	5 tsp
Brandy	1 tbsp	2½ tbsp
Tabasco sauce		
Red wine vinegar	100 ml	250 ml
Shallots, finely chopped	2	5
To serve		
Sprigs of parsley and lemon wedges, to garnish		
Chorizo sausage, warm, to garnish (optional)		

Preparing the dish

1. Cut the lobster in half lengthways. Remove the stomach and give the claws a crack to break the shell.
2. Open the crab, remove the 'dead man's fingers' and cut the body into four. Give the claws a few cracks to break the shell – this will make getting the meat out at the table easier.
3. Put the prawns, winkles, clams, cockles, mussels and langoustines into a pan with the white wine, parsley stalks, shallots and salt. Bring to the boil, cover and steam for 4 minutes until the mussels, clams and cockles open. Remove from the water and put on a tray to cool.
4. Open the oysters with an oyster knife.
5. Place a generous portion of crushed ice on a tray. Arrange the lobster, crab, langoustines, clams, mussels, cockles, winkles, prawns and oysters on the ice, garnishing with lemon and parsley.

Dead man's fingers are the crab's gills. You can see them inside the crab – they are grey and shaped like fingers.

To make the sauces

1. Divide the mayonnaise into thirds. Set one-third to one side.
2. Mix the chopped garlic into another third of the mayonnaise.
3. To make seafood sauce, mix the tomato ketchup, the brandy and a dash of Tabasco into the remaining mayonnaise.
4. To make shallot vinegar, mix together the red wine vinegar and the shallots.

SERVING SUGGESTION

Serve the fruits de mer with the mayonnaise, aioli (garlic mayonnaise), seafood sauce, shallot vinegar, lemon wedges and Tabasco, and chorizo sausage if desired.

Cold meat dishes and pies

40 Chicken salad

Energy	Calories	Fat	Saturated fat	Carbohydrates	Sugar	Protein	Fibre	Sodium
4,752 kJ	1,148 kcal	95.2 g	27.3 g	3.6 g	2.7 g	70.0 g	0.7 g	0.4 g

Ingredient	4 portions	10 portions
Fresh chicken	1.5 kg	3.75 kg
Black peppercorns	10	25
Bay leaves	3	7
Cumin seeds, ground	2 tsp	5 tsp
Almonds, sliced	25 g	60 g
For the dressing		
Greek yoghurt	2 tbsp	5 tbsp
Mayonnaise	3 tbsp	7 tbsp
Lemons, juice and zest	2	5
Cucumber, peeled and diced	1	2½
Fresh basil, picked and torn	25 g	60 g
To serve		
Mixed salad leaves	100 g	250 g
Vinaigrette	20 ml	50 ml

Cooking

1. Place the chicken in a large saucepan and cover with water.
2. Add the peppercorns and bay leaves and bring to a gentle simmer. Poach gently for about 40 minutes and leave to cool in the liquid.
3. Once cool, take the chicken out of the pan, remove the skin and shred the meat. Cover and place in a refrigerator.
4. Dry fry the cumin and almonds in a hot pan and leave to cool.
5. To make the dressing, mix the yoghurt, mayonnaise and lemon zest and juice in a large bowl.
6. Add the chicken, cucumber, cumin and almonds with the torn basil. Mix well and serve on a bed of the mixed salad leaves tossed lightly in vinaigrette.

41 Raised pork pie

Energy	Calories	Fat	Saturated fat	Carbohydrates	Sugar	Protein	Fibre	Sodium
3,005 kJ	721 kcal	47.7 g	19.3 g	49.2 g	1.7 g	26.7 g	2.7 g	1.2 g

Ingredient	4 portions	10 portions
Hot water paste		
Strong plain flour	250 g	500 g
Salt		
Lard or margarine (alternatively use 100 g lard and 25 g butter or margarine)	125 g	300 g
Water	125 ml	300 ml
Filling		
Shoulder of pork, without bone	300 g	1 kg
Bacon	100 g	250 g
Allspice (or mixed spice) and chopped sage	½ tsp	1½ tsp
Salt, pepper		
Bread, soaked in milk	50 g	125 g
Stock or water	2 tbsp	5 tbsp
Egg wash		
Stock, hot	125 ml	375 ml
Gelatine	5 g	12.5 g
Picked watercress and salad to serve		

Cooking

For the pastry

1. Sift the flour and salt into a basin. Make a well in the centre.
2. Boil the fat with the water and pour immediately into the flour.
3. Mix with a wooden spoon until cool enough to handle.
4. Mix to a smooth paste and use while still warm.

For the filling

1. Cut the pork and bacon into small even pieces and combine with the rest of the main ingredients (allspice, seasoning, bread, and the 2 tbsp of stock or water).
2. Keep one-quarter of the paste warm and covered.
3. Roll out the remaining three-quarters and carefully line a well-greased raised pie mould. Ensure that there is a thick rim of pastry.
4. Add the filling and press down firmly.
5. Roll out the remaining pastry for the lid and egg wash the edges of the pie.
6. Add the lid, seal firmly, neaten the edges, cut off any surplus paste; decorate if desired.
7. Make a hole 1 cm in diameter in the centre of the pie; brush all over with egg wash.
8. Bake in a hot oven (230–250°C) for approximately 20 minutes.
9. Reduce the heat to moderate (150–200°C) and cook for 1½–2 hours in all.
10. If the pie colours too quickly, cover with greaseproof paper or foil. Remove from the oven and carefully remove tin. Egg wash the pie all over and return to the oven for a few minutes.
11. Remove from the oven and fill with approximately 125 ml of good hot stock in which 5 g of gelatine has been dissolved.

Serve when cold, garnished with picked watercress and offer a suitable salad.

42 Veal and ham pie

Energy	Calories	Fat	Saturated fat	Carbohydrates	Sugar	Protein	Fibre
607 kJ	144 kcal	4.5 g	1.5 g	3.8 g	0.8 g	22.4 g	0.1 g

Ingredient	4 portions	10 portions
Hot water paste (see recipe 41)	125 ml	310 ml
Ham or bacon	150 g	375 g
Salt, pepper		
Hard-boiled egg	1	2½
Lean veal	250 g	625 g
Parsley and thyme	½ tsp	1¼ tsp
Lemon, grated zest of	1	2½
Stock or water	2 tbsp	5 tbsp
Bread, soaked in milk	50 g	125 g
Gelatine	5 g	12.5 g

Cooking

Proceed as for raised pork pie (recipe 41) but place the shelled egg in the centre of the mixture. Serve when cold, garnished with picked watercress, and offer a suitable salad.

Partly fill the pie, then place the egg(s) into the centre

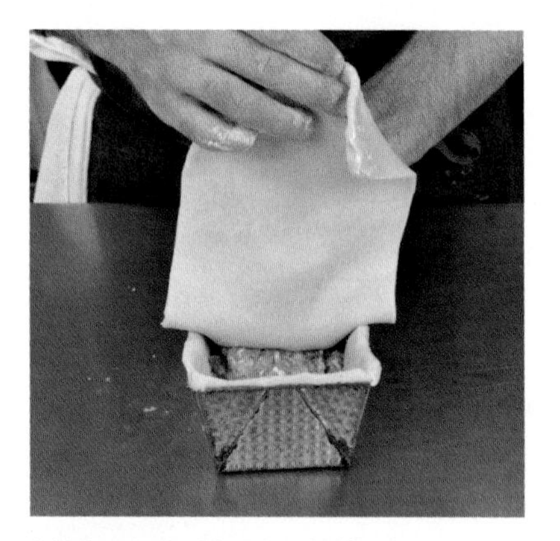

Add the pastry lid and seal it firmly

Pour gelatine dissolved in stock into the pie after baking

Pâtés and terrines

43 Liver pâté (*pâté de foie*)

Energy	Calories	Fat	Saturated fat	Carbohydrates	Sugar	Protein	Fibre
896 kJ	213 kcal	19.1 g	8.5 g	0.7 g	0.1 g	9.8 g	0.0 g

Ingredient	4 portions	10 portions
Liver (chicken, pig, calf, lamb, etc.)	100 g	250 g
Butter or oil	25 g	60 g
Onion, chopped	10 g	25 g
Garlic cloves	1	2½
Sprigs of parsley, thyme, chervil		
Fat pork	50 g	125 g
Salt, pepper		
Fat bacon	25 g	60 g

Cooking

1. Cut the liver into 2 cm pieces.
2. Toss quickly in the butter or oil in a frying pan over a fierce heat for a few seconds with the onion, garlic and herbs.
3. Allow to cool.
4. Pass the liver and fat pork together through a mincer, twice. Season.
5. Line an earthenware terrine with wafer-thin slices of fat bacon.
6. Place the mixture into the terrine. Cover with fat bacon.
7. Stand in a tray half full of water and bring to simmering point.
8. Cook in a moderate oven for 1 hour. Use a temperature probe to check that the centre reaches 70°C–72°C
9. Blast-chill. When quite cold, cut into 0.5 cm slices and serve on lettuce leaves. Usually served accompanied with freshly made toast.

This is a typical recipe for a home-made terrine, often seen on the menu as *pâté maison*.

HEALTHY EATING TIP

- Use an unsaturated oil (sunflower or olive). Lightly oil the pan and drain off any excess after the frying is complete.
- The bacon is high in salt so very little (or no) added salt is necessary.

44 Terrine of bacon, spinach and mushrooms

Energy	Calories	Fat	Saturated fat	Carbohydrates	Sugar	Protein	Fibre
1,436 kJ	347 kcal	30.4 g	7.2 g	1.2 g	1.0 g	17.0 g	1.4 g

Ingredient	12 portions
Collar of bacon	1 kg
Carrot	1
Onion clouté	1
Bouquet garni	1
Celery	2 sticks
Peppercorns	8
Fresh spinach	500 g
Butter	50 g
Mushrooms (preferably morels)	200 g

Mise en place

1. If necessary soak the bacon overnight.
2. Drain.

Cooking

1. Place the bacon in cold water, bring to the boil, add the carrot, onion, bouquet garni, celery and peppercorns.
2. Simmer until tender.
3. Pick some large leaves of spinach to line the terrine dish. Blanch the leaves, refresh and drain.
4. Lightly cook the rest of the spinach gently; refresh, drain and shred.
5. Alternatively, shred the spinach raw, quickly cook in butter, drain and then blast-chill.
6. Cook the mushrooms in a little butter, season and chill well.
7. When cool, remove the bacon from the cooking liquor and chop into small pieces.
8. Line the terrine with clingfilm, then the spinach leaves. Layer with bacon, mushrooms and spinach. Cover with spinach leaves and clingfilm. Wait for 12 hours or overnight.
9. When ready, turn out, slice and serve on plates, with leek and mushroom vinaigrette served separately.

HEALTHY EATING TIP

- Soaking the bacon overnight will remove some of the salt.
- Use only a little butter to cook the mushrooms.
- Use a minimum amount of salt to season the vinaigrette.
- Serve with warm bread rolls, butter optional.

Salads

45 Potato salad

Energy	Calories	Fat	Saturated fat	Carbohydrates	Sugar	Protein	Fibre
2013 kJ	479 kcal	34.9 g	5.1 g	40.0 g	1.3 g	4.0 g	2.6 g

Ingredient	4 portions	10 portions
Potatoes	200 g	500 g
Vinaigrette	1 tbsp	2½ tbsp
Mayonnaise, natural yoghurt or crème fraîche	125 ml	300 ml
Onion or chive (optional)	10 g	25 g
Parsley or mixed fresh herbs	½ tsp	1½ tsp
Salt		

Mise en place

1. Wash and peel the potatoes (or cook in skins and then peel).
2. Cook potatoes by boiling or steaming.
3. Cut potatoes into ½–1 cm dice or slices.
4. If desired, blanch the onion by placing in boiling water for 2–3 minutes, cooling and draining. (This will reduce its harshness.) Then chop it up.
5. Chop the herbs.
6. Prepare the vinaigrette (see recipe 6).

Preparing the dish

1. Put the potatoes into a bowl and sprinkle on the vinaigrette.
2. Mix in the mayonnaise, onion and chive.
3. Finally, chop and mix in the parsley or other herbs and season to taste.

VARIATION

- At the end, add chopped mint or chopped hard-boiled egg.

46 Vegetable salad

Energy	Calories	Fat	Saturated fat	Carbohydrates	Sugar	Protein	Fibre
1566 kJ	373 kcal	35.0 g	5.2 g	10.1 g	8.2 g	5.0 g	11.9 g

* Using mayonnaise, for 4 portions

Ingredient	4 portions	10 portions
Carrots	100 g	250 g
French beans	50 g	125 g
Turnip	50 g	125 g
Peas	50 g	125 g
Vinaigrette	1 tbsp	2–3 tbsp
Mayonnaise or natural yoghurt	125 ml	300 ml
Salt		

Mise en place

1. Peel and wash the carrots and turnips, and cut into neat dice (*macédoine*).
2. Top and tail the beans and cut into ½ cm pieces.
3. Prepare the vinaigrette (see recipe 6).

Preparing the dish

1. Cook the carrots, beans and turnips separately in lightly salted water, then refresh and drain well.
2. Cook, drain and refresh the peas. Drain well.
3. Mix all the vegetables in a basin with the vinaigrette and then add and mix in the mayonnaise or yoghurt.
4. Taste and correct the seasoning if necessary.

VARIATION

- Potato can be used in place of turnip.
- A little of any or a mixture of the following can be chopped and added: chives, parsley, chervil, tarragon.

ACTIVITY

Suggest two or three more ingredients that could be added.

47 Beetroot salad

Energy	Calories	Fat	Saturated fat	Carbohydrates	Sugar	Protein	Fibre	Sodium
331 kJ	78 kcal	1.9 g	0.2 g	12.7 g	11.8 g	2.9 g	3.8 g	127.0 g

Ingredient
Beetroot (quantity as required)
Vinaigrette, if desired

Mise en place

1. Wash the beetroot.
2. Prepare the vinaigrette (see recipe 6).

Preparing the dish

1. Cook the beetroots in their skin in a steamer or gently simmering water until tender.
2. Cool and test by rubbing the skin between your fingers and thumb. When cooked, the skin should peel (rub) off easily.
3. Cut into ½ cm dice and either serve plain or lightly sprinkled with vinaigrette.

VARIATION

- Sprinkle with chopped onion, or chive and parsley, or other fresh herbs. Freshly chopped mint and orange zest makes an interesting combination.

48 Tomato salad

Energy	Calories	Fat	Saturated fat	Carbohydrates	Sugar	Protein	Fibre	Sodium
210 kJ	49 kcal	1.8 g	0.3 g	7.4 g	7.2 g	1.4 g	2.3 g	29.7 g

* Using 15 g mixed salad leaves per portion. Not including onion or chives

Ingredient	4 portions	10 portions
Tomatoes	200 g	500 g
Lettuce leaves		
Vinaigrette	10 g	25 g
Onions (sliced) or chives (optional)		
Finely chopped parsley and/or fresh mixed herbs		

Mise en place

1. Wash and dry the tomatoes.
2. Remove the stem eyes.
3. Leave the skins on, or peel by plunging them into boiling water for ten seconds, then remove them and cool under cold running water.
4. Slice the onion and, if desired, blanch it in boiling water.

The amount of lettuce required will depend on type and size.

Preparing the dish

1. Slice the tomatoes.
2. Arrange them neatly on washed, well-drained lettuce leaves.
3. Sprinkle on the vinaigrette and the onion.
4. Chop the parsley or other herbs and sprinkle these on.

49 Coleslaw

Energy	Calories	Fat	Saturated fat	Carbohydrates	Sugar	Protein	Fibre
2514 kJ	599 kcal	59.0 g	8.8 g	11.7 g	11.4 g	5.9 g	7.2 g

* Using mayonnaise, for 4 portions

Ingredient	4 portions	10 portions
Cabbage, white or Chinese	200 g	500 g
Carrot	50 g	125 g
Onion (optional)	25 g	60 g
Mayonnaise or natural yoghurt	125 ml	300 ml
Salt		

Mise en place

1. Trim off and discard the outer cabbage leaves.
2. Wash and peel the carrot.
3. Finely shred the onion, and blanch and refresh it to remove the harsh taste (optional).

Preparing the dish

1. Cut the cabbage into quarters and cut out the hard centre stalk.
2. Wash the cabbage, finely shred it and drain it well.

3. Cut the carrot into fine strips (known as julienne – for large quantities this can be done in a food processor).
4. Mix the vegetables together.

5. Stir in the mayonnaise.
6. Taste and season very lightly with salt, only if necessary.

ACTIVITY

Prepare batches of coleslaw:

1. without onion
2. with onion
3. with blanched onion.

In a group, taste and assess the different coleslaws and note your findings.

50 Rice salad

Energy	Calories	Fat	Saturated fat	Carbohydrates	Sugar	Protein	Fibre	Sodium
137 kJ	33 kcal	0.6 g	0.1 g	5.6 g	1.1 g	1.0 g	0.8 g	154.0 g

* Using 1/4 tsp salt in recipe for 4 portions

Ingredient	4 portions	10 portions
Tomatoes	100 g	250 g
Long grain rice, cooked	50 g	125 g
Peas	30 g	75 g
Vinaigrette	1 tbsp	2½ tbsp
Salt		

Mise en place

1. Cook the rice.
2. Cook the peas.
3. Blanch and skin the tomatoes.
4. Prepare the vinaigrette (see recipe 6).

Preparing the dish

1. Cut the tomatoes into quarters, remove the seeds and cut into ½ cm dice.
2. Mix the tomatoes with the rice, peas and vinaigrette.
3. Taste and correct the seasoning.

51 Green salad

- A large number of salad leaves are available, including different varieties of lettuce. You can use whichever you choose, or a mixture of several.
- Green salad is a mixture of salad leaves, well washed and dried, served on a plate or in a bowl, with vinaigrette served separately.
- Tossed green salad is the same as green salad but with vinaigrette added. It is tossed in a salad bowl using two salad servers to coat the leaves in the dressing.
- Tossed green salad with herbs is a tossed salad with chopped fresh herbs mixed in.

52 Warm Asian bean salad with satay dressing

Energy	Calories	Fat	Saturated fat	Carbohydrates	Sugar	Protein	Fibre	Sodium
824 kJ	196 kcal	10.6 g	2.0 g	16.9 g	10.4 g	8.3 g	5.2 g	132.0 g

Ingredient	4 portions	10 portions
Butternut squash, peeled, deseeded and cut into 2 cm dice	250 g	625 g
Broad beans, cooked and skinned	240 g	600 g
Clear honey	1 tbsp	2 tbsp
Lime, grated zest and juice	½	2
Peanut satay (see note)	80 g	200 g
Coriander, chopped	6	15
Radishes, thinly sliced	4	10
Roasted cashew nuts, roughly chopped	50 g	125 g
Spring onions, chopped	4	10

Mise en place

1. Peel and deseed the butternut squash and cut into 2 cm dice.
2. Cook and shell the broad beans.
3. Wash and slice the radishes.
4. Roughly chop the spring onions.
5. Roast and chop the cashew nuts.

Satay is peanut sauce. You can buy this ready made or you can make it yourself. To make it, add the following ingredients to a food processor and blend until smooth:

- 4 tbsp peanut butter
- 2 tbsp sesame oil
- 1 tbsp soy sauce
- 1 tbsp honey
- 1 tbsp milk or water
- 1 garlic clove, peeled and crushed/chopped
- ½ lime, juice only

Preparing the dish

1. Blanch the butternut squash in boiling water for 3–4 minutes and drain.
2. Place the butternut squash in a large bowl with the cooked broad beans.
3. Prepare the dressing by mixing together the honey, lime juice and peanut satay.
4. Roughly chop the coriander and add this, along with the chopped spring onions, sliced radish and cashew nuts, to the squash and broad beans.
5. Mix in half the dressing.

SERVING SUGGESTION

Serve on plates, on a bed of mixed salad leaves. Drizzle over the remainder of the dressing and serve.

53 Asian rice salad

Energy	Calories	Fat	Saturated fat	Carbohydrates	Sugar	Protein	Fibre	Sodium
1225 kJ	293 kcal	13.6 g	1.7 g	35.5 g	6.1 g	6.0 g	3.7 g	487.0 g

Ingredient	4 portions	10 portions
Flat-leaf parsley, chopped	2 tbsp	5 tbsp
Coriander, chopped	2 tbsp	5 tbsp
Mint, chopped	1 tbsp	2½ tbsp
Garlic, finely chopped	1 clove	4 cloves
Ginger, finely chopped	2 cm	5 cm
Reduced-salt soy sauce	2½ tbsp	6 tbsp
Lime juice	1 tbsp	2½ tbsp
Honey	1 tbsp	2½ tbsp
Sunflower oil	4 tbsp	10 tbsp
Basmati rice, cooked	400 g	1 kg
Courgettes	1	3
Peas, lightly cooked	125 g	300 g
Spring onions	2	5

Mise en place

1. Lightly cook the peas.
2. Cook the rice lightly in salted water. Drain and cool.
3. Very finely dice the courgette and finely slice the spring onion, cutting on the slant – for this salad the pieces must be small.
4. Peel and finely chop the garlic and ginger.
5. Roughly chop the herbs.

Preparing the dish

1. Blitz the herbs, garlic, ginger, soy sauce, lime juice and honey in a food processor.
2. Slowly add the oil to create a glossy mixture.
3. To the rice add the courgettes, peas and spring onions and combine.
4. Stir through the dressing.

54 Pesto pasta salad

Energy	Calories	Fat	Saturated fat	Carbohydrates	Sugar	Protein	Fibre	Sodium
2393 kJ	568 kcal	21.0 g	2.8 g	69.0 g	3.9 g	23.7 g	5.2 g	192.0 g

* Using 1.5 small chicken breasts

Ingredient	4 portions	10 portions
Green pesto	70 g	200 g
Lemon juice	1 tbsp	3 tbsp
Mayonnaise or reduced-fat mayonnaise	2½ tbsp	6 tbsp
Penne pasta	400 g	1 kg
Extra virgin olive oil	1 tbsp	2 tbsp
Cooked chicken breasts	1 – 1½	3
Parsley, chopped	1 tbsp	5 tbsp

Mise en place

1. Cook the pasta al dente in boiling, lightly salted water. Drain and mix with oil.
2. Cook the chicken breasts by poaching, steaming, shallow frying or roasting. Remove the skin.

Preparing the dish

1. Mix the pesto, lemon juice and mayonnaise together and stir into the pasta.
2. Cut the chicken into thin slices and combine with the pasta.
3. Chop the parsley and stir through the pasta.

VARIATION

- If you leave out the chicken and mayonnaise this can be served as a simple pasta salad with pesto.

55 Green bean salad

Energy	Calories	Fat	Saturated fat	Carbohydrates	Sugar	Protein	Fibre	Sodium
78 kJ	19 kcal	0.6 g	0.1 g	2.1 g	1.6 g	1.1 g	1.8 g	152.0 g

* Using 1 tsp chives and 1/4 tsp salt per recipe for 4 portions

Ingredient	4 portions	10 portions
Green beans	200 g	500 g
Vinaigrette	1 tbsp	2½ tbsp
Onion, if required	15 g	40 g
Chives		
Salt		

Mise en place

1. Cook the green beans.
2. Chop and blanch the onions.
3. Prepare the vinaigrette (see recipe 6).

Preparing the dish

1. Combine all ingredients.
2. Taste and season as necessary.

VARIATION

- This recipe can also be made using any type of dried bean. Many dried beans are available ready cooked in cans.
- Make a three-bean salad using three different types of dried bean, such as red kidney, black-eyed and flageolet.

56 Greek salad

Energy	Calories	Fat	Saturated fat	Carbohydrates	Sugar	Protein	Fibre	Sodium
1099 kJ	266 kcal	24.7 g	7.5 g	4.2 g	3.7 g	7.2 g	2.0 g	676.0 g

* Using 1/4 tsp salt in recipe for 4 portions

Ingredient	4 portions	10 portions
Large tomatoes (preferably vine tomatoes)	2	6
Cucumber, sliced	½	1
Feta cheese, diced	150 g	400 g
Olive oil	60 ml	150 ml
Lemon juice	2 tbsp	6 tbsp
Salt and black pepper		
Oregano, to garnish	1 level tbsp	3 level tbsp
Pitted black olives, to garnish	6	15

Mise en place

1. Wash the tomatoes and cut them in half lengthwise. Cut out the core, and cut each half into four wedges.
2. Wash and slice the cucumber.
3. Dice the feta cheese.

If you are not keen on the idea of eating olives, just try them and see what you think. They go particularly well with the other flavours and texture of this salad.

Preparing the dish

1. Put the tomatoes into a large salad bowl and add the cucumber and feta cheese.
2. Spoon over the olive oil and lemon juice.
3. Season lightly with salt and black pepper. Go easy on the salt, as feta cheese is already salty!
4. Toss gently to mix.

SERVING SUGGESTION

Sprinkle the salad with fresh oregano and decorate with olives.

57 Garden salad

Energy	Calories	Fat	Saturated fat	Carbohydrates	Sugar	Protein	Fibre	Sodium
401 kJ	95 kcal	1.4 g	0.3 g	13.0 g	8.6 g	6.2 g	8.3 g	28.0 g

Ingredient	4 portions	10 portions
Medium lettuce (crispy variety like iceberg or cos), torn into pieces	½	1
Carrot, cut into fine julienne	1	2
Red cabbage, finely chopped	125 g	350 g
Radish, thinly sliced	2	8
Onions, thinly sliced	1	3
Red pepper, thinly sliced	1	2
Celery, thinly sliced	1 stick	3 sticks
Frozen peas, cooked	250 g	500 g

Mise en place

1. Bring the peas to the boil and cook until just tender.
2. Drain and refresh.

Preparing the dish

1. Wash and dry the lettuce, then tear into pieces.
2. Cut the carrots into julienne and finely slice the carrot, cabbage, radishes, onions, red pepper and celery.
3. Combine the ingredients in large bowl with the peas.

SERVING SUGGESTION

Drizzle with a salad dressing of your own choice, such as vinaigrette (recipe 6), or serve plain.

VARIATION

- This works well with bean sprouts for added crunch.
- Add flakes of canned tuna to make an interesting tuna salad.
- Add beans such as chickpeas or butter beans for a different texture.
- It also works well with 125 g or 300 g of feta cheese (for 4 or 10 portions, respectively).

58 Couscous and halloumi salad

Energy	Calories	Fat	Saturated fat	Carbohydrates	Sugar	Protein	Fibre	Sodium
3346 kJ	805 kcal	50.0 g	15.4 g	54.0 g	5.9 g	27.6 g	8.8 g	1,074.0 g

* Using 1/4 tsp salt in recipe for 4 portions

Ingredient	4 portions	10 portions
Couscous	250 g	625 g
Vegetable stock	250 ml	625 ml
Chickpeas, cooked	200 g	500 g
Courgettes	200 g	500 g
Olive oil	30 ml	75 ml
Halloumi cheese	250 g	625 g
Cherry tomatoes	200 g	500 g
Vinaigrette		
Lime juice	2	5
Garlic cloves, crushed and chopped	2	5
Fresh mint, finely chopped	2 tbsp	5 tbsp
Sugar	1 tsp	2 tsp
Olive oil	100 ml	250 ml
Seasoning		

Preparing the dish

1. Place the couscous in a bowl. Pour on the boiling stock and mix well. Leave for about 5 minutes. Drain off any excess liquid.
2. Make the vinaigrette. Place the lime juice, garlic, mint and sugar in a bowl. Whisk in the oil. Add the seasoning.
3. Add the chickpeas to the couscous. Add half the vinaigrette.
4. Slice the courgettes in 2 mm slices. Fry in oil both sides until lightly brown, remove and drain on kitchen paper.
5. Fry slices of halloumi in oil on both sides until crisp and brown.
6. Halve the cherry tomatoes and mix in the couscous.
7. Arrange the couscous mix on a suitable serving dish. Arrange the slices of courgette around the sliced halloumi on top.
8. Sprinkle with the remainder of the vinaigrette and serve.

59 Italian salad

Energy	Calories	Fat	Saturated fat	Carbohydrates	Sugar	Protein	Fibre	Sodium
2065 kJ	490 kcal	20.2 g	2.8 g	48.0 g	7.4 g	25.6 g	10.5 g	163.0 g

* Using 1/4 tsp salt in recipe for 4 portions

Ingredient	4 portions	10 portions
Puy lentils	400 g	1 kg
Spring onions, finely chopped	2	5
Seedless green grapes, halved	20	50
Seedless red grapes, halved	20	50
Small cucumber, peeled and finely diced	1	2
Red pepper, seeded and finely diced	1	2
Vinaigrette		
Fresh lemon juice	1 lemon	2 lemons
Extra virgin oil	75 ml	200 ml
Seasoning		

Preparing the dish

1. Place the lentils in a saucepan of water. Bring to the boil and cook until tender (about 20 minutes). Drain and cool.
2. Place the lentils in a basin. Add the spring onions, grapes, cucumber and red pepper.
3. To make the vinaigrette, place the lemon juice in a suitable bowl, whisk in the oil and season.
4. Add the vinaigrette to the salad and mix well. Serve immediately.

VARIATION

- Some fresh chopped herbs may be added to the salad, e.g. basil.

60 Melon, feta cheese and mint salad

Energy	Calories	Fat	Saturated fat	Carbohydrates	Sugar	Protein	Fibre	Sodium
651 kJ	157 kcal	10.3 g	6.8 g	7.7 g	7.6 g	8.6 g	1.7 g	672.0 g

* Using 1/4 tsp salt in recipe for 4 portions, adding 40 g mixed leaves per recipe for garnishing

Ingredient	4 portions	10 portions
Melon (watermelon, honeydew, charentais or Gallia)	500 g	1250 g
Feta cheese, diced	200 g	450 g
Mint, chopped	1 tsp	2 tsp
Seasoning		
Mixed salad leaves		

Preparing the dish

1 Dice the seeded melon into 1 cm cubes. Place into a basin with the diced feta cheese.

2 Add the chopped mint. Mix and season, adding more mint if required.

3 Serve on a bed of mixed salad leaves or sprinkle with micro herbs.

61 Cucumber quinoa salad

Energy	Calories	Fat	Saturated fat	Carbohydrates	Sugar	Protein	Fibre	Sodium
1824 kJ	438 kcal	32.3 g	7.1 g	25.0 g	5.5 g	11.4 g	4.1 g	424.0 g

* Using 1/4 tsp salt in recipe for 4 portions

Ingredient	4 portions	10 portions
Cucumber	1 medium size	2
Quinoa, cooked	500 g	1¼ g
Red onion, finely diced	50 g	125 g
Feta cheese, diced	100 g	250 g
Basil leaves, chopped	1 tbsp	2 tbsp
Vinaigrette		
Olive oil	100 ml	250 ml
Red wine vinegar	2 tbsp	5 tbsp
Lemon juice	½ lemon	2 lemons
Seasoning		

Cooking

1 Rinse the quinoa in water and drain. Cook the quinoa in sufficient boiling water or stock until all the liquid is absorbed. Fluff the quinoa with a fork and allow to cool.

2 Make the vinaigrette by whisking all the ingredients together.

3 Place the quinoa in a bowl and add all the other ingredients. Mix well and add the vinaigrette.

4 Serve immediately.

62 Avocado and bacon salad

Energy	Calories	Fat	Saturated fat	Carbohydrates	Sugar	Protein	Fibre	Sodium
1,462 kJ	354 kcal	34.4 g	7.6 g	2.4 g	0.7 g	9.0 g	4.9 g	1.0 g

Ingredient	4 portions	10 portions
Thin streaky bacon rashers, rind and excess fat trimmed	8	20
Fresh lemon juice	1 tbsp	2½ tbsp
Garlic clove, crushed finely	1	2½
Extra virgin olive oil	2 tbsp	5 tbsp
Salt and freshly ground black pepper		
Ripe avocados, medium	2	5
Snow pea sprouts, stems trimmed	50 g	125 g

Cooking

1. Grill the bacon rashers under a salamander until crisp. Transfer to a tray lined with kitchen paper and allow to cool.
2. Place the lemon juice and garlic in a mixing bowl and whisk in the olive oil. Season with salt and pepper.
3. Halve the avocados lengthways, remove the stones and peel the skin. Place the avocados on to a chopping board, cut side down, and cut in half lengthways, then crossways into slices 1 cm thick.
4. Layer the avocados, bacon and snow pea sprouts on serving plates, drizzling the dressing between the layers. Serve immediately.

ACTIVITY

Prepare six salads and present them in three or four different ways.

Cold desserts

63 Fresh fruit salad

Energy	Calories	Fat	Saturated fat	Carbohydrates	Sugar	Protein	Fibre
493 kJ	117 kcal	0.0 g	0.0 g	30.3 g	29.5 g	0.9 g	3.0 g

Ingredient	4 portions	10 portions
Stock syrup		
Caster sugar	50 g	125 g
Water	125 ml	310 ml
Lemon, juice of	½	1¼
Fruit		
Orange	1	2½
Dessert apple	1	2½
Dessert pear	1	2½
Cherries	50 g	125 g
Grapes	50 g	125 g
Banana	1	2½

Preparing the dish

1. For the syrup, boil the sugar with the water and place in a bowl.
2. Allow to cool, then add the lemon juice.
3. Peel and cut the orange into segments.
4. Peel, quarter and core the apple and pear, then cut each quarter into two or three slices, place in the bowl with the syrup and mix in the orange segments.
5. Stone the cherries but leave them whole.
6. Cut the grapes in half, peel if required, and remove any pips. Add the cherries and grapes to the fruit and syrup mix.
7. Mix the fruit salad carefully and place in a glass bowl in the refrigerator to chill.
8. Just before serving, peel and slice the banana and mix in.

VARIATION

- Any of the following fruits may be used: dessert apples, pears, pineapple, oranges, grapes, melon, strawberries, peaches, raspberries, apricots, bananas, cherries, kiwi fruit, plums, mangoes, paw paws and lychees. Allow about 150 g unprepared fruit per portion. All fruit must be ripe.
- Kirsch or an orange liqueur could be added to the syrup.
- Fruit juice (such as apple, orange, grape or passion fruit) can be used instead of syrup.

64 Crème caramel

Energy	Calories	Fat	Saturated fat	Carbohydrates	Sugar	Protein	Fibre
868 kJ	207 kcal	7.2 g	3.3 g	30.2 g	30.2 g	7.3 g	0.0 g

* Using whole milk.

Ingredient	4–6 portions	10–12 portions
Caramel		
Water	125 ml	250 ml
Sugar, granulated or cube	100 g	200 g
Cream		
Milk, whole or skimmed	0.5 litres	1 litre
Eggs	4	8
Sugar, caster or unrefined	50 g	100 g
Vanilla essence or a vanilla pod	3–4 drops	6–8 drops

Cooking

1. Prepare the caramel by placing three-quarters of the water in a thick-based pan, adding the sugar and allowing to boil gently, without shaking or stirring the pan.
2. When the sugar has cooked to a golden-brown caramel colour, add the remaining quarter of the water, reboil until the sugar and water mix, then pour into the bottom of dariole moulds.
3. Prepare the cream by warming the milk and whisking on to the beaten eggs, sugar and vanilla essence (or pod).
4. Strain and pour into the prepared moulds.
5. Place in a roasting tin half full of water.
6. Cook in a moderate oven at 150–160°C for 30–40 minutes.
7. When thoroughly cold, loosen the edges of the crème caramel with the fingers, shake firmly to loosen, and turn out on to a flat dish or plates.
8. Pour any caramel remaining in the mould around the creams.

SERVING SUGGESTION

Crème caramels may be served with whipped cream or a fruit sauce such as passion fruit, and accompanied by a sweet biscuit (e.g. shortbread, palmiers).

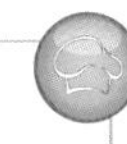

PROFESSIONAL TIP

Adding a squeeze of lemon juice to the caramel will invert the sugar, thus preventing recrystallisation.

65 Fruit mousse

Energy	Calories	Fat	Saturated fat	Carbohydrates	Sugar	Protein	Fibre
950 kJ	227 kcal	12.4 g	7.0 g	26.0 g	26.0 g	4.0 g	2.0 g

Ingredient	10 portions
Egg yolks	4
Sugar	50 g
Fruit purée	250 g
Lemon juice	
Gelatine	4 leaves
Lightly whipped cream	250 g
Italian meringue	
Sugar	112 g
Water, to saturate	
Egg whites	2
Cream of tartar	pinch
Glaze topping	
Stock syrup	150 ml
Gelatine	3 leaves, soaked in cold water
Fruit purée	150 ml

Cooking

1. Mix the egg yolks and sugar together, and slowly add the boiled fruit purée which has been flavoured with a squeeze of lemon juice.
2. Return to the stove and cook to 80°C until slightly thickened. Do not boil.
3. Add the previously softened gelatine to the warm purée and mix until fully dissolved. Chill down.
4. Prepare the Italian meringue by placing the sugar in a pan and saturating in water.
5. Boil the sugar to 115°C, then whisk the egg whites with a pinch of cream of tartar.
6. Once the egg whites are at full peak, gradually add the boiled sugar, which now should have reached the temperature of 121°C. Whisk until cold.
7. Once the purée is cold, but not set, incorporate the Italian meringue and whipped cream.
8. Place into piping bag and pipe into the desired ring mould, normally (but optional) lined with a suitable sponge such as a jaconde.
9. Level the surface using a palette knife and refrigerate.
10. Once set, glaze the surface, refrigerate.
11. To remove from the mould, warm the outside of it with a blow torch and remove the ring mould.

For the glaze

1. Warm the syrup. Add the gelatine and stir until dissolved, then add the desired fruit purée.
2. Apply to the surface of the chilled mousse while in a liquid state, but not hot.

66 Bavarois

Energy	Calories	Fat	Saturated fat	Carbohydrates	Sugar	Protein	Fibre
970 kJ	231 kcal	18.2 g	10.9 g	11.8 g	11.8 g	5.8 g	0.0 g

* Using whole milk and whipping cream.

Ingredient	6–8 portions
Gelatine	10 g
Eggs, pasteurised, separated	2
Caster sugar	50 g
Milk (whole, semi-skimmed or skimmed)	250 ml
Whipping or double cream (or non-dairy cream)	125 ml

Cooking

1. If using leaf gelatine, soak in cold water.
2. Cream the egg yolks and sugar in a bowl until almost white.
3. Bring the milk to the boil in a thick-based saucepan then whisk it into the egg yolk and sugar mixture; mix well.
4. Clean the milk saucepan and return the mixture to it.
5. Return to a low heat and stir continuously with a wooden spoon until the mixture coats the back of the spoon. The mixture must not boil.
6. Remove from the heat, add the gelatine and stir until dissolved.
7. Pass through a fine strainer into a clean bowl. Leave in a cool place, stirring occasionally until almost at setting point.
8. Fold in the lightly beaten cream.
9. Fold in the stiffly beaten egg whites.
10. Pour the mixture into a mould or individual moulds (which may be very lightly greased with almond oil).
11. Allow to set in the refrigerator.
12. Shake and turn out on to a flat dish or plates.

SERVING SUGGESTION

Bavarois may be decorated with sweetened, flavoured whipped cream (crème Chantilly).

FLAVOURS FOR BAVAROIS

- **Raspberry or strawberry bavarois** (as shown): when the custard is almost cool, add 200 g of picked, washed and sieved raspberries or strawberries. Decorate with whole fruit and whipped cream.
- **Chocolate bavarois**: melt 50 g chocolate couverture in the milk. Decorate with whipped cream and grated chocolate.
- **Coffee bavarois**: add coffee essence to the basic bavarois mixture, to taste.
- **Orange bavarois**: add the grated zest and juice of two oranges and one or two drops of orange colour to the mixture, and increase the gelatine by two leaves. Decorate with blanched, fine julienne of orange zest, orange segments and whipped cream.
- **Lemon or lime bavarois**: as for orange bavarois, but using lemons or limes in place of oranges.
- **Vanilla bavarois**: add a vanilla pod or a few drops of vanilla extract to the milk. Decorate with vanilla-flavoured sweetened cream (crème Chantilly).

HEALTH AND SAFETY

It is advisable to use pasteurised egg yolks and whites.

HEALTHY EATING TIP

- Use semi-skimmed milk and whipping cream to reduce the overall fat content.

67 Vanilla panna cotta served on a fruit compote

Energy	Calories	Fat	Saturated fat	Carbohydrates	Sugar	Protein	Fibre
1,565 kJ	378 kcal	34.0 g	21.1 g	16.1 g	16.1 g	2.9 g	1.5 g

Ingredient	6 portions
Milk	125 ml
Double cream	375 ml
Aniseeds	2
Vanilla pod	½
Gelatine (soaked)	2 leaves
Caster sugar	50 g
Fruit compote	
Apricot purée	75 g
Vanilla pod	½
Peach	1
Kiwi fruit	1
Strawberries	75 g
Blueberries	75 g
Raspberries	50 g

Cooking

1. Prepare the fruit compote by boiling the apricot purée and infusing with the vanilla pod. Remove the pod and allow the purée to cool.
2. Finely dice the peach and the kiwi, and quarter the strawberries. Mix, then add blueberries and raspberries.
3. Bind the fruit with the apricot purée. A little stock syrup (see page 302) may be required to keep the fruit free flowing.
4. For the panna cotta, boil the milk and cream, add aniseeds, infuse with the vanilla pod and remove after infusion.
5. Heat again and add the soaked gelatine and caster sugar. Pass through a fine strainer.
6. Place in a bowl set over ice and stir until it thickens slightly; this will allow the vanilla seeds to suspend throughout the mix instead of sinking to the bottom.
7. Fill individual dariole moulds.
8. Place the fruit compote on individual fruit plates, turn out the panna cotta from the moulds, place on top of the compote and finish with a tuile biscuit.

68 Fruit fool

Method 1

Energy	Calories	Fat	Saturated fat	Carbohydrates	Sugar	Protein	Fibre
942 kJ	222 kcal	2.6 g	1.6 g	50.3 g	4.5 g	2.4 g	1.6 g

Method 1 nutritional analysis for an apple fool made with whole milk.

Ingredient	4 portions	10 portions
Fruit (apple, gooseberry, rhubarb, etc.)	400 g	1 kg
Water	60 ml	150 ml
Sugar, granulated or unrefined	100 g	250 g
Cornflour	25 g	60 g
Milk, whole or semi-skimmed	250 ml	625 ml
Sugar, caster or unrefined	25 g	60 g
Sweetened whipped cream or non-dairy cream, to decorate		

Cooking

1. Cook the fruit to a purée in the water with the granulated sugar. Pass through a sieve.
2. Dilute the cornflour in a little of the milk and add the caster sugar.
3. Boil the remainder of the milk.
4. Pour on to the diluted cornflour and stir well.
5. Return to the pan on a low heat and stir to the boil.
6. Mix with the fruit purée. The quantity of mixture should not be less than 0.5 litres (for four portions).
7. Pour into glass coupes or suitable dishes and allow to set.
8. Decorate with sweetened whipped cream or non-dairy cream. The colour may need to be adjusted slightly with food colour.

Method 2

Energy	Calories	Fat	Saturated fat	Carbohydrates	Sugar	Protein	Fibre
1,540 kJ	370 kcal	25.3 g	15.8 g	35.7 g	35.7 g	2.0 g	1.2 g

Method 2 nutritional analysis for a strawberry fool.

Ingredient	4 portions	10 portions
Fruit purée (raspberry, strawberry, etc.)	400 g	1 kg
Caster sugar	100 g	250 g
Fresh whipped cream	250 ml	625 ml

Preparing the dish

1. Mix the ingredients and serve in coupes.

Method 3

Energy	Calories	Fat	Saturated fat	Carbohydrates	Sugar	Protein	Fibre
1,606 kJ	385 kcal	25.2 g	15.6 g	40.0 g	31.9 g	2.0 g	2.7 g

Method 3 nutritional analysis for a raspberry fool made with double cream.

Ingredient	4 portions	10 portions
Cornflour	35 g	85 g
Water	375 ml	940 ml
Sugar	100 g	250 g
Fruit purée (raspberry, strawberry, etc.)	400 g	1 kg
Cream	185 ml	460 ml

Cooking

1. Dilute the cornflour in a little of the water.
2. Boil the remainder of the water with the sugar and prepared fruit until soft.
3. Pass through a fine sieve.
4. Return to a clean pan and reboil.
5. Stir in the diluted cornflour and reboil. Allow to cool.
6. Lightly whisk the cream and fold into the mixture.
7. Serve as for method 1.

PROFESSIONAL TIP

In methods 2 and 3 the fat content may be reduced by using equal quantities of cream and natural Greek-style yoghurt.

69 Trifle

Energy	Calories	Fat	Saturated fat	Carbohydrates	Sugar	Protein	Fibre
2,280 kJ	543 kcal	29.1 g	17.1 g	66.2 g	51.3 g	8.2 g	1.9 g

Ingredient	6–8 portions
Sponge, pre-prepared	200 g
Jam	25 g
Tinned fruit (pears, peaches, pineapple) in syrup	1
Sherry (optional)	
Custard	
Custard powder	35 g
Milk, whole or skimmed	375 ml
Caster sugar	50 g
Cream (¾ whipped) or non-dairy cream	125 ml
Whipped sweetened cream or non-dairy cream	250 ml
Angelica	25 g
Glacé cherries	25 g
Optional glacé cherries and angelica	

Cooking

1. Cut the sponge in half, sideways, and spread with jam.
2. Place in a glass bowl or individual dishes and soak with fruit syrup drained from the tinned fruit; a few drops of sherry may be added.
3. Cut the fruit into small pieces and add to the sponge.
4. Dilute the custard powder in a basin with some of the milk and add the sugar.
5. Boil the remainder of the milk, pour a little on the custard powder, mix well, return to the saucepan and, over a low heat, stir to the boil. Allow to cool stirring occasionally to prevent a skin forming; fold in the ¾ whipped cream.
6. Pour on to the sponge. Leave to cool.
7. Decorate with the whipped cream, angelica and cherries, or with fresh fruit as in the photo. Alternatively, decorate with chocolate run outs or a combination of both.

VARIATION

- Other flavourings or liqueurs may be used in place of sherry (such as whisky, rum, brandy, coffee liqueur).
- For raspberry or strawberry trifle use fully ripe fresh fruit in place of tinned, and decorate with fresh fruit in place of angelica and glacé cherries.
- A fresh egg custard may be used with fresh egg yolks (see page 310).

71 Flan cases

Video: lining a flan, http://bit.ly/2nNoWvH

1. Allow 25 g flour per portion and prepare sugar pastry as per recipe 5.
2. Grease a flan ring and baking sheet.
3. Roll the pastry out so that the circumference is 2 cm larger than the flan ring. The pastry may be rolled between cling film or greaseproof or silicone paper.
4. Place the flan ring on the baking sheet.
5. Carefully place the pastry on the flan ring by rolling it loosely over the rolling pin, picking it up and unrolling it over the flan ring.
6. Press the pastry into shape without stretching it, being careful to exclude any air.
7. Allow a 0.5 cm ridge of pastry on top of the flan ring.
8. Cut off the surplus paste by rolling the rolling pin firmly across the top of the flan ring.
9. The rim can be left straight or moulded. Mould the edge with thumb and forefinger. Decorate either with pastry tweezers or with thumbs and forefingers, squeezing the pastry neatly to form a corrugated pattern.

NOTES

Some recipes call for the flan case to be baked blind, which means that it is baked before the filling is added. Line the pastry case with cling film and fill with baking beans (ceramic pie weights) or dried beans. Bake at 190 °C.

Place the pastry into the flan ring

Firm the pastry into the bottom of the ring

Bake blind, filled with beans, if the recipe requires

72 Fresh egg custard sauce (*sauce à l'anglaise*)

Energy	Calories	Fat	Saturated fat	Carbohydrates	Sugar	Protein	Fibre
1583 kJ	377 kcal	20.7 g	8.8 g	35.3 g	35.2 g	24.2 g	0.0 g

* Using whole milk

	300 ml	700 ml
Egg yolks, pasteurised	40 ml	100 ml
Caster or unrefined sugar	25 g	60 g
Vanilla extract or vanilla pod (seeds)	2-3 drops/½pod	5-7 drops/1 pod
Milk, whole or skimmed, boiled	250 ml	625 ml

Cooking

1. Mix the yolks, sugar and vanilla in a bowl.
2. Whisk in the boiled milk and return to a thick-bottomed pan.
3. Place on a low heat and stir with a wooden spoon until it coats the back of the spoon. Do not allow the mix to boil or the egg will scramble. A probe can be used to ensure the temperature does not go any higher than 85 °C.
4. Put through a fine sieve into a clean bowl. Set on ice to seize the cooking process and to chill rapidly.

VARIATION

Other flavours may be used in place of vanilla, for example, coffee, curaçao, chocolate, Cointreau, rum, Tia Maria, brandy, whisky, star anise, cardamom seeds, kirsch, orange flower water.

73 Fruit tart, tartlets or barquettes

Fruit tart

Energy	Calories	Fat	Saturated fat	Carbohydrates	Sugar	Protein	Fibre
1907 kJ	454 kcal	18.7 g	10.7 g	68.0 g	39.0 g	6.8 g	3.6 g

Ingredient	4 portions
Sweet paste (see page 156)	250 g
Fruit (e.g. strawberries, raspberries, grapes, blueberries)	500 g
Pastry cream (see page 109)	
Glaze	5 tbsp

Cooking

1. Line a flan ring with paste and cook blind at 190°C. Allow to cool.
2. Pick and wash the fruit, then drain well. Wash and slice/segment, etc. any larger fruit being used.
3. Pipe pastry cream into the flan case, filling it to the rim. Dress the fruit neatly over the top.
4. Coat with the glaze. Use a glaze suitable for the fruit chosen – for example, for a strawberry tart use a red glaze.

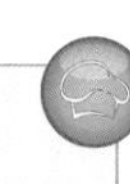

PROFESSIONAL TIP

Brush the inside of the pastry case with melted couverture before filling. This forms a barrier between the pastry and the moisture in the filling.

FAULTS

Although this strawberry tart may appear to be fine at first glance, the husks of the strawberries are visible. It would be better to present the strawberries with their tops pointing upwards or sliced and overlapping.

There is also quite a wide gap between the rows of strawberries, showing the pastry cream underneath. This should be avoided.

The second photo shows the importance of ensuring that fillings are prepared and/or cooked properly. In this case, the pastry cream has not been cooked sufficiently or prepared accurately as the filling is not structured sufficiently to support the fruit once the tart has been cut.

Tartlets

Energy	Calories	Fat	Saturated fat	Carbohydrates	Sugar	Protein	Fibre	Sodium
690 kJ	165 kcal	8.7g	2.7 g	21.1 g	6.3 g	2.0 g	1.2 g	0.1 g

Cooking

1. Roll out pastry 3 mm thick.
2. Cut out rounds with a fluted cutter and place them neatly in greased tartlet moulds. If soft fruit (such as strawberries or raspberries) is being used, the pastry should be cooked blind first.
3. After baking and filling (or filling and baking) with pastry cream, dress neatly with fruit and glaze the top.

Certain fruits (such as strawberries and raspberries) are sometimes served in boat-shaped moulds (barquettes). The preparation is the same as for tartlets. Tartlets and barquettes should be glazed and served allowing one large or two small per portion.

74 Apple flan

Energy	Calories	Fat	Saturated fat	Carbohydrates	Sugar	Protein	Fibre
1,428 kJ	340 kcal	13.8 g	5.8 g	53.8 g	36 g	3.5 g	2.9 g

Ingredient	4 portions	10 portions
Sweet pastry (see page 156)	100 g	250 g
Pastry cream (*crème pâtissière*) (see page 109)	250 ml	625 ml
Cooking apples	400 g	1 kg
Sugar	50 g	125 g
Apricot glaze	2 tbsp	6 tbsp

Cooking

1. Line a flan ring with sweet pastry. Pierce the bottom several times with a fork.
2. Pipe a layer of pastry cream into the bottom of the flan.
3. Peel, quarter and wash the selected apple.
4. Cut into neat thin slices and lay carefully on the pastry cream, overlapping each slice. Ensure that each slice points to the centre of the flan then no difficulty should be encountered in joining up the pattern neatly.
5. Sprinkle a little sugar on the apple slices and bake the flan at 200–220°C for 30–40 minutes.
6. When the flan is almost cooked, remove the flan ring carefully, return to the oven to complete the cooking. Mask with hot apricot glaze or flan jelly.

Pipe the filling neatly into the flan case

Slice the apple very thinly for decoration

Arrange the apple slices on top of the flan

Assessment strategies for Professional Cookery Technical Certificate

Chefs are assessed regularly in many different ways: each meal that is served is evaluated by the customer who will consider many things about their meal experience and often provide feedback which should enable the establishment to continue to develop its offer.

As part of professional development, through education, training and skills updating there are many opportunities for an individual chef to gain an indication of how well they are doing as well as offering opportunities to provide feedback on things that could be improved.

Assessment of the Level 2 Technical Certificate in Professional Cookery

For the Level 2 Technical Certificate the assessment takes place at given times through the development of the course, and covers a number of different tasks and assessment methods which will be formal and set by the awarding body (for example City and Guilds of London Institute CGLI) and the centre offering the programme. You will be marked on the quality and accuracy of your work.

The process known as 'Synoptic Assessment' is an approach where candidates have to make full use of the knowledge, understanding and skills they have built up during the course of learning and development to tackle problems/challenges/tasks.
As part of the process the full range of knowledge, skills and understanding will be incorporated into the assessment, and candidates will have the responsibility for transferring their knowledge, skills and understanding to the practical situation, fostering independence, autonomy and confidence in the way they approach the situation.

Assessment conditions and process for formal qualifications are set to meet three main criteria:

- Ensure the rigour of the assessment process
- Provide fairness for all candidates, wherever they complete the assessment
- Give confidence in relation to the outcome for both candidates and future employers.

There are two parts to the formal assessment process:

Knowledge assessment or written exam

Completion of set exercises, written or oral questioning that enable the candidate to show their individual understanding of a given subject area. This will include the current legislation in relation to providing food for sale, the techniques and methods used to produce dishes to meet customer requirements, product knowledge and an understanding of traditional and contemporary cooking methods which will be linked to the subject specifications. You may be asked to complete a paper-based or online multiple-choice test, answer a series of short-answer questions to test your knowledge, or complete an assignment. City and Guilds candidates will be asked to complete a short-answer exam either on paper or online.

Example question

Your chef supervisor has given you a list of mise-en-place required for the lunch time service as you start your shift at 0800, the list is as follows and lunch service starts at 1200.

- 4 kg of turned potatoes
- 5 lemon sole, filleted, skinned and stock from the bones
- 10 lemons segmented
- 2 kg shallots peeled and shredded
- 1 kg mirepoix of vegetables
- 250g chopped parsley

Produce a plan for the completion of this task list indicating time, equipment, resources and areas to consider (15 marks)

Responses could include the following indicative content:

- Points of clarification that you could ask the supervisor (which items are needed first, or how they will be used)
- Prioritisation of work/tasks
- Realistic timings for each task and order to complete them
- Equipment and materials to be used (knives, boards, storage and waste containers)
- Food safety, health and safety considerations (noting hazards, risks and control measures).

Mark Bands:

- **(Marks 1-5):** Minimal recognition that some items may be needed preparing before others, timings may be unrealistic or inaccurate, limited indication of resources or legislation to follow. Basic response, which is correct but only factual would only gain limited marks, the response may be disorganised or ambiguous in content.
- **(Marks 6-10):** Recognition that some items in the list would need to be prepared before others, a suggested logical sequence with some general realistic timing. Correctly identified suitable resources and equipment for tasks, links have been made to food safety, health and safety requirements, some justification against choices made. The response has demonstrated reasonable organisation and structure.
- **(Marks 11-15):** All tasks have been prioritised in a logical sequence. Timing is realistic and accurate. Equipment and materials required are suitable and appropriate for the task (e.g. filleting knife, turning knife, blue board etc.). Food safety, health and safety have been fully integrated into the response, with clear justification for the response and reasoning which is in a structured format and well organised.

Practical assessment (Synoptic tests)

Technical qualifications are based around developing knowledge, understanding and the skills for an individual to have the capability to work as a chef. This is a practical skills test, but would normally take the form of a given brief that would replicate an industry-type scenario. This would reflect a menu concept for a given event with multiple dishes and covering a wide variety of skills; it will be set at an appropriately levelled, substantial, occupationally relevant problem or task to achieve. It is often set to show kitchen and pastry skills.

This could be in the form of a given task, as in a briefing from a potential customer for a meal experience that would enable each candidate to select and carry out processes required to meet the customers' requirements as would happen in the work place.

Example scenario

The hotel where you work have been approached by the local rugby club to provide catering for the end season event; they have requested a sample menu to be produced before the contract is confirmed.

You have been tasked with planning and producing two portions of this menu. Your supervisor has provided you with the following menu and recipe specifications.

- Crab cake with dressing and salad garnish
- Roast loin of pork with braised onions, and boulangère potato
- Red wine poached pear with sauce anglais.

This task would be split into two parts, each of which would contribute to the overall mark.

- **Part 1:** with the menu and recipes you will be required to complete the following under supervised conditions in a a time limit (2 hours)
  - Plan of work (often called a time plan)
  - Allergen chart (correctly indicating the allergens, indicate alternatives)

  Your plan should include timings for cooking and presenting the dishes, the order in which you will complete the tasks, a list of equipment and tools you will require for the tasks, considerations for food safety, and health and safety considerations.

  This has to be your own work and marks will be awarded against:
- **Part 2:** produce a three course menu for 2 covers. Working methodically, clean as you go, adhering to appropriate food safety, health and safety procedures at all times (you will have 3 hours to complete this).

  There is a requirement to complete an evaluation of the dishes produced as part of the final stage; photographs or video clips may be used to support the marking of the whole task.
  - You will be marked on the dishes produced, which should be in correct order
  - You will need to produce a written self-evaluation of the dishes, which may be restricted in the number of words.

Skills assessments (Practical tasks)

These are a set of practical tasks that are set across all areas of the programme; these normally cover one complete dish. Tutors or mentors use this process to evaluate progress being made and are part of a development programme for individual chefs. These will not form part of the overall result but are used to ensure that you are prepared to take the synoptic assessment.

How can you prepare?

Prior planning and preparation is important to enable you to achieve the maximum from any assessment – you cannot beat the feeling of receiving the highest mark possible. To do that you will have to work in a methodical manner, be prepared to practise and listen to feedback as well as personally reflecting on what you have completed.

1. Read the instructions or brief that is given to you; make sure you understand what you have to do. This includes the criteria you will be judged or assessed on, which could include use of equipment, professional standards, use of materials, skills and techniques to be covered, time allowed, any preparations that can be completed before the test starts.
2. Carry out any research, find or develop your recipes and consider which ingredients and skills you will need to include within the test.
3. Prepare and plan your time; this could be a time plan for the actual assessment. This isn't only for the day but how you may prepare before the test date.
4. Prepare a list of equipment you will require to complete the task; make sure you have available what you need. It may be helpful to check if there is time to set out your work station before the assessment takes place.

On the day of assessment, you should ensure you arrive at the assessment centre in plenty of time. You may be allowed time to set up and ensure that you have all your equipment in place before the assessment starts; make good use of that time if it is available.

Tips from Chef

Time planning

Think about how long dishes take to cook and prepare, especially where there are a number of elements in a dish

- E.g. Roast loin of pork: Does the pork need to be boned? How long does the oven take to come to temperature? What garnishes and sauces are required?
- E.g. Poached pear in red wine: Prepare the cooking liquor before peeling the pears, as it is a cold dish how long will it take to cool. Do you have access to a blast chiller?

To write up the time plan if you have 3 hours think of 180 minutes and start from where you wish to finish and work back to that start (0 minutes); schedule in a break time if it is longer.

Professional practice

This area covers what you do while producing your dishes. The assessor will be looking at how you conduct yourself in the kitchen area. Things to consider:

- Personal hygiene and turnout – this will cover your dress. It is a good idea to ensure your whites are clean and pressed. Personal hygiene standards will cover things like jewellery, hair and nails. Ensure that you are seen washing hands as required.
- Craft skills – use the correct ones that are appropriate for the dish, including knife skills; the ease of the technique used and the consistency of skills shown are also important.
- Correct use of equipment – the correct tools or equipment used safely and correctly to complete tasks. This will include use of pans and could include energy. Do you really need to have the grill on 120 minutes before you glaze a fish dish?
- Work methods – ensure you work in a logical and organised manner, using appropriate time and temperature controls for food items. 'Clean as You Go' is the mantra used across kitchens, and be aware of cross-contamination threats to your dishes.

Culinary practice and finished dishes

This area covers the selection of ingredients, choice of cooking methods and techniques, application of knowledge and skills to a level appropriate with the assessment set out. The checking of the finished dish will cover presentation, portioning, flavour, texture, seasoning and of course cooking.

- Use of food items – have you selected ingredients that balance in terms of texture, colour and flavours in relation to overall dish? In some settings you may be asked to consider seasonality as part of the assessment or the impact of allergens on your dish choice.
- Techniques or skill – preparation skills for ingredients that these are completed in a logical sequence and with an understanding and awareness of portion sizes or waste from trimming and peeling.
- Cooking methods – the correct use of these for the dish requirements and ingredients being used. You will need to consider the use of time and temperature to ensure that dishes are cooked correctly and ready for the target service time.
- Monitoring cooking process – the tasting and evaluating elements of the dish prior to finishing will cover consistency and will enable you to correct the balance of the dish through the process.
- Presentation – the final stage of any practical assessment is how the dish is finished to present to the potential customer. This is an opportunity to show final flair and creativity as a chef, how you garnish and finish the dish. Make sure you don't allow the food to go cold while trying to get it on the plate.

Using this book to help you to prepare for assessment

Throughout the book you will find a number of opportunities that can support your learning and development:

- Test your knowledge: these will help you prepare for assessments and questioning
- Activities where you will look at a situation or issue in providing dishes and reviewing alternatives to meet customer expectations
- Within the recipes there are features which are annotated as:
  - assessment dishes that may form part of your preparation for practical skills reviews,
  - tips and notes considering alternative ingredients or garnishes that could be used.

Other types of assessment

There are also other times which could be considered as an assessment opportunity or a review of knowledge and skills of a chef these include:

- **Competitions** – many of these are set through each year at local, regional, national and even international levels. These could be based on an individual skill like cutting a chicken for sauté, all the way to a full menu or display products as culinary arts. Sponsorship is often linked to most of these with some quite prestigious development opportunities; there is also the opportunity to represent your region or country through cookery competitions both as an individual and as part of a team. The following websites give an insight in to the types of competitions that could be considered: www.worldskillsuk.org; www.nestle-toquedor.co.uk
- **Skills test (basket of goods)** – as part of employment and application processes many employers are now using skills assessment. For some this is a simple stage in the kitchen or a complete mystery basket test to assess practical skills as well as working practices prior to offering employment to an individual.

Glossary

Aerated To introduce air into. An 'aerated storeroom' is one that air is allowed to circulate through

Al dente Cooked until firm, crisp and with a bite

Allergenic A reaction by the immune system to certain foods or ingredients

Allergy When the immune system reacts to or rejects certain foods or ingredients

Amino acid The structural units of protein

Anaphylactic shock Anaphylaxis is a severe, potentially life-threatening allergic reaction that can develop rapidly

Antioxidants Molecules that help prevent cancer cells forming in the body. Prevent oxidation of products

Aromats Herbs such as parsley, chervil and basil used as a flavour base; may also include vegetables such as onions and celery

Balanced diet A balanced diet contains sufficient amounts of fibre and the various nutrients (carbohydrates, fats, proteins, vitamins and minerals) to ensure good health; food should also provide the appropriate amount of energy and adequate amounts of water

Basting Moistening meat periodically, especially while cooking, using a liquid such as melted butter or a sauce

Batting (out) Cuts of meat and poultry are batted out using a meat hammer or bat to give an even thickness and start breaking down the connective tissue to assist even cooking, resulting in a more tender final product

Best before date Date coding appearing on packaged foods that are stored at room temperature and are an indication of quality. Use of the food within the date is not legally binding but it is bad practice to use foods that have exceeded this date

Binary fission The process by which bacteria divide in half and multiply

Biological contamination Contamination by living organisms

Bivalves Molluscs with a single spiral shell; for example, winkles or whelks

Blanching Plunging food into boiling water for a brief time before plunging into cold water to halt the cooking process. The purpose of blanching is to soften and/or partly cook the food without colouring it

Blanquette A white stew; the sauce is made by thickening the cooking liquor at the end of the cooking process

Boiling Heating to boiling point. This method is unique to the production of choux paste, where the butter is initially melted in boiling water before being made into a paste with the addition of flour and then eggs

Bran Outer layers of the cereal

Broth A soup consisting of a stock or water in which meat or fish and/or vegetables have been simmered

Brown rice Any rice that has had the outer covering removed, retaining its bran

Brown stock Stock produced by browning vegetables and bones before covering in water, boiling and simmering

Brunoise A French term meaning to cut a vegetable into small cubes of precise and uniform measurement

Bulk fermentation The time it takes for the dough to double in size. Fermentation in bulk

Bulk fermentation time A proving/fermentation process in which a leavened dough will double in size

Bullying Threatening and oppressive behaviour towards an individual or group of individuals over a period of time

Catering The provision of facilities, including food and drinks

Centralised kitchen A production kitchen producing dishes that are then chilled or frozen and transported to finishing kitchens, often as part of a restaurant group or chain

Centrifuge A piece of laboratory equipment, driven by a motor, which spins liquid samples at high speed. Centrifuges work by the sedimentation principle to separate substances of greater and lesser density

Cephalopods Molluscs with a soft body and an internal shell; for example squid and octopus

Cereal The edible fruit of any grass used for food

Chef de partie In charge of a specific section within the kitchen

Chemical contamination Contamination by chemical compounds used for a variety of purposes such as cleaning and disinfection

Cholesterol A substance produced by the body that can clog the arteries to the heart; not all cholesterol is bad – some types of cholesterol are important for the nervous system and other body functions

Clean in place Cleaning items where they are rather than moving them to a sink. This is used for large equipment such as mixing machines

Cleaning schedule Planned and recorded cleaning of all areas and equipment

Cleaning The removal of dirt and grease, usually with the assistance of hot water and detergent

Coagulate The transformation of liquids or moisture in meat to a solid form

Coagulation To change consistency from a fluid into a thickened mass

Coarse cut Cuts from the neck legs and forequarters; these are tougher cuts and therefore often cooked using slower methods such as braising and stewing. Roughly cut

Coeliac disease A disease in which a person is unable to digest the protein gluten (found in wheat and other cereals). Gluten causes the person's immune system to attack its own tissues, specifically the lining of the small intestine. Symptoms include diarrhoea, bloating, abdominal pain, weight loss and malnutrition

Collagen White protein found in connective tissue

Commensurate Completed at the right level for the job being undertaken

Commercial sector Businesses such as hotels, restaurants, cafés, pubs and clubs that operate to make a profit

Commis chef A junior chef working under the supervision of the sous chef

Connective tissue Animal tissue that binds together the fibres of meat

Consommé a completely clear broth/stock

Contact dermatitis A skin reaction suffered by people who are allergic to certain food items, chemicals, plastics or cleaning materials

Contamination Anything in food that should not be there; contaminated food could cause harm or may just be unpleasant

Control measure Measures put in place to minimise risk

Convalescent carrier Someone recovering from a salmonella-related or other bacterial illness who still carries the organism

Cook/chill meals Pre-cooked foods that are rapidly chilled and packaged then held at chiller temperatures before being reheated for use

Corrosive Something that can eat away or destroy solid materials

COSHH Regulations Legal requirement for employers to control and list substances that are hazardous to health to prevent any possible injury to those using the substances

Cost sector/secondary service sector Businesses working in the public sector (which was traditionally non-profit making) but who aim to make a profit

Creaming Creaming refers to the initial mixing of sugar and butter or margarine together using a wooden spoon or electric mixer until a smooth mixture is formed. This is often used in the production of sweet/sugar pastry

Crème renversée Egg custard mixture made using eggs, milk and cream

Critical control point (CCP) A point in a procedure or process where a hazard could occur if controls were not in place

Cross-contamination Contaminants such as pathogenic bacteria transferred from one place to another. This is frequently from raw food to cooked/high risk food

Crustaceans Shellfish with tough outer shells and flexible joints to allow quick movement; for example, crab and lobster

Danger zone The temperature range at which bacteria are most likely to multiply. Danger zone temperature range is between 5°C and 63°C with most rapid activity around 37°C

Deglaze To add wine stock or water to the pan in which the fish was cooked to use the sediments and flavours left in the pan

Demersal fish Live in deep water and feed from the bottom of the sea; they are almost always white fleshed fish and can be round or flat

Descaler A substance to remove the hard deposit formed by chemicals in some water supplies. A descaler is often used on kettles, coffee machine pipes and water boilers

Detergent A substance that is soluble in water and breaks down grease and holds dirty particles in suspension in water; it may be in the form of liquid, powder, gel or foam; detergent will not kill pathogens

Diabetes A medical condition where the body cannot regulate the glucose levels in the body

Disinfectant Destroys pathogenic bacteria, bringing it to a safe level

Disinfection Action to bring micro-organisms to a safe level; this can be done with chemical disinfectants or heat

Double sink method Items are washed in one sink with detergent and hot water; they are then placed in racks and rinsed in very hot water in a second sink and allowed to air dry

Due diligence Written and recorded proof that a business took all reasonable precautions to avoid food safety problems and food poisoning

EHO/EHP Environmental Health Officer. Employed by local authorities to ensure that the required standards of food safety are met

Elastin Yellow protein found in connective tissue. This needs to be removed

Emulsifier Emulsifiers are made up of molecules with one water-loving (hydrophilic) and one oil-loving (hydrophobic) end. They make it possible for liquids that are normally immiscible to become finely dispersed in each other, creating a stable, homogenous, smooth emulsion

Emulsion An emulsion is a mixture of two or more liquids that are normally immiscible (non-mixable or un-blendable)

Endosperm The middle layer of the wheat grain containing starch and protein and used to make flour

Environmental cause Accidents due to a person's surroundings or location

Environmental health officer (EHO) A person employed by the local authority to advise upon, inspect and enforce food safety legislation in their area. An EHO is now sometimes called an environmental health practitioner (EHP)

Enzyme Biological catalyst. Proteins that speed up the rate of a chemical reaction, causing food to ripen, deteriorate and spoil

Fermentation Fermentation occurs when yeast and/or bacteria convert carbohydrates to carbon dioxide causing gas bubbles to form. This has a leavening (raising) effect on products such as dough when making bread

FIFO First in–first out; refers to using older food stocks before new deliveries

Fixed costs Regular charges, such as labour and overheads, that do not vary according to the volume of business

Flat fish Have a flatter profile and always have white flesh because the oils are stored in the liver. They include sole, plaice, dabs, turbot, brill, bream, flounder and halibut

Food intolerance Does not involve the immune system, but it does cause a reaction to some foods

Food poisoning A range of illnesses of the digestive system, usually caused by consuming food and drinks that have become contaminated with pathogenic bacteria (bacteria that causes bacterial infection), viruses, chemicals or toxins

Food safety Putting measures in place to ensure food is safe to eat and will not cause illness

Food spoilage Foods spoiled by the action of bacteria, moulds yeasts or enzymes. The food may smell or taste unpleasant, be sticky, slimy, dry, wrinkled or discoloured. Food spoilage is usually detectable by sight, smell or touch

Forequarter The front section of the side of meat (beef)

Franchise When a company grants permission for someone to open and run a branch of their company and sell their products

Fricassée A white stew; the sauce is thickened as part of the cooking process

Gelatine A nearly transparent, glutinous substance, obtained by boiling the bones, ligaments, etc., of animals, and used in making jellies

Germ The smallest part of the grain

Glaze a reduced stock with a concentrated flavour. Often used to enhance the flavour of soups and sauces

Global Worldwide or universal, applying to the whole world. For example we talk about the global economy, to signify the economy of the whole world

Grain Edible fruit of cereals

Gross profit The difference between the cost of an item and the price at which it is sold

Hand contact surfaces Anything in the kitchen that hands touch, including surfaces, equipment and a wide range of objects used in the kitchen

Harassment One or more serious incidents that create an intimidating, hostile or offensive environment. This can take many forms and happen for many reasons. It may be related to a person's age, sex, race, disability, religion, sexuality or any other personal characteristic of an individual

Hazard Any area, activity or procedure with the potential to cause harm

Hazard analysis Identifying all the possible hazards and putting in measures to prevent them causing harm

Hazard Analysis Critical Control Point (HACCP) A system for identifying the food safety hazards within a business or procedure and putting suitable controls in place to make them safe. Details of the system must be recorded and available for inspection. All food businesses must now have a food safety system based on HACCP

HDL High-density lipoprotein, 'good cholesterol'

Head chef Has overall responsibility for the organisation and management of the kitchen

Health and Safety Executive (HSE) The national independent authority for work-related health, safety and illness. It acts to reduce work-related death and serious injury across Great Britain's workplaces

Healthy carrier Someone carrying salmonella in their intestine without showing any signs of illness

High-ratio cakes A high ratio cake is prepared with a relatively high proportion of sugar and eggs compared to flour

Hindquarter The back part of the side of meat

Hogget A sheep over a year old

Homogenise A process in the production of milk in which the fats are emulsified so that the cream does not separate

Hospitality The friendly and generous treatment of guests

Human carrier Someone carrying bacteria (usually salmonella) in their intestines but not showing any signs of illness. They may pass on the salmonella bacteria to food they work with and this could then cause food poisoning in others

Human cause Accidents due to your own or another person's actions

Human Resources (HR) Department within an organisation that manages employee and employer relations. Responsible for recruitment and dismissal of staff and usually handle employee complaints or disputes. HR is sometimes needed to act as a moderator between employer and employee, or between two employees

Humectant A humectant is a hygroscopic (helps to retain water) substance used to keep products moist. Honey is an example used in this way

Hydrogenated A substance that has had hydrogen gas added to it. This is used to harden oils in margarine

Hydrolysis A chemical reaction in which a compound – like sugar – breaks down by reacting with water

Hydrometer Equipment used to measure density on the Baumé scale

Immune system A system of structures and processes in the human body that defend against harmful substances and maintain good health; occasionally the immune system in some people recognises ordinary food as harmful and a reaction occurs

Impermeable Something that liquid cannot pass through

Improvement notice A business is given a set amount of time to improve health and safety issues highlighted by an enforcement officer

Insecticide A chemical substance that is used to kill insects

International When two or more countries are involved in an industry or business

Intolerance The body reacts to certain types of food but does not involve the immune system; symptoms may vary

Knocking back Re-kneading the dough once proved

Lactic fermentation Lactic fermentation is a biological process in which sugars (e.g. sucrose or lactose) are converted into cellular energy

Lamb a sheep under a year old

Lamination Lamination is the term for the process of alternating layers of dough and butter when making puff pastry, croissants or Danish pastries

LDL Low-density lipoprotein, 'bad cholesterol'

Leavened Bread that has risen

Leavening The process where a substance, such as yeast or baking powder, is used to produce fermentation in a dough or batter

Legal requirement Something that must be done by law

Liaison A mixture of egg yolks and cream that is used to thicken a sauce, a thickening agent

Limited liability company A business in which the amount the owners will have to pay to cover the business's debts if it fails or if it is sued is limited to the value of the shares each shareholder (owner) owns

Linear workflow A flow of work that allows the processing of food to be moved smoothly in one direction through the premises from the point of delivery to the point of sale or service

Liquefied Petroleum Gas (LPG) Also referred to as propane or butane; it is used to fuel some cooking appliances

Local Specific to a local area such as a small family-run restaurant or local cheeses

Long-grain rice A narrow, pointed grain that has had the full bran and most of the germ removed. Used for plain boiling and in savoury dishes

Maillard reaction The chemical reaction that occurs when heat is applied to meat, causing browning

Mandatory Something that must be done, for example rubber gloves must be worn when handling certain chemicals

Marbling White flecks of fat within meat

Marinating Items are pre-soaked or coated in a marinade to help flavour, tenderise and in some cases colour food before the cooking process starts

Metamyoglobin Created when myoglobin is oxidised (reacts with oxygen in the air). This changes the colour of meat to dark red or brown

Mirepoix A mixture of roughly cut onion, carrot, leek and celery

Mise en place A French phrase that means 'putting in place'; it refers to the set-up required before cooking or before service, and may include the preparation of ingredients or garnishes, and is an essential part of the work of a professional kitchen

Modified atmosphere packaging Food is placed in a package then surrounded with a gas mixture that helps to slow down its deterioration (often the oxygen has been removed). The package is sealed to keep the food in its own atmosphere. This method is used for a variety of foods including salads, prepared fruit and meat

Molluscs Shellfish with either a hinged double shell, such as mussels, or a spiral shell, such as winkles

Multinational A term to describe a company that operates in several countries

Muscle Wastage when muscles wither away

Mutton Meat from a mature sheep

Myoglobin Pigment in the tissues which gives meat its bright red colour

National Available in one country, for example a chain of fish and chip restaurants only operating in the UK

Navarin A brown lamb stew; the sauce is thickened as part of the cooking process

Net profit The difference between the selling price of an item and the total cost of the product (this includes food, labour and overheads)

Nutrient A chemical providing nourishment and purpose in the diet

Obesity A medical condition in which excess body fat has accumulated to the extent that it may have an adverse effect on health, leading to reduced life expectancy and/or increased health problems

Occupational cause Accidents that are work- or activity-related

Oily fish Are always round and, because the fish oils are dispersed through the flesh (rather than stored in the liver as in white fish), the flesh is darker. These include mackerel, salmon, sardines, trout, herrings and tuna

Osteoporosis A disease in which the density or thickness of the bones breaks down, putting them at greater risk of fracture. Exercise and good nutrition can reduce the risk of developing osteoporosis

Overheads Expenses associated with operating the business, such as rent, rates, heating, lighting, electricity, gas, maintenance and equipment

Pané Coating the fish with a light coating of seasoned flour, beaten egg then breadcrumbs

Papin An enzyme that is sometimes injected into animals before slaughter to speed up the softening of fibres and muscles

Partie system A food production system devised by French chef, August Escoffier, in which different sections of the kitchen are delegated to carry out specific jobs

Partnership Consists of two or more people working together as the owners of a business; the partners take all the risks, stand any losses and keep any profits

Passed A thin soup such as a consommé, served by passing through a fine muslin cloth to remove the solid particles

Pasteurisation Pasteurisation is a process where heat is applied to products such as milk and cream for a short period of time before being cooled quickly. This helps to kill harmful bacteria and extend shelf-life whilst maintaining flavour properties

PAT testing Portable appliance testing of electrical appliances and equipment by a qualified electrician to make sure they are safe to use. A record is kept of this and a label or sticker is placed on the appliance to show that it has been tested

Pathogenic bacteria Bacteria that can cause illness either by infection or by the toxins they may produce. Disease farming bacteria

Pelagic fish Live in more shallow or mid-depth waters and are usually round, oily fish such as mackerel, herrings and sardines

Personal development plan A statement outlining a person's career aspirations and work-related goals, and a description of the steps to be taken to ensure the plan is achieved

Personal hygiene Keeping yourself clean and hygienic to avoid contaminating food

Physical contamination By an object which can be of any shape, size or type

Potage A soup

PPE Personal protective equipment (and clothing) worn for safety reasons at work

Primary service sector Hospitality in banks, law firms and other large corporate businesses

Prime cut The leanest and most tender cuts of meat; these come from the hindquarters

Prohibition notice A business or business procedure is deemed to be unsafe by an enforcement officer and the activity must stop immediately

Prohibition Something that is not allowed and must not be done, for example smoking in certain outside areas

Prove Process of allowing dough to rise and increase in size

Provenance Where food comes from, for example, where it is grown, reared, produced or finished

Public (service) sector Establishments such as schools, hospitals, care homes, armed services and prisons

Public limited company (PLC) A company that can sell shares to the public

Purée A soup with a vegetable base that has been puréed

Raising agent A substance added to a cake or bread mixture which produces gases that give lightness to the product. Baking powder is an example of a raising agent

Refractometer Equipment used to measure sweetness on the Brix scale

Regional Applies to a specific region or area, for example small hotel businesses operating only in Wales or the Lake District

Restaurant runner A member of the restaurant team who collects food from the kitchen and delivers it to the waiter for service; they would also assist with clearing

Retarding dough Reducing the fermentation process of a dough by placing it in chilled conditions

Rickets A disease of the bones

RIDDOR Reporting Injuries, Diseases and Dangerous Occurrences Act 1996. All injuries, diseases and dangerous occurrences happening in the workplace or because of work carried out on behalf of the employer must be reported to the Health and Safety Executive. This is a legal requirement and it is the employer's responsibility to make any such reports

Risk The possibility that someone could be harmed by a hazard

Risk assessment The process of identifying and evaluating hazards and risks, and putting measures in place to control them; this process should be recorded and reviewed

Rodenticide A chemical substance that is used to kill rodents such as rats and mice

Round fish Can vary greatly in size from small sardines to very large tuna. They can either have white flesh, such as bass, grouper, mullet, haddock and cod, or darker, oily flesh such as tuna, mackerel, herring, trout and salmon

Roux A soup thickened with a traditional roux of fat and flour

Rubbing in Rubbing in is a technique where flour is rubbed into a fat to make products such as short pastry and crumbles. Using the fingertips, flour and butter are rubbed gently together until the mixture resembles fine breadcrumbs

Safety shoes Strong, enclosed shoes with reinforced toecaps to protect the feet from heavy or sharp objects and hot liquids

Sanitiser A chemical with detergent and disinfecting properties; it breaks down dirt and grease and controls bacteria and usually comes in spray form

Satellite kitchen A kitchen where food produced in a centralised kitchen would be finished

Sautéing To sauté (meaning to toss or jump) tender cuts of meat and poultry, cook them in a sauté pan or frying pan in the same way as for shallow frying

Scurvy A disease that can cause bleeding gums and other symptoms

Self-assisted service Someone is on duty to help the customer choose; in some cases there will be a section on a buffet where a chef will be cooking fresh items such as stir fry, omelettes, waffles and pancakes. Here the guest is helped to choose and will take the finished item to their table. This is also known as 'theatre cookery'

Self-service Customers serve themselves from a self-service counter or buffet

Septic Cuts, burns and so on infected with pathogenic bacteria; they are often wet, with a white or yellow appearance

Septicaemia Blood poisoning. It occurs when an infection in the bloodstream causes the body's immune system to begin attacking the body itself

Shortening Fat used in pastry making; it is made from oils and is 100 per cent fat

Shortening agent A fat used to help prevent the development of gluten strands when making pastry. This helps to make the texture of the product more crumbly

Short-grain rice A short, rounded grain with a soft texture. Suitable for sweet dishes and risotto

Small- to medium-sized enterprise (SME) Businesses with up to 250 employees

Socio-cultural The customs, beliefs, values and language which may shape a person's identity, lifestyle and expectations

Sole trader The simplest form of a business; the sole trader owns the business, takes all the risks, is liable for any losses and keeps any profits

Solvent A liquid that is able to dissolve other substances

Sous chef Takes overall responsibility for the kitchen when the head chef is absent; may have a specific area of responsibility

Spoilage bacteria Cause food to change and spoil, for example, develop a bad smell or go slimy

Spore A resistant, resting phase for some bacteria when they form protection around the essential part of the cell that can then survive, boiling, freezing and disinfection

Stabiliser A stabiliser is a substance added to foods to help to preserve its structure

Sterilisation Sterilisation is another process where heat is applied but at much higher temperatures. This increases shelf-life further than pasteurisation but products treated this way tend to lose some of their flavour properties

Steriliser Can be chemical or through the action of extreme heat. It will kill all living micro-organisms

Still room An area between the kitchen and the restaurant, or somewhere close to both, where tea, coffee and other drinks may be prepared, along with other tasks such as slicing/preparing bread for the restaurant

Stock rotation Managing stock by using older items before newer items, provided the older items are in sound condition and are still within use by or best before dates

Syneresis Loss of water from a mixture

Toxin A poison produced by some bacteria as they multiply in food or as they die in the human body

Traceability Use of records to track food from its source through production and distribution to help control hazards

Turning A turn is the term used to describe the process of producing the layers in laminated pastry. Each time the paste is rolled and folded, it is referred to as a turn

Univalves Molluscs with an external hinged double shell; for example, scallops and mussels

Unpassed A thin soup such as a broth which is served along with all the ingredients used

Use-by date Date coding appearing on packaged perishable foods that need to be stored in the refrigerator; use of the food within this date is a legal requirement

Variable costs Costs that vary according to the volume of business; includes food and materials costs

Vegan A vegetarian who also does not eat eggs or milk, or anything containing eggs or milk

Velouté A basic white sauce made using stock and a blond roux

Virus Micro-organism even smaller than bacteria. It does not multiply in food but can enter the body via food where it then invades living cells

Water retention When the body does not get rid of enough water

Wheatgerm Part of the wheat grain containing oil which is removed in the milling process

White stock A stock produced by blanching but not browning vegetables and bones, to give a clear stock

Index of recipes

This index lists every recipe in the book, grouped by major commodity and by type of dish.

There is a full topic index at the pack of the book.

Index

Page references in **bold** indicate key terms